Applied Probability and Statistics (Continued)

CHEW · Experimental Designs in Industry
CLARK · An Introduction to Statistics
COCHRAN · Sampling Techniques, *Second Edition*
COCHRAN and COX · Experimental Designs, *Second Edition*
CORNELL · The Essentials of Educational Statistics
COX · Planning of Experiments
DEMING · Sample Design in Business Research
DEMING · Some Theory of Sampling
DODGE and ROMIG · Sampling Inspection Tables, *Second Edition*
FRYER · Elements of Statistics
GOLDBERGER · Econometric Theory
GOULDEN · Methods of Statistical Analysis, *Second Edition*
GUTTMAN and WILKS · Introductory Engineering Statistics
HALD · Statistical Tables and Formulas
HALD · Statistical Theory with Engineering Applications
HANSEN, HURWITZ, and MADOW · Sample Survey Methods and Theory, Volume I
HAUSER and LEONARD · Government Statistics for Business Use, *Second Edition*
HOEL · Elementary Statistics
JOHNSON and LEONE · Statistics and Experimental Design: In Engineering and the Physical Sciences, Volumes I and II
KEMPTHORNE · An Introduction to Genetic Statistics
MEYER · Symposium on Monte Carlo Methods
PRABHU · Queues and Inventories: A Study of Their Basic Stochastic Processes
RICE · Control Charts in Factory Management
SARHAN and GREENBERG · Contributions to Order Statistics
TIPPETT · Technological Applications of Statistics
WILLIAMS · Regression Analysis
WOLD and JURÉEN · Demand Analysis
YOUDEN · Statistical Methods for Chemists

Tracts on Probability and Statistics

BILLINGSLEY · Ergodic Theory and Information

QUEUES and INVENTORIES

QUEUES and INVENTORIES

A Study of Their Basic Stochastic Processes

N. U. PRABHU
Associate Professor
Cornell University

John Wiley & Sons, Inc., New York · London · Sydney

Library of Congress Catalog Card Number: 65-21434
Printed in the United States of America

To Sumi

Preface

Similarities between the mathematical formalisms of queueing and inventory models had been observed at a fairly early stage in their development. Briefly, an amount of material held in stock for future use may be compared to a group of customers waiting for service at a counter offering certain facilities; models describing these two situations therefore give rise to stochastic processes with the same basic features. The purpose of this book is to give a unified treatment of these processes. I have made no attempt, however, to establish a unified theory, from which results for queues and inventories can be deduced as corollaries. I have treated each topic separately by unified methods, using unified notation, and the similarities between the results have been pointed out wherever they exist. I hope that this treatment will be less tedious and more interesting to the readers.

There now exists voluminous literature on queues and inventories, and obviously it is not possible to give a comprehensive treatment of the subject in a book of this kind. The topics presented here are mainly single server waiting systems and storage systems; this selection is based on my research interests. Chapter 1 contains an introductory account of queueing systems. Here the nature of the basic stochastic processes is carefully explained; for Markov processes, it is shown how the forward Kolmogorov equations can be used to obtain the queue-length and waiting time distributions, and the imbedded Markov chain technique is explained and applied to several particular cases, where the basic processes are non-Markovian. In the next two chapters, a detailed investigation of the systems $M/G/1$ and $GI/M/1$ is made. Results for busy and idle periods, waiting time, and queue-length distributions are obtained in Chapter 2, and the imbedded Markov chain analysis of these two systems is carried out in Chapter 3. The emphasis is placed here on explicit results, and the methods used are based on direct probabilistic arguments. These methods are seen to be applicable to systems with modified arrival and service schemes.

No treatment of queueing theory is complete without an account of recent results for the system $GI/G/1$, based on the pioneering work of E. Sparre Andersen and Frank Spitzer on the fluctuation theory of random variables. This account is given in Chapter 4, and, as particular cases, the systems $GI/E_s/1$ and $E_s/G/1$, and the bulk queue $M^{(X)}/G^{(Y)}/1$ are studied.

In Chapter 5 several inventory models are discussed. The main concern here is the study of the stochastic processes underlying the models, and, except in a few cases, the equally important problem of optimization is not considered. In particular, the theory of collective risk, developed by Swedish actuaries, is described.

The theory of storage systems (or dams) was formulated by P. A. P. Moran in 1954. An excellent account of the theory, describing results obtained up to 1958, is contained in Moran's [(1959), Methuen, London] monograph. Considerable progress has since been made in several directions: the study of the time-dependent behavior of stochastic processes underlying Moran's original model, modifications of this model, as well as the formulation and solution of new models. Chapters 6 and 7 give a detailed account of these developments. Chapter 6 is concerned with Moran's discrete time dam process, and continuous time storage processes are studied in Chapter 7.

At the end of each chapter there are problems and complementary results. These results are mostly direct consequences of those derived in the text, but sometimes they arise from other methods of investigation, of models treated here or related models. I hope that these problems and further results will help the reader to gain a deeper insight into the theory. References are given at the end of each chapter rather than in the form of a consolidated bibliography. Comprehensive bibliographies on queues and inventories are being published frequently and therefore the lists of references are restricted here only to those research papers and books actually referred to.

I have assumed that readers have a knowledge of modern probability theory and stochastic processes at an introductory level. However, only the basic concepts of these topics are actually used in the book, and these are carefully explained at every stage. Since the methods used are direct, detailed results in the theory of stochastic processes are not used and the treatment is therefore largely self-contained.

My interest in queues was stimulated by the research on storage theory done in collaboration with J. Gani during the years 1956, 1957, and 1962. To him go my special thanks. For criticisms of the preliminary draft of the book I am indebted to U. Narayan Bhat and C. Heyde. Finally, I am grateful to Miss Christine Bourke for her efficient typing of the manuscript, and to the University of Western Australia for a research grant toward the preparation of the manuscript.

N. U. PRABHU

The University of Western Australia
May 1965

Contents

Chapter 1

Some Queueing Systems

1.1 INTRODUCTION

A queue or waiting line is formed when customers arrive at a counter offering certain facilities and demand service. As examples we may consider subscribers' calls arriving at a telephone exchange, patients waiting in a doctor's reception room, machines waiting to be serviced by repairmen, and cars waiting at a traffic intersection. A queueing system is completely described by (1) the input, (2) the queue-discipline, and (3) the service mechanism. These are defined as follows.

The *input* describes the way customers arrive and join the system. The number of customers may be finite or infinite, and they may arrive individually or in groups. If each arriving customer joins the system we have a *waiting (or delay) system*. However, it is possible that the system does not accept a customer when it is fully occupied; then we have a *loss system*. A customer may also leave if, on arrival, he finds too long a queue (or, perhaps, too short a queue)—such behavior is called *balking*. Finally, a customer may be forced to leave if he does not find any standing space in the system.

The *queue-discipline* is the rule determining the formation of the queue and the manner of the customers' behavior while waiting. The simplest discipline is "first come, first served," according to which customers are served in the order of their arrival. If this order is reversed, we have the "last come, first served" discipline; several other disciplines are possible. In a system with several counters, a customer may have a choice as to the counter he could join, but the queue at each counter would be subject to some specified discipline. Furthermore, there is scope for differences in the customers' behavior; thus for instance, having waited for some time, a customer may become impatient and leave the system (that is, he may *renege*).

Finally, the *service mechanism* describes the arrangements for serving the customers with the facilities they seek. In general, there are s servers, where $s \geqslant 1$. We assume that these servers will be always available, but there are situations where one or more of them will be absent from the system at certain times. If $s = \infty$, then all customers will be served immediately on arrival, and there will be no queue. If there are a finite number of servers, they attend to the customers in a specified order. In particular, the "first come, first served" queue-discipline implies that the first of the s servers to be free attends to the customer at the top of the queue. In *bulk service* systems customers are served in batches, rather than individually. Furthermore, in some systems customers might be served in a certain order of *priorities*.

Let us suppose that the facilities provided have been so planned that any predictable congestion, such as, for instance, because of peak hour rush, can be reasonably dealt with; we are concerned with congestion arising from unpredictable factors such as the irregularity of the input or the service mechanism, and we assume that this irregularity is statistical in nature. Our aim is therefore to study the statistical fluctuations in the queueing phenomena, with a view to a proper understanding of the system, and we hope that on the basis of our study, a better planning of the facilities can be undertaken.

The pioneering work on the theory of queues was done by A. K. Erlang of the Copenhagen Telephone Company during 1909 to 1920 [for a study of Erlang's work from the modern point of view, see Jensen (1948)]. Independently, valuable work was done by Fry (1928). Mention must also be made of major contributions to the theory by Palm [see, in particular, his paper (1943) on the machine interference problem], Khintchine and Pollaczek [see the English translation (1960) of Khintchine's book and the two monographs in French by Pollaczek (1957, 1961)]. A systematic treatment of the theory from the point of view of stochastic processes is due to Kendall (1951, 1953), and this has greatly influenced subsequent work in this field.

In the present work we are mainly concerned with waiting systems, where the population of customers is infinite, customers arrive individually, and there is no balking, reneging, or priorities in service. The systems we consider are specified by the following assumptions.

1. *The input.* Let the successive customers arrive at the instants t_0, $t_1, t_2, \ldots$; the interarrival times are then $u_r = t_r - t_{r-1}$ $(r = 1, 2, \ldots)$. We assume that $u_1, u_2, u_3, \ldots$ are random variables which are mutually independent and have the same distribution function (d.f.) $A(u)$ $(0 \leqslant u < \infty)$. We may describe this briefly by stating that the sequence of random variables $\{u_r, r = 1, 2, \ldots\}$ is a renewal process.

This assumption implies that the arrival pattern is stationary in time. This is not always a valid assumption; for example, telephone calls arrive at an exchange more frequently during busy hours and doctors may have more patients during certain seasons. However, in most situations it seems reasonable to assume that the input process does not vary with time.

2. *The queue-discipline* is "first come, first served."

3. *The service-mechanism.* The number of servers is s, where $1 \leqslant s < \infty$. The time which elapses while a particular customer is being served is called his service time. We assume that the service times $v_1, v_2, v_3, \ldots$ of the successive customers are random variables, which are mutually independent, and also independent of $u_1, u_2, u_3, \ldots$; they have the same d.f. $B(v)$ $(0 \leqslant v < \infty)$.

These assumptions regarding the service mechanism imply that the customers are all identical with respect to their demand for service; if, as in some post offices, different counters provide different facilities, we assume that each customer goes to the appropriate counter, and we have in effect several independent queueing systems. It is further implied by our assumptions that the server does not get tired and slacken service at any time, and that he is not in any way influenced by the queue-length (for instance, he does not expedite his service when he sees a long queue being formed).

Let $E(u_i) = a$, $E(v_i) = b$ denote respectively the mean interarrival time and mean service time; we shall assume that $0 < a < \infty$, $0 < b < \infty$. For a single server system, the ratio

$$\rho = \frac{b}{a} = \frac{\text{mean service time}}{\text{mean interarrival time}} \qquad (0 < \rho < \infty) \tag{1.1}$$

is called the relative traffic intensity expressed in "erlangs" (the international unit of telephone traffic); actually, this is a dimensionless quantity. Now, from renewal theory applied to the sequence $\{u_r\}$ we find that as time $t \rightarrow \infty$,

$$\text{expected number of arrivals per unit time} \sim \frac{1}{a}, \tag{1.2}$$

so that we can write

$$\rho \sim \text{expected number of arrivals per mean service time}, \tag{1.3}$$

which indicates that ρ is a measure of congestion in the system; ρ is, in fact, of great importance in the analysis of queueing systems. For an s-server queue $(s < \infty)$ we define the traffic intensity to be $\rho = b/as$.

As special cases of the input we consider the following.

1. *D* (*derministic or regular input*). Here customers arrive at regular intervals of a units of time; the interarrival times have therefore the d.f. given by

$$A(u) = 0 \quad \text{if} \quad u < a, \qquad \text{and}$$
$$= 1 \quad \text{if} \quad u \geqslant a \qquad (0 < a < \infty). \tag{1.4}$$

2. *M* (*Markovian or Poisson input*). Here the customers arrive in a Poisson process at a rate λ $(0 < \lambda < \infty)$. Thus the number of arrivals during a time interval $(0, t]$ has the Poisson distribution $e^{-\lambda t}(\lambda t)^n/n!$ $(n = 0, 1, \ldots)$, and from the well-known property of this distribution it follows that the intervals of time between successive arrivals have the negative exponential distribution

$$dA(u) = \lambda e^{-\lambda u}\, du \qquad (0 < u < \infty). \tag{1.5}$$

Since this distribution has the Markovian property

$$Pr\{u < u_i < u + du \mid u_i \geqslant u_0\} = \frac{dA(u)}{1 - A(u_0)} = \lambda e^{-\lambda(u-u_0)}\, du, \tag{1.6}$$

we call this input "Markovian"; it is also called a *completely random* input.

3. E_k (*Erlangian input*). Here the interarrival time distribution is given by

$$dA(u) = \frac{(\lambda k)^k}{(k-1)!}\, e^{-\lambda k u} u^{k-1}\, du \qquad (0 < u < \infty), \tag{1.7}$$

where k is a positive integer. When $k = 1$, this reduces to the negative exponential distribution (1.5), whereas, as $k \to \infty$, we find that the characteristic function (c.f.) of (1.7),

$$\int_0^\infty e^{i\theta u}\, dA(u) = \left(1 - \frac{i\theta}{k\lambda}\right)^{-k} \to e^{i\theta/\lambda}, \tag{1.8}$$

where $e^{i\theta/\lambda}$ is the c.f. of the distribution (1.4) with $a = \lambda^{-1}$; this shows that the Erlangian input tends to the regular input as $k \to \infty$. In the general case where $1 < k < \infty$, the distribution (1.7) is the k-fold convolution of the distribution (1.5) and can therefore be considered as representing an arrival process which occurs in k successive stages such that the time required for each stage has the negative exponential distribution (1.5) independently of the others, and the arrival takes place only at the completion of these k stages; when this happens, the process starts with the first stage of the next arrival. The intervals of time between successive arrivals therefore have the distribution (1.7).

We may also consider special cases of the service time distribution similar to the foregoing. In particular, a service of the Erlangian type E_k can be considered as constituted of k "phases" of service, each phase requiring time which is distributed as in (1.5). In the general case Kendall, to whom the above classification is due, denotes the queueing system by $GI/G/S$, where GI indicates an input of the "general independent" type, G indicates a service time distribution of the general type, and s is the number of servers.

Some of the important problems which arise in the analysis of a queueing system are concerned with the following.

1. *The queue-length.* Let $Q(t)$ be the number of customers present in the system at time t. If $s < \infty$, $Q(t)$ is the number of persons either being served or waiting in the queue; we call $Q(t)$ the queue-length. If $s = \infty$, $Q(t)$ is the number of busy servers.
2. *The waiting time.* The time spent by a customer in the queue before the commencement of his service is called his waiting time. The total time spent by him in the system is his waiting time plus service time.
3. *The busy period.* Suppose that the server is free initially and a customer arrives; he will be served immediately. During his service time some more customers will arrive and will be served in their turn. This process will continue in this way until no customer is left and the server becomes free again. When this happens, we say that a busy period has just ended. In contrast, we have idle periods during which no customers are present in the system. A busy period and the idle period following it together constitute a *busy cycle*, and the whole process is a succession of such cycles.

Because our basic assumptions emphasize the random nature of the irregularities in the system, our queueing models give rise to stochastic processes, which have to be analyzed in the course of investigating the above problems. It is the purpose of this book to study these stochastic processes systematically. In the remainder of this chapter we discuss several important queueing systems with reference to concepts and methods. Detailed analysis of special systems will be carried out in the next few chapters.

1.2 THE QUEUE $M/M/1$

a. Transforms

We shall start our discussion by considering a queueing system in which customers arrive in a Poisson process at a rate λ and are served by a single server on a "first come, first served" basis, the service time of a customer having the negative exponential distribution $\mu e^{-\mu v}\,dv$ $(0 < v < \infty)$.

The mean interarrival time is clearly λ^{-1} and the mean service time is given by

$$(1.9)\qquad b = \int_0^\infty \mu e^{-\mu v} v\, dv = \mu^{-1},$$

so that the traffic intensity is $\rho = \lambda/\mu$. If $A(t)$ denotes the number of arrivals during $(0, t]$, then $A(t)$ has the probability distribution

$$(1.10)\qquad Pr\{A(t) = n\} = e^{-\lambda t}\frac{(\lambda t)^n}{n!} \qquad (n = 0, 1, 2, \ldots);$$

similarly, if $D(t)$ is the number of customers who complete their service and leave the system during $(0, t]$, then since the service time is distributed negative exponentially, $D(t)$ is also a Poisson process with

$$(1.11)\qquad Pr\{D(t) = n\} = e^{-\mu t}\frac{(\mu t)^n}{n!} \qquad (n = 0, 1, 2, \ldots).$$

Furthermore, the arrivals and departures during $(t, t + s]$ occur independently of the development of the process during $(0, t]$. Therefore, if $Q(t)$ is the number of customers present in the system (either being served or waiting) at time $t \geqslant 0$, it follows that $Q(t)$ is a Markov process; it is clear that $Q(t)$ is a denumerable, time-homogeneous process with states $0, 1, 2, \ldots$. Let its transition probabilities be denoted by

$$(1.12)\qquad P_{ij}(t) = Pr\{Q(t) = j \mid Q(0) = i\} \qquad (t > 0)$$

$$(1.13)\qquad P_{ij}(0) = \delta_{ij} = \begin{cases} 1 & \text{if } i = j, \\ 0 & \text{if } i \neq j. \end{cases}$$

We shall use the convention that $P_{ij}(t) \equiv 0$ whenever one or both of the suffixes i, j are negative. Now, during an infinitesimal time interval $(t, t + dt]$, the probability of an arrival is $\lambda\, dt + o(dt)$ and the probability of a departure is $\mu\, dt + o(dt)$; therefore

$$(1.14)\qquad \begin{aligned} P_{ii+1}(dt) &= \lambda\, dt + o(dt) \\ P_{ii-1}(dt) &= \mu\, dt + o(dt) \\ P_{ii}(dt) &= 1 - (\lambda + \mu)\, dt + o(dt), \end{aligned}$$

and $P_{ij}(dt) = o(dt)$ for all other combinations of i and j. The equations (1.14) indicate that $Q(t)$ is a birth and death process [see Feller (1957)]. Substituting (1.14) in the Chapman-Kolmogorov equations

$$(1.15)\qquad P_{ij}(t + dt) = \sum_{k=0}^{\infty} P_{ik}(t)P_{kj}(dt) \qquad (i, j \geqslant 0),$$

we obtain

$$(1.16)\quad P_{ij}(t + dt) = P_{ij}(t)(1 - \lambda\, dt - \mu\, dt) + P_{ij-1}(t)\lambda\, dt + P_{ij+1}(t)\mu\, dt + o(dt),$$

which gives

$$(1.17)\quad \frac{P_{ij}(t + dt) - P_{ij}(t)}{dt} = -(\lambda + \mu)P_{ij}(t) + \lambda P_{ij-1}(t) + \mu P_{ij+1}(t) + \frac{o(dt)}{dt} \qquad (i, j \geqslant 0).$$

From (1.16) we find that $P_{ij}(t + dt) \to P_{ij}(t)$ as $dt \to 0$; similarly, replacing t by $t - dt$ in (1.16) we have that $P_{ij}(t - dt) \to P_{ij}(t)$. Thus $P_{ij}(t)$ is continuous at each $t > 0$. A similar procedure with (1.17), using the continuity property of $P_{ij}(t)$, shows that $P_{ij}(t)$ has a derivative at each $t > 0$. At $t = 0$ continuity and differentiability both hold, but from the right. It follows from (1.17) that

$$(1.18)\quad \begin{aligned} P'_{i0}(t) &= -\lambda P_{i0}(t) + \mu P_{i1}(t) \\ P'_{ij}(t) &= -(\lambda + \mu)P_{ij}(t) + \lambda P_{ij-1}(t) + \mu P_{ij+1}(t) \qquad (j > 0); \end{aligned}$$

the difference-differential equations (1.18) are called the forward Kolmogorov equations of the process. To solve these equations we first introduce the generating function (transform)

$$(1.19)\quad G(z, t) = \sum_{j=0}^{\infty} P_{ij}(t)z^j \qquad (|z| \leqslant 1),$$

where, using (1.13), we find that $G(z, 0) = z^i$ $(i \geqslant 0)$. We have also $\dfrac{\partial G}{\partial t} = \sum_0^\infty P'_{ij}(t)z^j$. Multiplying the equations (1.18) successively by $1, z, z^2, \ldots$ and adding, we obtain

$$\sum_0^\infty P'_{ij}(t)z^j = -(\lambda + \mu)\sum_0^\infty P_{ij}(t)z^j + \lambda \sum_{j=1}^\infty P_{ij-1}(t)z^j + \mu \sum_{j=0}^\infty P_{ij+1}(t)z^j + \mu P_{i0}(t)$$

which, after some simplification, gives

$$(1.20)\quad z\frac{\partial G}{\partial t} = [\lambda z^2 - (\lambda + \mu)z + \mu]G - \mu(1 - z)P_{i0}(t).$$

Next, let us define the Laplace transforms with respect to time of $G(z, t)$ and $P_{ij}(t)$ as

$$(1.21)\quad G^*(z, \theta) = \int_0^\infty e^{-\theta t}G(z, t)\, dt$$

and

(1.22) $$P_{ij}^*(\theta) = \int_0^\infty e^{-\theta t} P_{ij}(t)\, dt \qquad [\mathrm{Re}\,(\theta) > 0].$$

Integration by parts yields the relation

(1.23) $$\int_0^\infty e^{-\theta t} \frac{\partial G}{\partial t}\, dt = [e^{-\theta t} G(z, t)]_0^\infty + \theta \int_0^\infty e^{-\theta t} G(z, t)\, dt$$
$$= -z^i + \theta G^*(z, \theta).$$

Multiplying both sides of (1.20) by $e^{-\theta t}$ and integrating over $(0 \leqslant t < \infty)$, we obtain

$$\theta z G^*(z, \theta) - z^{i+1} = [\lambda z^2 - (\lambda + \mu) z + \mu] G^*(z, \theta) - \mu(1 - z) P_{i0}^*(\theta),$$

or

(1.24) $$G^*(z, \theta) = \frac{z^{i+1} - \mu(1 - z) P_{i0}^*(\theta)}{(\lambda + \mu + \theta) z - \mu - \lambda z^2}.$$

The denominator on the right-hand side of (1.24) has two zeros, namely,

(1.25) $$\xi \equiv \xi(\theta) = \frac{\lambda + \mu + \theta - \sqrt{(\lambda + \mu + \theta)^2 - 4\lambda\mu}}{2\lambda}$$
$$\eta \equiv \eta(\theta) = \frac{\lambda + \mu + \theta + \sqrt{(\lambda + \mu + \theta)^2 - 4\lambda\mu}}{2\lambda},$$

where the square root is taken so that its real part is positive. Clearly, $|\xi| < |\eta|$, and moreover,

(1.26) $$\xi + \eta = \frac{\lambda + \mu + \theta}{\lambda}, \qquad \xi\eta = \frac{\mu}{\lambda}.$$

For $|z| = 1$ and $\mathrm{Re}\,(\theta) > 0$ we have

(1.27) $$|(\lambda + \mu + \theta) z| = |\lambda + \mu + \theta| > \lambda + \mu \geqslant |\mu + \lambda z^2|,$$

so that by Rouche's theorem $(\lambda + \mu + \theta) z - \mu - \lambda z^2$ has only one zero in the unit circle; this is clearly $z = \xi$. Now since the Laplace transform $G^*(z, \theta)$ converges in the region $|z| = 1$, $\mathrm{Re}\,(\theta) > 0$, the zeros of the numerator and denominator on the right-hand side of (1.24) must coincide, and therefore

(1.28) $$P_{i0}^*(\theta) = \frac{\xi^{i+1}}{\mu(1 - \xi)}.$$

Substituting (1.28) in (1.24) we obtain the result

$$G^*(z, \theta) = \frac{z^{i+1} - (1-z)\xi^{i+1}/(1-\xi)}{\lambda(z-\xi)(\eta - z)} \tag{1.29}$$

for the transform of the transition probabilities of the process $Q(t)$.

This method of analysis and the results are due to Bailey (1954); earlier, Ledermann and Reuter (1954) had carried out the spectral analysis of the general birth and death process, of which this queueing process is a special case. The probabilities $P_{ij}(t)$ can be obtained by inverting the transform (1.29) (see Complements 3, 4); however, we describe below Champernowne's (1956) combinatorial method for deriving these probabilities explicitly.

b. The Basic Process $X(t)$

Let $A(t)$ and $D(t)$ be the number of arrivals and departures respectively during $(0, t]$; their probability distributions are given by (1.10) and (1.11). Now consider the process $X(t) = A(t) - D(t)$ and let

$$k_j(t) = Pr\{X(t) = j\} \qquad (j = \ldots, -1, 0, 1, 2, \ldots) \tag{1.30}$$

denote the distribution of $X(t)$. Since $A(t)$ and $D(t)$ are independent processes, we have

$$k_j(t) = Pr\{A(t) - D(t) = j\} = \sum_{n=0}^{\infty} Pr\{D(t) = n;\ A(t) = n + j\}$$

$$\begin{aligned} &= \sum_{n=0}^{\infty} Pr\{D(t) = n\}Pr\{A(t) = n + j\} \\ &= \sum_{n=0}^{\infty} e^{-\mu t}\frac{(\mu t)^n}{n!} \cdot e^{-\lambda t}\frac{(\lambda t)^{n+j}}{(n+j)!} \\ &= e^{-(\lambda+\mu)t}\rho^{j/2} I_j(2\sqrt{\lambda\mu}\, t), \end{aligned} \tag{1.31}$$

where

$$I_j(x) = \sum_{n=0}^{\infty} \frac{(x/2)^{2n+j}}{n!\,(n+j)!} \tag{1.32}$$

is the modified Bessel function of index j. Since $I_j(x) = I_{-j}(x)$, we have

$$\begin{aligned} k_{-j}(t) &= e^{-(\lambda+\mu)t}\rho^{-j/2} I_j(2\sqrt{\lambda\mu}\, t) \\ &= \rho^{-j} k_j(t). \end{aligned} \tag{1.33}$$

When $\lambda = \mu$, this gives $k_{-j}(t) = k_j(t)$, as it should, since $X(t)$ is now a symmetric random process. The Laplace transform of $I_j(x)$ is given by

$$\int_0^\infty e^{-\theta x} I_j(x)\, dx = (\theta^2 - 1)^{-\frac{1}{2}}(\theta + \sqrt{\theta^2 - 1})^{-j} \tag{1.34}$$

so that, for $j \geqslant 0$, we obtain

$$\int_0^\infty e^{-\theta t} k_j(t)\, dt = \int_0^\infty e^{-\theta t-(\lambda+\mu)t} \rho^{j/2} I_j(2\sqrt{\lambda\mu}\, t)\, dt$$

$$= \int_0^\infty e^{-(\theta+\lambda+\mu)x/2\sqrt{\lambda\mu}} \rho^{j/2} I_j(x) \frac{dx}{2\sqrt{\lambda\mu}}$$

$$(1.35) \qquad = \frac{\rho^{j/2}}{2\sqrt{\lambda\mu}} \left[\frac{(\theta+\lambda+\mu)^2}{4\lambda\mu} - 1\right]^{-1/2}$$

$$\cdot \left[\frac{\theta+\lambda+\mu}{2\sqrt{\lambda\mu}} + \sqrt{\frac{(\theta+\lambda+\mu)^2}{4\lambda\mu} - 1}\right]^{-j}$$

$$= \frac{\eta^{-j}}{\lambda(\eta-\xi)} \qquad (j \geqslant 0).$$

Similarly, using (1.33) we find that for $j \geqslant 0$,

$$(1.36) \qquad \int_0^\infty e^{-\theta t} k_{-j}(t)\, dt = \int_0^\infty e^{-\theta t} \rho^{-j} k_j(t)\, dt$$

$$= \frac{(\rho\eta)^{-j}}{\lambda(\eta-\xi)} = \frac{\xi^j}{\lambda(\eta-\xi)} \qquad \text{from (1.26).}$$

The probability generating function of $X(t)$ is given by

$$\sum_{j=0}^{\infty} k_j(t) z^j = E[z^{X(t)}] = E[z^{A(t)-D(t)}]$$

$$(1.37) \qquad = E[z^{A(t)}] E\left[\left(\frac{1}{z}\right)^{D(t)}\right]$$

$$= e^{-\lambda t(1-z)} \cdot e^{-\mu t(1-1/z)}$$

$$= e^{[\lambda z-(\lambda+\mu)+\mu/z]t}.$$

Letting $z \to 1$ in (1.37) we find that

$$(1.38) \qquad Pr\{X(t) < \infty\} = \sum_0^\infty k_j(t) = 1,$$

which shows that $X(t)$ assumes only finite values. Finally, we have

$$K_j(t) = \sum_{-\infty}^{j} k_v(t)$$

$$(1.39) \qquad = Pr\{A(t) - D(t) \leqslant j\}$$

$$= \sum_{\Delta(j)}\sum e^{-(\lambda+\mu)t} \frac{\lambda^a \mu^b}{a!\, b!} t^{a+b},$$

where $\Delta(j)$ denotes the set of integers a, b, such that $a \geqslant 0$, $b \geqslant 0$, $a - b \leqslant j$.

c. Combinatorial Methods

We now describe Champernowne's (1956) method for deriving an explicit expression for the transition probabilities $P_{ij}(t)$. Let us first observe that the process $X(t)$ increases or decreases by unity at random points of time, and that the intervals between successive points of increase and the intervals between successive points of decrease are random variables which are distributed according to negative exponential laws with means λ^{-1} and μ^{-1} respectively, all intervals being mutually independent. A typical realization of this process is shown in Figure 1.1.

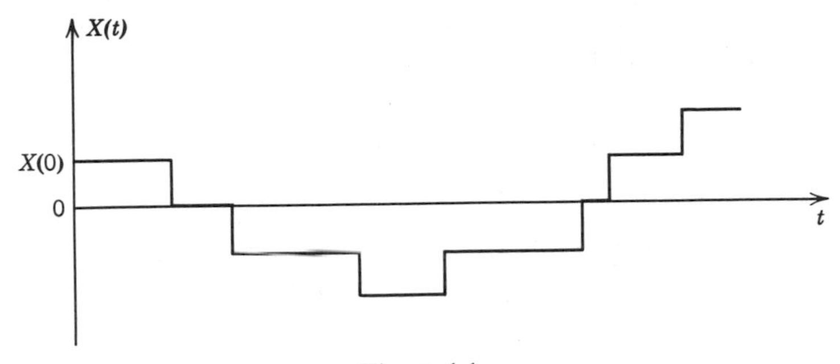

Figure 1.1

The process $Q(t)$ shares the same properties as $X(t)$, with the important difference that $Q(t)$ has an impenetrable barrier at 0, such that when $Q(t)$ reaches zero, it remains at zero until the process $X(t)$ takes the first upward jump (of unit magnitude), and at this point $Q(t) = 1$. The process $Q(t)$ then repeats itself. It will be found that

$$Q(t) = \max\left\{\sup_{0\leqslant\tau\leqslant t}[X(t) - X(\tau)],\ Q(0) + X(t)\right\}. \tag{1.40}$$

This representation is typical of many of the processes which will be encountered in this book; a rigorous proof will be given in Section 7.9. We can write (1.40) as

$$Q(t) = \max\,[X(t) - \sigma(t),\ Q(0) + X(t)], \tag{1.41}$$

where

$$\sigma(t) = \inf_{0\leqslant\tau\leqslant t} X(\tau) = \inf_{\leqslant\tau\leqslant t}[A(\tau) - D(\tau)]. \tag{1.42}$$

Since $A(0) = D(0) = 0$, it follows that $\sigma(t) \leqslant 0$ with probability one; the distribution of $\sigma(t)$ can be obtained as follows.

Let us consider the various points of increase or decrease in the process $A(t) - D(t)$ during $(0, t]$, subject to the condition that $A(t) = a$, $D(t) = b$; if we plot the "state" of the process (that is, its value) against the cumulated number of jumps, we obtain a path consisting of the points $(0, 0)$, $(1, s_1)$, $(2, s_2), \ldots, (a + b, s_{a+b})$, where $s_x - s_{x-1} = \pm 1$ $(x = 1, 2, \ldots, a + b)$ and $s_{a+b} = a - b$. Such a path can be considered as the path of a particle performing the classical random walk [see Feller (1957), Chapter III]. The numbers of such paths is $\binom{a+b}{a}$, and since clearly all these are equally likely, the probability of each path is $\binom{a+b}{a}^{-1}$. Now if $\sigma(t) \leqslant \nu$, then this path meets or crosses the line $x = \nu$, and by the "reflection principle" of D. André, the number of such paths equals the number of paths from $(0, \nu)$ to $(a + b, a - b - \nu)$, which is $\binom{a+b}{a-\nu}$. Hence it follows that

$$Pr\{\sigma(t) \leqslant \nu \mid A(t) = a,\ D(t) = b\}$$

$$(1.43) \qquad = \frac{\binom{a+b}{a-\nu}}{\binom{a+b}{a}} = \begin{cases} \dfrac{a!\, b!}{(a-\nu)!\,(b+\nu)!} & \text{if } \nu < \min(0, a-b) \\ 1 & \text{if } \nu \geqslant \min(0, a-b). \end{cases}$$

Using (1.43) we therefore obtain from (1.41)

$$\begin{aligned} Pr\{Q(t) \leqslant j \mid Q(0) = i\} \\ &= \sum_{a,b}\sum Pr\{A(t) = a;\ D(t) = b\} Pr\{Q(t) \leqslant j \mid Q(0) = i, \\ &\qquad\qquad A(t) = a,\ D(t) = b\} \\ &= \sum_{\Delta(j-i)}\sum e^{-(\lambda+\mu)t} \frac{\lambda^a \mu^b t^{a+b}}{a!\, b!} Pr\{\sigma(t) \geqslant a - b - j\} \\ (1.44) \qquad &= \sum_{\Delta(j-i)}\sum e^{-(\lambda+\mu)t} \frac{\lambda^a \mu^b t^{a+b}}{a!\, b!}\left[1 - \frac{a!\, b!}{(b+j+1)!\,(a-j-1)!}\right] \\ &= \sum_{\Delta(j-i)}\sum e^{-(\lambda+\mu)t} \frac{\lambda^a \mu^b t^{a+b}}{a!\, b!} - \sum_{\Delta(-j-i-2)}\sum e^{-(\lambda+\mu)t} \frac{\lambda^{a+j+1} \mu^{b-j-1} t^{a+b}}{a!\, b!} \\ &= K_{j-i}(t) - \rho^{j+1} K_{-j-i-2}(t) \qquad \text{[from (1.39)].} \end{aligned}$$

Hence

$$\begin{aligned} P_{ij}(t) &= Pr\{Q(t) = j \mid Q(0) = i\} \\ &= Pr\{Q(t) \leqslant j \mid Q(0) = i\} - Pr\{Q(t) \leqslant j - 1 \mid Q(0) = i\} \\ (1.45) \qquad &= [K_{j-i}(t) - \rho^{j+1} K_{-j-i-2}(t)] - [K_{j-1-i}(t) - \rho^j K_{-j-i-1}(t)] \\ &= k_{j-i}(t) + \rho^j k_{-j-i-1}(t) + (1 - \rho)\rho^j K_{-j-i-2}(t); \end{aligned}$$

using (1.33) we can write this as

$$P_{ij}(t) = k_{j-i}(t) + \rho^{-i-1}k_{j+i+1}(t) + (1-\rho)\rho^j K_{-j-i-2}(t). \tag{1.46}$$

When $\rho = 1$, this simplifies to

$$P_{ij}(t) = k_{j-i}(t) + k_{j+i+1}(t), \tag{1.47}$$

where $k_j(t) = e^{-2\lambda t}I_j(2\lambda t)$. From (1.45) we find that

$$\begin{aligned}\sum_{j=0}^{\infty} P_{ij}(t) &= \sum_{j=0}^{\infty} k_{j-i}(t) + \sum_{j=0}^{\infty} \rho^j k_{-j-i-1} + (1-\rho)\sum_{j=0}^{\infty}\rho^j \sum_{-\infty}^{-j-i-2} k_\nu \\ &= \sum_{-i}^{\infty} k_\nu(t) + \sum_{-\infty}^{-i-1} \rho^{-\nu-i-1}k_\nu + \sum_{-\infty}^{-i-1} k_\nu(1-\rho^{-\nu-i-1}) \\ &= \sum_{-\infty}^{\infty} k_\nu(t) = 1 \qquad \text{[from (1.38)];}\end{aligned} \tag{1.48}$$

thus in finite time there is no possibility of an unduly long queue.

d. The Limiting Distribution of $Q(t)$

From the property

$$I_j(x) \sim \frac{e^x}{\sqrt{2\pi x}} \qquad \text{as} \quad x \to \infty \tag{1.49}$$

we find that

$$\begin{aligned} k_j(t) &\sim e^{-(\lambda+\mu)t}\rho^{j/2}\frac{e^{2\sqrt{\lambda\mu}\,t}}{2(\pi t)^{1/2}(\lambda\mu)^{1/4}} \\ &= \frac{e^{-(\sqrt{\lambda}-\sqrt{\mu})^2 t}\rho^{j/2}}{2(\pi t)^{1/2}(\lambda\mu)^{1/4}} \qquad \text{as} \quad t\to\infty. \end{aligned} \tag{1.50}$$

Therefore, if $\rho > 1$,

$$K_j(t) = \sum_{-\infty}^{j} k_\nu(t) \sim \frac{e^{-(\sqrt{\lambda}-\sqrt{\mu})^2 t}}{2(\pi t)^{1/2}(\lambda\mu)^{1/4}}\sum_{-\infty}^{j}\rho^{\nu/2} < \infty, \tag{1.51}$$

whereas, if $\rho < 1$,

$$1 - K_j(t) = \sum_{j+1}^{\infty} k_\nu(t) \sim \frac{e^{-(\sqrt{\lambda}-\sqrt{\mu})^2 t}}{2(\pi t)^{1/2}(\lambda\mu)^{1/4}}\sum_{j+1}^{\infty}\rho^{\nu/2} < \infty. \tag{1.52}$$

Hence we see that as $t \to \infty$

$$K_j(t) \to \begin{cases} 0 & \text{if} \quad \rho > 1 \\ 1 & \text{if} \quad \rho < 1 \end{cases} \tag{1.53}$$

for all j. Using (1.50) and (1.53) in (1.46) and (1.47) we have that

$$\lim_{t\to\infty} P_{ij}(t) = \begin{cases} 0 & \text{if} \quad \rho \geqslant 1 \\ (1-\rho)\rho^j & \text{if} \quad \rho < 1. \end{cases} \tag{1.54}$$

This result implies that independently of its initial length i, the queue grows unduly long at the end of an indefinitely long period of time if $\rho \geqslant 1$, whereas if $\rho < 1$, the queue-length attains statistical equilibrium and tends to have the geometric distribution $(1-\rho)\rho^j$ $(j = 0, 1, 2, \ldots)$ This limiting distribution is stationary in the sense that if the initial queue-length $Q(0)$ has this distribution, so does the queue-length $Q(t)$ for any $t > 0$. For we have

$$
\begin{aligned}
Pr\{Q(t) \leqslant j\} &= \sum_{i=0}^{\infty} Pr\{Q(0) = i\} Pr\{Q(t) \leqslant j \mid Q(0) = i\} \\
&= \sum_{i=0}^{\infty} (1-\rho)\rho^i [K_{j-i}(t) - \rho^{j+1} K_{-j-i-2}(t)] \\
&= (1-\rho) \sum_{0}^{\infty} \rho^i \sum_{-\infty}^{j-i} k_v(t) - (1-\rho) \sum_{0}^{\infty} \rho^{i+j+1} \sum_{-\infty}^{-j-i-2} k_v(t) \qquad (1.55) \\
&= \sum_{-\infty}^{j+1} k_v(t)(1 - \rho^{j-v+1}) - \sum_{-\infty}^{-j-2} k_v(t)(\rho^{j+1} - \rho^{-v}) \\
&= \left[\sum_{-\infty}^{j+1} k_v(t) - \rho^{j+1} \sum_{-j-1}^{\infty} k_v(t)\right] - \left[\rho^{j+1} \sum_{-\infty}^{-j-2} k_v(t) - \sum_{j+2}^{\infty} k_v(t)\right] \\
&= 1 - \rho^{j+1},
\end{aligned}
$$

which proves our assertion.

e. The Busy Period; Zero-Avoiding Transitions

Suppose that initially the system contains i ($\geqslant 1$) customers, and let T_i be the next subsequent epoch of time at which the server is free; T_i is called the busy period initiated by i customers. We can express T_i as

$$T_i = \inf\, [t \mid Q(t) = 0,\, Q(0) = i]. \tag{1.56}$$

Clearly, T_i is a random variable; let its distribution function (d.f.) be $G_i(t)$, so that

$$G_i(t) = Pr\{T_i \leqslant t\} \qquad (0 \leqslant t < \infty). \tag{1.57}$$

We also define

$${}^0P_{ij}(t) = Pr\{Q(t) = j;\, T_i > t \mid Q(0) = i\} \qquad (i, j \geqslant 1) \tag{1.58}$$

as the probability that there will be j customers in the system at time t, the server being busy throughout the interval $[0, t]$. We call ${}^0P_{ij}(t)$ the zero-avoiding transition probabilities of the Markov process $Q(t)$.

In view of (1.40) we can write (1.56) as

$$T_i = \inf [t \mid i + X(t) \leqslant 0], \tag{1.59}$$

and therefore

$$\begin{aligned} {}^0P_{ij}(t) &= Pr\{i + X(\tau) > 0 \; (0 \leqslant \tau \leqslant t);\; i + X(t) = j\} \\ &= Pr\{i + \sigma(t) > 0;\; i + X(t) = j\}. \end{aligned} \tag{1.60}$$

From (1.41) and (1.60) we obtain

$$\begin{aligned} Pr\{Q(t) < j \mid Q(0) = i\} &= Pr\{X(t) - \sigma(t) < j;\, i + X(t) < j\} \\ &= \sum_{\nu=i+1}^{\infty} Pr\{X(t) - \sigma(t) < j;\, X(t) = j - \nu\} \\ &= \sum_{i+1}^{\infty} Pr\{\nu + \sigma(t) > 0;\, \nu + X(t) = j\} \\ &= \sum_{i+1}^{\infty} {}^0P_{\nu j}(t), \end{aligned} \tag{1.61}$$

a relation connecting the zero-avoiding transition probabilities with the ordinary ones. In particular we have

$$P_{i0}(t) = \sum_{i+1}^{\infty} {}^0P_{\nu 1}(t). \tag{1.62}$$

From (1.61) it follows that

$$\begin{aligned} {}^0P_{ij}(t) &= Pr\{Q(t) \leqslant j - 1 \mid Q(0) = i - 1\} - Pr\{Q(t) \leqslant j - 1 \mid Q(0) = i\} \\ &= [K_{j-i}(t) - \rho^j K_{-j-i}(t)] - [K_{j-i-1}(t) - \rho^j K_{-j-i-1}] \\ &= k_{j-i}(t) - \rho^j k_{-j-i}(t) \\ &= k_{j-i}(t) - \rho^{-i} k_{j+i}(t) \qquad (i, j \geqslant 1). \end{aligned} \tag{1.63}$$

The Laplace transform of ${}^0P_{ij}(t)$ is given by

$$\begin{aligned} {}^0P^*_{ij}(\theta) &= \int_0^\infty e^{-\theta t}\, {}^0P_{ij}(t)\, dt \\ &= \int_0^\infty e^{-\theta t} k_{j-i}(t)\, dt - \rho^{-i} \int_0^\infty e^{-\theta t} k_{j+i}(t)\, dt. \end{aligned}$$

Using (1.35) and (1.36) we find that

$$(1.64)\qquad {}^0P^*_{ij}(\theta) = \begin{cases} \dfrac{\eta^{-j}(\eta^i - \xi^i)}{\lambda(\eta - \xi)} & \text{if } j \geqslant i \\[2ex] \dfrac{\xi^i(\xi^{-j} - \eta^{-j})}{\lambda(\eta - \xi)} & \text{if } j \leqslant i, \end{cases}$$

where ξ, η are given by (1.25).

The distribution of the busy period T_i is given by

$$\begin{aligned} dG_i(t) &= {}^0P_{i1}(t)\mu\, dt \\ &= [\rho^{1-i}k_{i-1}(t) - \rho^{-i}k_{i+1}(t)]\mu\, dt \\ &= e^{-(\lambda+\mu)t}[\rho^{-i+1}\rho^{(i-1)/2}I_{i-1}(2\sqrt{\lambda\mu}\, t) - \rho^{-i}\rho^{(i+1)/2}I_{i+1}(2\sqrt{\lambda\mu}\, t)]\mu\, dt \\ &= e^{-(\lambda+\mu)t}\rho^{(i-1)/2}\{I_{i-1}(2\sqrt{\lambda\mu}\, t) - I_{i+1}(2\sqrt{\lambda\mu}\, t)\}\mu\, dt \\ &= e^{-(\lambda+\mu)t}\rho^{-(i-1)/2}\left(\frac{2i}{2\sqrt{\lambda\mu}\, t}\right)I_i(2\sqrt{\lambda\mu}\, t)\mu\, dt \\ &= \frac{i}{t}\, k_{-i}(t)\, dt, \end{aligned}$$

which shows that $dG_i(t) = g_i(t)\, dt$, where the frequency function (fr.f.) $g_i(t)$ is given by

$$(1.65)\qquad g_i(t) = \frac{i}{t}\, k_{-i}(t) \qquad (i \geqslant 1, t > 0).$$

The Laplace transform of this distribution is given by

$$(1.66)\qquad \begin{aligned} g_i{}^*(\theta) &= \int_0^\infty e^{-\theta t} g_i(t)\, dt = \int_0^\infty e^{-\theta t}\, {}^0P_{i1}(t)\mu\, dt \\ &= \frac{\xi^i(\xi^{-1} - \eta^{-1})}{\lambda(\eta - \xi)}\mu = \xi^i \qquad \text{[from (1.64)]}. \end{aligned}$$

From (1.66) we see that

$$(1.67)\qquad Pr\{T_i < \infty\} = \lim_{\theta \to 0+} g_i{}^*(\theta) = \begin{cases} 1 & \text{if } \rho \leqslant 1 \\ \rho^{-i} & \text{if } \rho > 1 \end{cases}$$

since $\xi(\theta) \to 1$ or ρ^{-1} depending on whether $\rho \leqslant 1$ or $\rho > 1$; thus the busy period will terminate eventually if $\rho \leqslant 1$, whereas if $\rho > 1$ there is a positive probability that it will continue indefinitely. When $i = 1$ we have the busy period T_1 initiated by a single customer (as defined in

Section 1.1); the Laplace transform of its distribution is $g_1^*(\theta) = \xi$, and from (1.66) we see that the fr.f. $g_i(t)$ is the i-fold convolution of $g_1(t)$. Thus T_i can be considered as the sum of i mutually independent random variables, each having the same distribution as T_1—a result which is intuitively obvious.

The result (1.63) is due to Bailey (1954), and (1.65) due (for $i = 1$) to Kendall (1952), and (for $i > 1$) to Good [see discussion in Kendall (1952)]. The methods used by these authors are, however, different from ours (see Complement 5).

f. The Waiting Time

The waiting time $W(t)$ is the time required to serve all the customers present in the system at time t. Thus

$$(1.68)\qquad W(t) = \begin{cases} 0 & \text{if } \quad Q(t) = 0 \\ v_1' + v_2 + v_3 + \cdots + v_{Q(t)} & \text{if } \quad Q(t) > 0, \end{cases}$$

where v_1' is the residual service time of the customer being served, and $v_2, v_3, \ldots, v_{Q(t)}$ the service times of those waiting at time t. From (1.68) it is easily seen that $W(t)$ is a Markov process. Let its transition d.f. be denoted by

$$(1.69)\quad F(x, t) = Pr\{W(t) \leqslant x \mid W(0) = 0\} \qquad (0 \leqslant x < \infty, 0 \leqslant t < \infty),$$

where we have assumed for convenience that initially the system is empty. From (1.68) we obtain at once

$$(1.70)\qquad F(0, t) = P_{00}(t).$$

Now let $Q(t) = j \geqslant 1$. On account of the Markovian property of the negative exponential distribution [see equation (1.6)], the distribution of the residual service time v_1' is the same as that of $v_2, v_3, \ldots, v_j$ (that is, $\mu e^{-\mu v}\, dv$), and since these variables are mutually independent it follows that the distribution of their sum $v_1' + v_2 + v_3 + \cdots + v_j$ is the j-fold convolution of this distribution, that is, the gamma distribution

$$\frac{e^{-\mu v}\mu^j v^{j-1}\, dv}{(j-1)!}.$$

Therefore the distribution of $W(t)$ is given by

$$(1.71)\qquad \begin{aligned} d_xF(x, t) &= Pr\{x < W(t) < x + dx \mid W(0) = 0\} \\ &= \sum_{j=1}^{\infty} \frac{P_{0j}(t)e^{-\mu x}\mu^j x^{j-1}\, dx}{(j-1)!} \qquad (0 < x < \infty). \end{aligned}$$

Since the probabilities $P_{0j}(t)$ have been already determined, the last expression can be evaluated. [$F(x, t)$ will be obtained more explicitly in Chapter 2.] The distribution of the waiting time thus has a discontinuity at the origin [given by (1.70)] and is continuous in the range $0 < x < \infty$. The Laplace-Stieltjes transform (L.S.T.) of this distribution is given by

$$
\begin{aligned}
\Phi(\omega, t) &= \int_{0-}^{\infty} e^{-\omega x}\, d_x F(x, t) \qquad [\text{Re}\,(\omega) > 0] \\
&= F(0, t) + \sum_{j=1}^{\infty} P_{0j}(t) \int_{0}^{\infty} e^{-\omega x - \mu x} \mu^j \frac{x^{j-1}}{(j-1)!}\, dx \\
&= P_{00}(t) + \sum_{1}^{\infty} P_{0j}(t) \left(\frac{\mu}{\mu + \omega}\right)^j \\
&= \sum_{0}^{\infty} P_{0j}(t) \left(\frac{\mu}{\mu + \omega}\right)^j = G\left(\frac{\mu}{\mu + \omega}, t\right),
\end{aligned} \tag{1.72}
$$

where $G(z, t)$ is the generating function defined by (1.19). Taking Laplace transforms with respect to time of both sides of (1.72) and using (1.29), we obtain

$$
\begin{aligned}
\Phi^*(\omega, \theta) &= \int_{0}^{\infty} e^{-\theta t} \Phi(\omega, t)\, dt = G^*\left(\frac{\mu}{\mu + \omega}, \theta\right) \\
&= \frac{[\mu/(\mu + \omega)] - [\omega/(\mu + \omega)]\xi/(1 - \xi)}{\lambda\left(\dfrac{\mu}{\mu + \omega} - \xi\right)\left(\dfrac{\mu}{\lambda\xi} - \dfrac{\mu}{\mu + \omega}\right)} \\
&= \frac{\xi}{\mu(1 - \xi)}\left(1 + \frac{\lambda\xi}{\mu + \omega - \lambda\xi}\right) \qquad [\text{Re}\,(\theta) > 0].
\end{aligned} \tag{1.73}
$$

To obtain the limiting distribution of $W(t)$ as $t \to \infty$, we note that taking limits inside the summation in (1.71) is justified. Thus $F(x, t) \to F(x)$, where

$$
F(0) = 1 - \rho, \tag{1.74}
$$

$$
\begin{aligned}
dF(x) &= \sum^{\infty} (1 - \rho)\rho^j e^{-\mu x} \mu^j x^{j-1} \frac{dx}{(j-1)!} \\
&= \lambda(1 - \rho) e^{-\mu x} \sum_{1}^{\infty} \frac{(\lambda x)^{j-1}}{(j-1)!}\, dx \\
&= \lambda(1 - \rho) e^{-(\mu - \lambda)x}\, dx \qquad (0 < x < \infty),
\end{aligned} \tag{1.75}
$$

these results being valid if $\rho < 1$; if $\rho \geqslant 1$, $F(x, t) \to 0$ as $t \to \infty$. These results imply, as in the case of queue-length, that if $\rho \geqslant 1$, the waiting time increases indefinitely as $t \to \infty$, whereas if $\rho < 1$, it tends to be distributed according to the negative exponential law (1.75) in the range $0 < x < \infty$, the probability of not having to wait being $1 - \rho$.

1.3 THE QUEUE $M/M/s$

We next consider the system $M/M/s$, where the input process and the service time distribution are the same as in the last section, but there are s servers, where $1 \leqslant s < \infty$. Customers are served on a "first come, first served" basis. Let $Q(t)$ be the number of customers present in the system (including those being served) at time t; here again $Q(t)$ is a birth and death process. For transitions occurring in an infinitesimal interval $(t, t + dt]$ we have

$$\begin{aligned} P_{ii+1}(dt) &= \lambda\, dt + o(dt) \\ P_{ii-1}(dt) &= \mu_i\, dt + o(dt) \\ P_{ii}(dt) &= 1 - (\lambda + \mu_i)\, dt + o(dt), \end{aligned} \tag{1.76}$$

where

$$\mu_i = \begin{cases} i\mu & \text{if } 0 \leqslant i \leqslant s \\ s\mu & \text{if } i \geqslant s; \end{cases} \tag{1.77}$$

$P_{ij}(dt) = o(dt)$ for all other combinations of i and j. Substituting (1.76) in (1.15) and proceeding as in the last section we find the forward Kolmogorov equations of the process to be

$$P'_{ij}(t) = -(\lambda + \mu_j)P_{ij}(t) + \lambda P_{ij-1}(t) + \mu_{j+1}P_{ij+1}(t) \qquad (i, j \geqslant 0). \tag{1.78}$$

Using (1.77) we can write (1.78) as

$$\begin{aligned} P'_{i0}(t) &= -\lambda P_{i0}(t) + \mu P_{i1}(t) \\ P'_{ij}(t) &= -(\lambda + j\mu)P_{ij}(t) + \lambda P_{ij-1}(t) + \mu(j + 1)P_{ij+1}(t) \\ &\qquad\qquad\qquad\qquad\qquad\qquad (1 \leqslant j \leqslant s - 1) \\ P'_{ij}(t) &= -(\lambda + s\mu)P_{ij}(t) + \lambda P_{ij-1}(t) + s\mu P_{ij+1}(t) \qquad (j \geqslant s). \end{aligned} \tag{1.79}$$

These equations have been solved by Saaty (1960) by an extension of Bailey's method of generating functions, which was described in Section 1.2a; the solution for $s > 1$ is rather complicated and will not be given here. Let us, however, consider the limiting probabilities

$$\lim_{t \to \infty} P_{ij}(t) = u_j \qquad (j \geqslant 0). \tag{1.80}$$

Assuming that the probabilities u_j exist independently of the initial state i, we see that they satisfy the equations (1.79) with $P'_{ij}(t) = 0$. Thus

$$\begin{aligned} \mu u_1 - \lambda u_0 &= 0 \\ \mu(j+1)u_{j+1} - (\lambda + j\mu)u_j + \lambda u_{j-1} &= 0 \qquad (1 \leqslant j \leqslant s-1) \\ s\mu u_{j+1} - (\lambda + s\mu)u_j + \lambda u_{j-1} &= 0 \qquad (j \geqslant s). \end{aligned} \tag{1.81}$$

Solving these equations successively, we obtain

$$u_1 = \frac{\lambda}{\mu} u_0, \qquad u_2 = \frac{1}{2}\left(\frac{\lambda}{\mu} + 1\right)u_1 - \frac{\lambda}{2\mu} u_0 = \frac{1}{2}\left(\frac{\lambda}{\mu}\right)^2 u_0,$$

$$u_3 = \frac{1}{3}\left(\frac{\lambda}{\mu} + 2\right)u_2 - \frac{\lambda}{3\mu} u_1 = \frac{1}{3}\left(\frac{\lambda}{\mu} + 2\right)\frac{1}{2}\left(\frac{\lambda}{\mu}\right)^2 u_0 - \frac{1}{3}\left(\frac{\lambda}{\mu}\right)^2 u_0$$

$$= \frac{1}{3!}\left(\frac{\lambda}{\mu}\right)^3 u_0$$

. . . .

$$u_s = \frac{1}{s!}\left(\frac{\lambda}{\mu}\right)^s u_0 \tag{1.82}$$

$$u_{s+1} = \left(\frac{\lambda}{s\mu} + 1\right)u_s - \frac{\lambda}{s\mu} u_{s-1}$$

$$= \left(\frac{\lambda}{s\mu} + 1\right)\frac{1}{s!}\left(\frac{\lambda}{\mu}\right)^s u_0 - \frac{1}{s!}\left(\frac{\lambda}{\mu}\right)^s u_0 = \frac{1}{s \cdot s!}\left(\frac{\lambda}{\mu}\right)^{s+1} u_0$$

$$u_{s+2} = \left(\frac{\lambda}{s\mu} + 1\right)u_{s+1} - \frac{\lambda}{s\mu} u_s$$

$$= \left(\frac{\lambda}{s\mu} + 1\right)\frac{1}{s \cdot s!}\left(\frac{\lambda}{\mu}\right)^{s+1} u_0 - \frac{1}{s \cdot s!}\left(\frac{\lambda}{\mu}\right)^{s+1} u_0 = \frac{1}{s^2 \cdot s!}\left(\frac{\lambda}{\mu}\right)^{s+2} u_0$$

. . . .

For the limiting queue-length Q we thus have

$$Pr\{Q = j\} = u_j = \begin{cases} \dfrac{u_0}{j!}\left(\dfrac{\lambda}{\mu}\right)^j & (0 \leqslant j \leqslant s) \\ \dfrac{u_0}{s^{j-s} \cdot s!}\left(\dfrac{\lambda}{\mu}\right)^j & (j \geqslant s), \end{cases} \tag{1.83}$$

where u_0 is determined by the condition that $u_0 + u_1 + u_2 + \cdots = 1$, which gives

$$u_0\left[\sum_0^{s-1} \frac{1}{j!}\left(\frac{\lambda}{\mu}\right)^j + \frac{s^s}{s!}\sum_s^{\infty} \rho^j\right] = 1, \tag{1.84}$$

where $\rho = \lambda/\mu s$ is the relative traffic intensity of the system. The infinite series on the left-hand side of (1.84) converges if and only if $\rho < 1$, so that the limiting distribution (1.80) exists only in this case. The condition (1.84) gives

$$u_0 = \left[\sum_0^{s-1} \frac{1}{j!}\left(\frac{\lambda}{\mu}\right)^j + \frac{1}{s!}\left(\frac{\lambda}{\mu}\right)^s (1-\rho)^{-1}\right]^{-1}. \tag{1.85}$$

The mean queue-length is given by

$$\begin{aligned} E(Q) &= \sum_0^{\infty} j u_j = \sum_0^{s} j \frac{u_0}{j!}\left(\frac{\lambda}{\mu}\right)^j + \sum_{s+1}^{\infty} j \frac{u_0}{s! \cdot s^{j-s}}\left(\frac{\lambda}{\mu}\right)^j \\ &= s\rho u_0 \sum_0^{s-1} \frac{1}{j!}\left(\frac{\lambda}{\mu}\right)^j + \frac{u_0}{s!}\left(\frac{\lambda}{\mu}\right)^s \sum_1^{\infty} (j+s)\rho^j \\ &= s\rho u_0 \sum_0^{s-1} \frac{1}{j!}\left(\frac{\lambda}{\mu}\right)^j + \frac{u_0}{s!}\left(\frac{\lambda}{\mu}\right)^s \left[\frac{\rho}{(1-\rho)^2} + \frac{s\rho}{(1-\rho)}\right] \\ &= s\rho + \frac{\rho u_s}{(1-\rho)^2} \qquad \text{[using (1.85)]}. \end{aligned} \tag{1.86}$$

If we are interested only in the number Q', of customers actually waiting in the system, the distribution and the mean of Q' (in the limiting case) can be found by using the preceding results for Q. For we have $Q' = \max(0, Q - s)$, and therefore

$$\begin{aligned} v_0 &= Pr\{Q' = 0\} = Pr\{Q \leqslant s\} = u_0 \sum_0^{s} \frac{1}{j!}\left(\frac{\lambda}{\mu}\right)^j, \\ v_j &= Pr\{Q' = j\} = Pr\{Q = j + s\} = \frac{u_0}{s^j \cdot s!}\left(\frac{\lambda}{\mu}\right)^{j+s} \qquad (j \geqslant 1), \end{aligned} \tag{1.87}$$

and

$$E(Q') = \sum_0^{\infty} j v_j = \frac{u_0}{s!}\left(\frac{\lambda}{\mu}\right)^s \sum_1^{\infty} j\rho^j = \frac{\rho u_s}{(1-\rho)^2}. \tag{1.88}$$

The distribution of W, the waiting time after an indefinitely long period of time, can also be obtained from the preceding results. For, if this customer, on entering the system, finds j customers ahead of him, then he will be served immediately if $j < s$, whereas if $j \geqslant s$, he will have to wait till the $(j - s + 1)$th customer completes his service. Therefore the probability that he does not have to wait is given by

$$F(0) = Pr\{W = 0\} = Pr\{Q < s\} = u_0 \sum_0^{s-1} \frac{1}{j!}\left(\frac{\lambda}{\mu}\right)^j. \tag{1.89}$$

If all the servers are busy, then the intervals of time between successive departures are independent random variables having a negative exponential distribution with mean $(s\mu)^{-1}$, and therefore the total time until the $(j-s+1)$th departure is the $(j-s+1)$-fold convolution of this distribution. Hence it follows that

$$\begin{aligned} dF(x) &= Pr\{x < W < x + dx\} \\ &= \sum_{s}^{\infty} u_j \, e^{-s\mu x}(s\mu)^{j-s+1} x^{j-s} \, dx/(j-s)! \\ &= \frac{u_0 s\mu}{s!}\left(\frac{\lambda}{\mu}\right)^s e^{-s\mu x} \sum_{s}^{\infty} \frac{(\lambda x)^{j-s}}{(j-s)!} \, dx \\ &= s\mu u_s \, e^{-x(s\mu-\lambda)} \, dx \qquad (0 < x < \infty). \end{aligned} \tag{1.90}$$

The distribution of W thus has a discrete probability at the origin and a continuous fr.f. in the range $0 < x < \infty$. The mean waiting time is given by

$$\begin{aligned} E(W) &= \int_0^\infty x s\mu u_s \, e^{-x(s\mu-\lambda)} \, dx \\ &= \frac{s\mu u_s}{(s\mu-\lambda)^2} = \frac{u_s}{s\mu(1-\rho)^2}. \end{aligned} \tag{1.91}$$

The results of this section are due to Erlang (1917); this system has also been considered by Vaulot (1924), Molina (1927), and Fry (1928).

1.4 THE SYSTEM WITH AN INFINITE NUMBER OF SERVERS

If the number of servers in the system considered in Section 1.3 is infinite, then each customer will be served immediately on arrival, and $Q(t)$ is the number of busy servers at time t. The forward Kolmogorov equations of the process become in this case

$$\begin{aligned} P'_{i0}(t) &= -\lambda P_{i0}(t) + \mu P_{i1}(t) \\ P'_{ij}(t) &= -(\lambda + j\mu)P_{ij}(t) + \lambda P_{ij-1}(t) \\ &\quad + \mu(j+1)P_{ij+1}(t) \qquad (j \geqslant 1). \end{aligned} \tag{1.92}$$

To solve (1.92) we introduce the generating function $G(z, t)$ defined by (1.19). We have

$$\frac{\partial G}{\partial z} = \sum_{1}^{\infty} jP_{ij}(t)z^{j-1}, \qquad \frac{\partial G}{\partial t} = \sum_{1}^{\infty} P'_{ij}(t)z^j. \tag{1.93}$$

Multiplying the equations (1.92) successively by $1, z, z^2, \ldots,$ and adding, we obtain

$$\sum_0^\infty P'_{ij}(t)z^j = -\sum_0^\infty (\lambda + j\mu)P_{ij}(t)z^j + \mu \sum_0^\infty (j+1)P_{ij+1}(t)z^j + \lambda \sum_1^\infty P_{ij-1}(t)z^j,$$

from which, simplifying and using (1.93), we obtain

$$\frac{\partial G}{\partial t} - \mu(1-z)\frac{\partial G}{\partial z} = -\lambda(1-z)G(z,t). \tag{1.94}$$

We have thus reduced the system of equations (1.92) to a single partial differential equation (1.94). To solve (1.94) we consider the associated equations

$$\frac{dt}{1} = \frac{dz}{-\mu(1-z)} = \frac{dG}{-\lambda(1-z)G}, \tag{1.95}$$

where the denominators are proportional to the coefficients of $\partial G/\partial t$, $\partial G/\partial z$, and G in (1.94); this latter system contains two independent equations. The first of these can be taken as $dt = -dz/\mu(1-z)$, which has the solution

$$e^{-\mu t}(1-z) = c_1 \qquad \text{(constant);} \tag{1.96}$$

the second can be taken as $dz = \mu\, dG/\lambda G$, which gives

$$G = c_2 e^{(\lambda/\mu)z} \qquad (c_2 \text{ constant}). \tag{1.97}$$

The general solution of (1.95) is obtained by eliminating one of the two constants c_1, c_2 from (1.96) and (1.97); thus

$$G(z,t) = e^{(\lambda/\mu)z}\phi\{e^{-\mu t}(1-z)\}. \tag{1.98}$$

Using the boundary condition $G(z, 0) = z^i$, we find that

$$e^{(\lambda/\mu)z}\phi(1-z) = z^i,$$

which gives

$$\phi(z) = e^{-(\lambda/\mu)(1-z)}(1-z)^i. \tag{1.99}$$

Using (1.99) in (1.98), we finally obtain

$$G(z,t) = e^{-(\lambda q/\mu)(1-z)}(q + pz)^i \tag{1.100}$$

as the solution of our equation (1.94); here $p = e^{-\mu t}$ and $q = 1 - p$. We note that the right-hand side of (1.100) is the product of two probability generating functions, the first one that of a Poisson distribution with mean $\lambda q/\mu$ and the second that of a binomial distribution with index i; the conditional distribution of $Q(t)$ is therefore the convolution of these two distributions. The transition probabilities of $Q(t)$ are therefore given by

$$P_{ij}(t) = \sum_{k=0}^{j} \binom{i}{j-k} e^{-\lambda q/\mu} p^{j-k} q^{i-j+2k} \left(\frac{\lambda}{\mu}\right)^k. \tag{1.101}$$

The conditional mean and variance of $Q(t)$ for a given $Q(0) = i$ are given respectively by

$$\begin{aligned} M &= \frac{\lambda q}{\mu} + ip = \frac{\lambda}{\mu} + \left(i - \frac{\lambda}{\mu}\right) e^{-\mu t} \\ V &= \frac{\lambda q}{\mu} + ipq = \frac{\lambda}{\mu} + \left(i - \frac{\lambda}{\mu}\right) e^{-\mu t} - ie^{-2\mu t}. \end{aligned} \tag{1.102}$$

These results are due to Palm (1943).

As $t \to \infty$, $p \to 0$, $q \to 1$ and therefore $G(z, t) \to U(z)$, where

$$U(z) = e^{-(\lambda/\mu)(1-z)}. \tag{1.103}$$

This shows that the limiting probabilities (1.80) existing independently of the initial state i are given by

$$u_j = \lim_{t\to\infty} P_{ij}(t) = e^{-\lambda/\mu} \frac{\left(\frac{\lambda}{\mu}\right)^j}{j!} \qquad (j \geqslant 0). \tag{1.104}$$

We thus obtain a Poisson distribution for the number of busy servers in statistical equilibrium; as in Section 1.2d, it can be proved that this distribution is stationary. From (1.102) we find that $M \to \lambda/\mu$, $V \to \lambda/\mu$ as $t \to \infty$, which shows that the mean and variance of the distribution (1.104) are both equal to λ/μ. This result also follows from (1.103).

1.5 THE SYSTEM WITH SERVICE IN PHASES

a. Transforms

Let us consider the single server system $M/E_k/1$, in which customers arrive in a Poisson process with mean λt, and the service time has the Erlangian distribution

$$dB(v) = \frac{e^{-\mu k v}(k\mu)^k v^{k-1}\, dv}{(k-1)!} \qquad (0 < v < \infty). \tag{1.105}$$

The mean service time is found to be

$$b = \int_0^\infty v\, dB(v) = \mu^{-1} \tag{1.106}$$

so that the relative traffic intensity is $\rho = \lambda b = \lambda/\mu$. Since the distribution (1.105) does not have the Markovian property, we see that the queue-length process in this system is not Markovian. However, let us observe that the service here can be interpreted as being offered in k consecutive phases, the times required for these phases being mutually independent random variables with the negative exponential distribution $k\mu e^{-k\mu v}\, dv$ $(0 < v < \infty)$, and the service of a customer being completed at the end of the kth phase. The arrival of each customer introduces k phases into the system, and the phases are completed successively in a Poisson process at a rate $k\mu$. If, therefore, $Q_1(t)$ denotes the number of phases in the system at time t, it is clear that $Q_1(t)$ is a denumerable Markov process. The transitions occurring in an infinitesimal interval $(t, t + dt]$ are characterized by the probabilities

$$P_{ij}(dt) = a_{ij}\, dt + o(dt) \qquad (i \neq j)$$
$$P_{ii}(dt) = 1 - a_{ii}\, dt + o(dt), \tag{1.107}$$

where

$$a_{00} = \lambda, \qquad a_{ii} = \lambda + k\mu \qquad (i \geqslant 1)$$
$$a_{i,i-1} = k\mu \qquad (i \geqslant 1), \qquad a_{i,i+k} = \lambda \qquad (i \geqslant 0), \tag{1.108}$$

a_{ij} being zero for all other combinations of i and j. This process is time homogeneous, but is slightly more general than Feller's (1957) birth and death process. Proceeding as in Section 1.2, we obtain the forward Kolmogorov equations of the process as

$$P'_{ij}(t) = -a_{jj}P_{ij}(t) + \sum_{v \neq j} P_{iv}(t)a_{vj} \qquad (i, j \geqslant 0). \tag{1.109}$$

Substituting (1.108) in (1.109) we can write these as

$$P'_{i0}(t) = -\lambda P_{i0}(t) + k\mu P_{i1}(t)$$
$$P'_{ij}(t) = -(\lambda + k\mu)P_{ij}(t) + k\mu P_{ij+1}(t) \qquad (1 \leqslant j < k) \tag{1.110}$$
$$P'_{ij}(t) = -(\lambda + k\mu)P_{ij}(t) + k\mu P_{ij+1}(t) + \lambda P_{ij-k}(t) \qquad (j \geqslant k).$$

Introducing the generating function $G(z, t)$ once again, we reduce (1.110) to the differential equation

$$z\frac{\partial G}{\partial t} = [k\mu - (\lambda + k\mu)z + \lambda z^{k+1}]G - k\mu(1 - z)P_{i0}(t). \tag{1.111}$$

Taking Laplace transforms with respect to time of both sides, we then obtain

$$G^*(z, \theta) = \frac{z^{i+1} - k\mu(1 - z)P^*_{i0}(\theta)}{(\theta + \lambda + k\mu)z - k\mu - \lambda z^{k+1}} \qquad (|z| < 1, \quad \mathrm{Re}\,(\theta) > 0). \tag{1.112}$$

In the region $|z| = 1$, $\text{Re}(\theta) > 0$, we have

$$(1.113) \quad |(\theta + \lambda + k\mu)z| = |\theta + \lambda + k\mu| > \lambda + k\mu > |\lambda z^{k+1} + k\mu|,$$

so that, by Rouché's theorem, the denominator on the right-hand side of (1.112), viz., $(\theta + \lambda + k\mu)z - k\mu - \lambda z^{k+1}$, has only zero in the unit circle. Let $\xi \equiv \xi(\theta)$ denote this zero. The arguments used in Section 1.2*a* then give

$$(1.114) \qquad P_{i0}^*(\theta) = \frac{\xi^{i+1}}{k\mu(1 - \xi)}$$

and

$$(1.115) \qquad G^*(z, \theta) = \frac{z^{i+1} - (1 - z)\xi^{i+1}/(1 - \xi)}{(\theta + \lambda + k\mu)z - k\mu - \lambda z^{k+1}}.$$

Since $G^*(z, \theta) \to \theta^{-1}$ as $z \to 1$, we have $\sum_0^\infty P_{ij}(t) = 1$, so that $Q_1(t)$ remains finite in finite time.

b. Limiting Distributions

Let us assume that the limiting probability distribution (u_j) of $Q_1(t)$ exists, where

$$(1.116) \qquad \lim_{t \to \infty} P_{ij}(t) = u_j \geqslant 0 \qquad (j \geqslant 0).$$

We have then

$$(1.117) \qquad u_0 = \lim_{t \to \infty} P_{i0}(t) = \lim_{\theta \to 0+} \theta P_{i0}^*(\theta)$$

and, moreover, from (1.112),

$$(1.118) \qquad \lim_{t \to \infty} G(z, t) = \lim_{\theta \to 0+} \theta G^*(z, \theta) = \frac{k\mu(1 - z)u_0}{k\mu - (\lambda + k\mu)z + \lambda z^{k+1}} \qquad (|z| \leqslant 1).$$

Now, consider the zeros of the denominator of this last expression; these are the roots of the equation

$$(1.119) \qquad z = K(z)$$

where $K(z) = (\lambda z^{k+1} + k\mu)/(\lambda + k\mu)$. Clearly, $K(z)$ is the p.g.f. of a random variable, with mean $K'(1) = (\lambda k + \lambda)/(\lambda + k\mu)$. From the theory of branching processes it is known (see Complement 17) that the equation (1.119) has a root ζ such that $0 < \zeta < 1$ if and only if $K'(1) > 1$, that is if $\rho > 1$. It is clear that if there is such a root, then as $\theta \to 0+$, $\xi(\theta) \to \zeta$, and otherwise $\xi(\theta) \to 1$. Furthermore, in the case $\rho \leqslant 1$, the relation $(\theta + \lambda + k\mu)\xi - k\mu + \lambda\xi^{k+1} = 0$ gives, on differentiation with respect to θ,

$$(\theta + \lambda + k\mu)\xi'(\theta) + \xi(\theta) - \lambda(k + 1)\xi^k\xi'(\theta) = 0,$$

from which, putting $\theta = 0+$, we obtain

$$\xi'(0+) = \begin{cases} \infty & \text{if} \quad \rho = 1 \\ [k(\lambda - \mu)]^{-1} & \text{if} \quad \rho < 1. \end{cases} \tag{1.120}$$

Using (1.120) in (1.117) we find that if $\rho \leqslant 1$, then

$$\lim_{t\to\infty} P_{i0}(t) = \lim_{\theta\to 0+} \frac{[\xi(0+)]^{i+1}}{-k\mu\xi'(0+)}$$

$$= \begin{cases} 0 & \text{if} \quad \rho = 1 \\ 1 - \rho & \text{if} \quad \rho < 1; \end{cases} \tag{1.121}$$

moreover, if $\rho > 1$, (1.117) shows directly that $P_{i0}(t) \to 0$ as $t \to \infty$, since $\zeta(\theta) \to \zeta < 1$ as $\theta \to 0+$. Summarizing these results, we see that if $\rho \geqslant 1$, $P_{i0}(t) \to 0$, and hence from (1.118), $G(z, t) \to 0$ as $t \to \infty$, whereas if $\rho < 1$, then $P_{i0}(t) \to u_0 = 1 - \rho$, and $G(z, t) \to \sum_0^\infty u_j z^j = U(z)$, where

$$U(z) = \frac{k\mu(1 - \rho)(1 - z)}{k\mu - (\lambda + k\mu)z + \lambda z^{k+1}} \qquad (|z| \leqslant 1). \tag{1.122}$$

For a further simplification of the result (1.122) we have to investigate the roots of the equation (1.119). Since $K(z)$ is a polynomial of degree $k + 1$, (1.119) has $k + 1$ roots, of which $z = 1$ is obviously one. Proceeding as in (1.113) we find that if $\rho < 1$, the other roots $z_1, z_2, \ldots, z_k$ are such that $|z_i| > 1$ $(i = 1, 2, \ldots, k)$. Let us assume that these roots are all distinct. Since

$$k\mu - (\lambda + k\mu)z + \lambda z^{k+1} = (1 - z)[k\mu - \lambda(z + z^2 + \cdots + z^k)],$$

it is clear that $z_1, z_2, \ldots, z_k$ are the roots of the equation

$$z^k + z^{k-1} + \cdots + z = \frac{\rho}{k}. \tag{1.123}$$

Furthermore we can write

$$k\mu - (\lambda + k\mu)z + \lambda z^{k+1} = \lambda(-1)^{k+1}(1 - z)\prod_{i=1}^{k}(z_i - z),$$

so that

$$U(z) = \frac{k\mu(1 - \rho)(-1)^{k+1}}{\lambda \prod_1^k (z_i - z)}.$$

Since $U(0) = u_0 = 1 - \rho$, we must have $\lambda z_1 z_2 \ldots z_k = k\mu(-1)^{k+1}$, and therefore

$$U(z) = \frac{1-\rho}{\prod_1^k (1 - zm_i)} \tag{1.124}$$

where $m_i = z_i^{-1}$, $|m_i| < 1$ $(i = 1, 2, \ldots, k)$. We can now express the last result in terms of partial fractions, viz.,

$$U(z) = (1-\rho)\sum_1^k \frac{A_\nu}{(1 - zm_\nu)}, \tag{1.125}$$

where

$$A_\nu = \lim_{z \to m_\nu^{-1}} \frac{1 - zm_\nu}{\prod_1^k (1 - zm_i)} = \prod_{i \neq \nu} \left(1 - \frac{m_i}{m_\nu}\right)^{-1} \qquad (1 \leqslant \nu \leqslant k). \tag{1.126}$$

Expanding the νth term on the right-hand side of (1.125) as a power series in z, convergent in the region $|z| < m_\nu^{-1}$, we obtain

$$U(z) = (1-\rho)\sum_1^k A_\nu \sum_0^\infty (zm_\nu)^j \tag{1.127}$$

$$|z| < \min\left(\left|\frac{1}{m_1}\right|, \left|\frac{1}{m_2}\right|, \ldots, \left|\frac{1}{m_k}\right|\right).$$

Hence we find that the limiting distribution of $Q_1(t)$ is given by

$$u_0 = 1 - \rho, \qquad u_j = (1-\rho)\sum_1^k A_\nu (m_\nu)^j \qquad (j \geqslant 1); \tag{1.128}$$

u_j is thus a weighted sum k of geometric terms.

As in Section 1.3, let W be the waiting time of a customer who joins the system after an indefinitely long period of time. If the system is empty, $W = 0$, but if the system contains $j \geqslant 1$ phases, then W is the time required to complete these j phases. Hence we find that

$$F(0) = Pr\{W = 0\} = 1 - \rho \tag{1.129}$$

$$\begin{aligned} dF(x) &= Pr\{x < W < x + dx\} \\ &= \sum_{j=1}^\infty \left[(1-\rho)\sum_1^k A_\nu m_\nu{}^j\right] e^{-k\mu x} \frac{(k\mu)^j}{(j-1)!} x^{j-1}\, dx \\ &= (1-\rho)\sum_1^k A_\nu m_\nu k\mu e^{-k\mu(1-m_\nu)x}\, dx \qquad (0 < x < \infty). \end{aligned} \tag{1.130}$$

Thus in the range $0 < x < \infty$, W has a continuous frequency function which is the weighted sum of k negative exponential terms.

The concept of phase type service is due to Erlang (1920), who obtained the above limiting distributions (see Complement 18). Before concluding this section we remark that the queue-length $Q(t)$ and the number of phases $Q_1(t)$ are connected by the relation

$$Q(t) = \left[\frac{Q_1(t) + k - 1}{k}\right] \tag{1.131}$$

where $[x]$ is the largest integer contained in x.

1.6 THE SYSTEM WHERE CUSTOMERS ARRIVE IN STAGES

We have seen in Section 1.1 that if the interarrival times have the Erlangian distribution

$$dA(u) = e^{-k\lambda u}(k\lambda)^k u^{k-1} \frac{du}{(k-1)!} \qquad (0 < u < \infty),$$

then we have in effect a scheme of arrivals according to which customers will have to pass through k different stages before they can actually join the system, the time required to complete each stage having the negative exponential distribution $k\lambda e^{-k\lambda u}\,du$. In this section we consider the single server system $E_k/M/1$, with Erlangian arrivals, and the service time distribution $\mu e^{-\mu v}\,dv$ $(0 < v < \infty)$. The mean interarrival time is $a = \lambda^{-1}$, so that the traffic intensity is $\rho = \lambda/\mu$. Let $Q_1(t)$ be the number of stages completed at time t, so that if $Q_1(t) = jk + \nu$ $(0 \leqslant \nu \leqslant k-1)$, then the queue-length is $Q(t) = j$; thus

$$Q(t) = \left[\frac{Q_1(t)}{k}\right]. \tag{1.132}$$

The successive stages enter the system at a Poisson rate $k\lambda$, whereas the departure of each customer removes k stages from it. Thus $Q_1(t)$ is a denumerable Markov process, whose transitions during $(t, t+dt]$ are characterized by the probabilities (1.107), where

$$\begin{aligned} &a_{ii} = k\lambda \quad (0 \leqslant i < k), \qquad a_{ii} = (k\lambda + \mu) \quad (i \geqslant k), \\ &a_{ii+1} = k\lambda \quad (i \geqslant 0), \qquad a_{ii-k} = \mu \quad (i \geqslant k), \\ &a_{ij} = 0 \qquad \text{if } j \neq i, \ \neq i+1, \ \neq i-k. \end{aligned} \tag{1.133}$$

The forward Kolmogorov equations of the process are found to be

$$\begin{aligned} &P'_{i0}(t) = -k\lambda P_{i0}(t) + \mu P_{ik}(t) \\ &P'_{ij}(t) = -k\lambda P_{ij}(t) + k\lambda P_{ij-1}(t) + \mu P_{ij+k}(t) \qquad (1 \leqslant j \leqslant k-1) \\ &P'_{ij}(t) = -(k\lambda + \mu)P_{ij}(t) + k\lambda P_{ij-1}(t) + \mu P_{ij+k}(t) \qquad (j \geqslant k). \end{aligned} \tag{1.134}$$

From these equations, an expression for the transform $G^*(z, \theta)$ can then be derived exactly as in Section 1.5a. However, Jackson and Nickols (1956) obtain the limiting probability distribution (u_j) of $Q_1(t)$ by solving these equations after setting $P'_{ij}(t) = 0$. Thus the u_j satisfy the equations

$$\begin{aligned} k\lambda u_0 &= \mu u_k \\ k\lambda u_j &= k\lambda u_{j-1} + \mu u_{j+k} \qquad (1 \leqslant j \leqslant k-1) \\ (k\lambda + \mu)u_j &= k\lambda u_{j-1} + \mu u_{j+k} \qquad (j \geqslant k). \end{aligned} \tag{1.135}$$

To solve (1.135), let us define the generating function

$$U(z) = \sum_0^\infty u_j z^j \quad (|z| \leqslant 1); \tag{1.136}$$

multiplying the equations (1.135) successively by 1, z, z^2, . . . and adding, we obtain

$$\begin{aligned} k\lambda U(z) + \mu\left[U(z) - \sum_0^{k-1} u_j z^j\right] &= k\lambda \sum_1^\infty u_{j-1} z^j + \mu \sum_0^\infty u_{j+k} z^j \\ &= k\lambda z U(z) + \mu z^{-k}\left[U(z) - \sum_0^{k-1} u_j z^j\right], \end{aligned}$$

which gives

$$U(z) = \frac{(1 - z^k) \sum_0^{k-1} u_j z^j}{k\rho z^{k+1} - (1 + k\rho)z^k + 1}. \tag{1.137}$$

Now for $|z| = 1 + \delta$, where δ is sufficiently small and positive, we have

$$\begin{aligned} \left|\frac{1 + k\rho z^{k+1}}{(1 + k\rho)z^k}\right| &\leqslant \frac{(1 + \delta)^{-k} + k\rho(1 + \delta)}{1 + k\rho} \\ &= 1 + \frac{(1 + \delta)^{-k} - (1 - k\rho\delta)}{1 + k\rho} \\ &= 1 + \frac{[1 - k\delta + \frac{1}{2}k(k + 1)\delta^2 + \cdots] - (1 - k\rho\delta)}{1 + k\rho} \\ &= 1 + \frac{k(\rho - 1)\delta + \cdots}{1 + k\rho}, \end{aligned} \tag{1.138}$$

and since $\rho < 1$, this last quantity is <1. By Rouché's theorem it follows that the equation

$$k\rho z^{k+1} - (1 + k\rho)z^k + 1 = 0 \tag{1.139}$$

has exactly k roots within the circle $|z| = 1 + \delta$; the remaining root z_0 (say) is such that $|z_0| > 1$. To see the nature of this root, let us replace z by z^{-1} in this equation and simplify; we then find that z_0^{-1} is the only root within the unit circle of the equation $z^{k+1} - (1 + k\rho)z + k\rho = 0$ or $z = K(z)$, where $K(z) = (z^{k+1} + k\rho)/(1 + k\rho)$. Here $K(z)$ is a p.g.f., with the mean $K'(1) = (k + 1)/(1 + k\rho) > 1$ since $\rho < 1$. From the remarks following equation (1.119) we see that $0 < z_0^{-1} = \zeta_0 < 1$. We also note the useful relation

$$k\rho(1 - \zeta_0) = \zeta_0(1 - \zeta_0^{\,k}). \tag{1.140}$$

Since the p.g.f. $U(z)$ is regular in the region $|z| \leqslant 1$, it is clear that the $k - 1$ zeros of the polynomial $\sum_0^{k-1} u_j z^j$ and the denominator on the right-hand side of (1.137) must coincide in this region. We must thus have

$$A[k\rho z^{k+1} - (1 + k\rho)z^k + 1] = (z - 1)(z - z_0) \sum_0^{k-1} u_j z^j, \tag{1.141}$$

where A is a constant. Substituting (1.141) in (1.137) and simplifying, we obtain

$$U(z) = A \frac{\sum_0^{k-1} z^j}{z_0 - z};$$

the condition $U(1 - 0) = 1$ gives $A = (z_0 - 1)/k$, so that finally

$$U(z) = \frac{1}{k}\left(\sum_0^{k-1} z^\nu\right)\frac{1 - \zeta_0}{1 - z\zeta_0} \qquad (|z| \leqslant 1). \tag{1.142}$$

Expanding $(1 - z\zeta_0)^{-1}$ as a power series in z, we obtain

$$\begin{aligned} U(z) &= \frac{1 - \zeta_0}{k} \sum_0^{k-1} z^\nu \sum_0^{\infty} (z\zeta_0)^j \\ &= \frac{1 - \zeta_0}{k}\left[\sum_0^{k-1} z^j \sum_{\nu=0}^{j} \zeta_0^{j-\nu} + \sum_k^{\infty} z^j \sum_{\nu=0}^{k-1} \zeta_0^{j-\nu}\right] \\ &= \frac{1}{k}\sum_0^{k-1} z^j(1 - \zeta_0^{j+1}) + \frac{1}{k}\sum_k^{\infty} z^j \zeta_0^{j-k+1}(1 - \zeta_0^{\,k}) \\ &= \frac{1}{k}\sum_0^{k-1} z^j(1 - \zeta_0^{j+1}) + \rho(1 - \zeta_0)\sum_k^{\infty} z^j \zeta_0^{j-k} \end{aligned}$$

where we have used (1.140). It follows that the limiting distribution of $Q_1(t)$ is given by

$$u_j = \begin{cases} \dfrac{1}{k}(1 - \zeta_0^{j+1}) & (0 \leqslant j \leqslant k - 1) \\ \rho(1 - \zeta_0)\zeta_0^{j-k} & (j \geqslant k). \end{cases} \tag{1.143}$$

Using (1.132) we find that the limiting distribution of the queue-length $Q(t)$ is given by (v_j), where

$$
\begin{aligned}
v_0 &= \sum_{0}^{k-1} u_\nu = 1 - \frac{\zeta_0(1-\zeta_0^k)}{k(1-\zeta_0)} = 1 - \rho \qquad \text{using (1.140)} \\
v_j &= \sum_{jk}^{jk+k-1} u_\nu = \rho(1-\zeta_0^k)\zeta_0^{k(j-1)} \qquad (j \geqslant 1);
\end{aligned} \tag{1.144}
$$

(v_j) is a geometric distribution with a modified initial term. For the limiting distribution of the waiting time, we have

$$
\begin{aligned}
dF(0) &= v_0 = 1 - \rho \\
dF(x) &= \sum_{1}^{\infty} v_j e^{-\mu x} \mu^j x^{j-1} \frac{dx}{(j-1)!} \\
&= \lambda(1-\zeta_0^k) e^{-\mu x(1-\zeta_0^k)}\, dx \qquad (0 < x < \infty).
\end{aligned} \tag{1.145}
$$

1.7 THE SYSTEM $M/D/s$

a. Limiting Distributions

In this system the customers arrive in a Poisson process at a rate λ, there are s servers, and each customer is served for exactly b units of time on a "first come, first served" basis. This system was considered by Erlang (1920) and Crommelin (1932); the following elegant treatment is due to Crommelin.

Let $Q(t)$ be the number of customers present in the system at time t; $Q(t)$ is a non-Markovian process. Let

$$
P_j(t) = Pr\{Q(t) = j\} \qquad (j \geqslant 0); \tag{1.146}
$$

by considering $Q(t)$ over the consecutive intervals $(0, t]$, $(t, t+b]$, we obtain the relation

$$
P_j(t+b) = \sum_{i=0}^{s} P_i(t) e^{-\lambda b} \frac{(\lambda b)^j}{j!} + \sum_{i=s+1}^{\infty} P_i(t) e^{-\lambda b} \frac{(\lambda b)^{j-i+s}}{(j-i+s)!}. \tag{1.147}
$$

Assuming that the limiting probability distribution (u_j) exists, where

$$
u_j = \lim_{t\to\infty} P_j(t), \tag{1.148}
$$

we obtain from (1.147) the equation

$$
u_j = (u_0 + u_1 + \cdots + u_s)a_j + \sum_{s+1}^{j+s} u_i k_{j-i+s}, \tag{1.149}
$$

where $k_j = e^{-\lambda b}(\lambda b)^j/j!$ $(j \geqslant 0)$. Let us now define the generating functions

$$U(z) = \sum_0^\infty u_j z^j, \qquad K(z) = \sum_0^\infty k_j z^j = e^{-\lambda b(1-z)}. \tag{1.150}$$

Multiplying the equations (1.149) successively by $1, z, z^2, \ldots$, adding and simplifying, we obtain

$$U(z) = \frac{\sum_0^{s-1} u_i(z^i - z^s)}{1 - z^s/K(z)}. \tag{1.151}$$

The expression for $U(z)$ contains s unknowns $u_0, u_1, \ldots, u_{s-1}$; to determine these we write (1.151) in the slightly different form

$$U(z) = \frac{(1-z)\sum_0^{s-1} v_i z^i}{1 - z^s e^{\lambda b(1-z)}}, \tag{1.152}$$

where $v_j = u_0 + u_1 + \cdots + u_j$ $(j \geqslant 0)$. The condition $U(1-0) = 1$ then readily yields the result

$$\sum_0^{s-1} v_i = s - \lambda b, \tag{1.153}$$

which is meaningful if and only if $s > \lambda b$ or if $\rho < 1$, where $\rho = \lambda b/s$ is the traffic intensity of the system. Thus the limiting distribution (1.148) exists only in this case. Now for $|z| = 1 + \delta$, where δ is sufficiently small and positive, we have

$$|e^{-\lambda b(1-z)}| \leqslant e^{-\lambda b + \lambda b\,|z|} = e^{\lambda b \delta} < (1+\delta)^s = |z|^s \tag{1.154}$$

if $\rho < 1$, so that by Rouché's theorem, the equation $e^{-\lambda b(1-z)} - z^s = 0$ has exactly s roots within the region $|z| = 1 + \delta$. Let these roots be denoted by $z_1, z_2, \ldots, z_{s-1}, z_s\,(=1)$; it is easily seen that $1, z_1, z_2, \ldots, z_{s-1}$ are all distinct. Since the p.g.f. $U(z)$ is regular within the region $|z| \leqslant 1$, it follows from (1.152) that $\sum_0^{s-1} v_i z^i$ should vanish at $z = z_1, z_2, \ldots, z_{s-1}$. Thus we must have

$$\sum_{i=0}^{s-1} v_i z_j^i = 0 \qquad (j = 1, 2, \ldots, s-1). \tag{1.155}$$

The equations (1.155) and (1.153) together constitute a system of s equations for the s unknowns $v_0, v_1, \ldots, v_{s-1}$. The determinant of these equations is given by

$$\Delta \equiv \begin{vmatrix} 1 & 1 & 1 & \cdot & \cdot & 1 \\ 1 & z_1 & z_1^2 & \cdot & \cdot & z_1^{s-1} \\ 1 & z_2 & z_2^2 & \cdot & \cdot & z_2^{s-1} \\ \cdot & \cdot & \cdot & \cdot & \cdot & \cdot \\ \cdot & \cdot & \cdot & \cdot & \cdot & \cdot \\ 1 & z_{s-1} & z_{s-1}^2 & \cdot & \cdot & z_{s-1}^{s-1} \end{vmatrix}, \tag{1.156}$$

and this determinant does not vanish since $1, z_1, z_2, \ldots, z_{s-1}$ are all different; therefore $v_0, v_1, \ldots, v_{s-1}$ are uniquely determined. The relations $u_0 = v_0$, $u_j = v_j - v_{j-1}$ $(j \geqslant 1)$ then yield $u_0, u_1, \ldots, u_{s-1}$, and the p.g.f. $U(z)$ is thus completely determined.

To obtain the limiting distribution of the waiting time, we define the probabilities

$$b_\nu(t) = Pr(\text{at most } \nu \text{ among those present at time } t_0 \text{ will remain at } t_0 + t) \qquad (0 < t \leqslant b, \nu \geqslant 0), \tag{1.157}$$

and the p.g.f. $B(z) = \sum_0^\infty b_\nu(t) z^\nu$. Then in statistical equilibrium we have the relation

$$\sum_0^j u_i = \sum_{\nu=0}^j b_\nu(t) e^{-\lambda t} \frac{(\lambda t)^{j-\nu}}{(j-\nu)!}, \tag{1.158}$$

which gives

$$\frac{U(z)}{1-z} = B(z) e^{-\lambda t(1-z)},$$

or, using (1.152),

$$B(z) = e^{\lambda t(1-z)} \frac{\sum_0^{s-1} v_i z^i}{1 - z^s e^{\lambda b(1-z)}}. \tag{1.159}$$

Now if z_1 is the root with the minimum modulus, we must obviously have $|e^{-\lambda b(1-z)}| > |z|^s$ for $|z| < |z_1|$, so that in this region we can expand $[1 - z^s e^{\lambda b(1-z)}]^{-1}$ as a power series in $z^s e^{\lambda b(1-z)}$. Thus

$$B(z) = \sum_0^{s-1} v_i z^i \sum_{r=0}^\infty z^{rs} e^{(\lambda t + \lambda r b)(1-z)}, \tag{1.160}$$

whence we find that the probabilities $b_\nu \equiv b_\nu(t)$ are given by

$$b_{ns+\nu} = \sum_{i=0}^{s-1} v_i \sum_{r=0}^{n} e^{\lambda(t+rb)} \frac{[-\lambda(t+rb)]^{ns-rs-i+\nu}}{(ns-rs-i+\nu)!} \quad (n \geqslant 0, \quad 0 \leqslant \nu \leqslant s-1). \tag{1.161}$$

For the limiting waiting time d.f. $F(x)$ we have

$$\begin{aligned} F(x) &= b_{ns+s-1} \quad \text{if} \quad x = nb + t \quad (n \geqslant 0, \quad 0 \leqslant t < b) \\ &= \sum_0^{s-1} v_i \sum_0^n e^{\lambda(x-rb)} \frac{[-\lambda(x-rb)]^{rs+s-1-i}}{(rs+s-1-i)!} \\ &= \sum_0^{s-1} v_{s-i-1} \sum_0^n e^{\lambda(x-rb)} \frac{[-\lambda(x-rb)]^{rs+i}}{(rs+i)!}. \end{aligned} \tag{1.162}$$

When $s = 1$, the result (1.151) becomes

$$U(z) = \frac{u_0(1-z)}{1 - ze^{\lambda b(1-z)}}, \tag{1.163}$$

where it is easily seen that $u_0 = 1 - \rho$, $\rho(=\lambda b)$ being the traffic intensity of the system. Furthermore, (1.162) reduces to

$$F(x) = (1-\rho) \sum_0^n e^{\lambda(x-rb)} \frac{[-\lambda(x-rb)]^r}{r!} \quad \text{if} \quad x = nb + t, \quad n \geqslant 0, \quad 0 \leqslant t < b. \tag{1.164}$$

By using a heuristic argument, Erlang (1920) showed that the waiting time d.f. $F(x)$ in the system $M/D/s$ satisfies the integral equation

$$F(x) = \int_0^\infty F(x+u-b) e^{-\lambda u} \frac{\lambda^s u^{s-1}}{(s-1)!} \, du, \tag{1.165}$$

where $F(x) = 0$ for $x < 0$. Prabhu (1962) proved that this equation yields a solution of the type (1.162), but an interpretation of the constants v_i in terms of the queue-length does not appear to be possible. When $s = 1$, (1.165) simplifies to

$$F(x) = \int_0^\infty F(x+u-b) \lambda e^{-\lambda u} \, du, \tag{1.166}$$

and it can be easily proved that (1.166) has the solution (1.164) [see Erlang (1909)].

b. The Busy Period in the System $M/D/1$

We now discuss the busy period problem in the system $M/D/1$. Clearly, the length of a busy period initiated by i customers ($i \geqslant 1$) is given by

$T_i = N_i b$, where N_i is the number of customers served during this period. The distribution of the random variable N_1 was obtained by Borel (1942), to whom the concept of the busy period is due. The following treatment is different from Borel's [see also Tanner (1953, 1961)].

Let the probability distribution of N_i be denoted by $(f_n^{(i)})$, where

$$f_n^{(i)} = Pr\{N_i = n\}. \tag{1.167}$$

Clearly, $f_n^{(i)} = 0$ for $n < i$, whereas for $n = i$ we have

$$f_i^{(i)} = e^{-\lambda ib} \tag{1.168}$$

since the busy period terminates with the service of the ith initial customer if and only if no new customers arrive during their total service period ib. On the other hand, if r ($\geqslant 1$) new customers arrive during this period, then the busy period will continue beyond $t = ib$, and $N_i - i$ customers will be served before it terminates. Therefore we obtain the relation

$$f_n^{(i)} = \sum_{r=1}^{n-i} e^{-\lambda ib} \frac{(\lambda ib)^r}{r!} f_{n-i}^{(r)} \qquad (n \geqslant i+1). \tag{1.169}$$

Putting $n = i + 1$ in (1.169) and using (1.168), we obtain

$$f_{i+1}^{(i)} = e^{-\lambda ib}(\lambda ib) f_1^{(1)} = e^{-\lambda(i+1)b}(\lambda ib), \tag{1.170}$$

and putting $n = i + 2$ in (1.169) and using (1.168) and (1.170), we find that

$$\begin{aligned} f_{i+2}^{(i)} &= e^{-\lambda ib}(\lambda ib) f_2^{(1)} + e^{-\lambda ib} \frac{(\lambda ib)^2}{2} f_2^{(2)} \\ &= e^{-\lambda ib}(\lambda ib) e^{-2\lambda b} \lambda b + e^{-\lambda ib} \frac{(\lambda ib)^2}{2} e^{-2\lambda b} \\ &= e^{-\lambda(i+2)b} \frac{(\lambda b)^2}{2!} (i^2 + 2i) \\ &= \frac{i}{i+2} e^{-\lambda(i+2)b} \frac{[\lambda(i+2)b]^2}{2!}. \end{aligned} \tag{1.171}$$

These results suggest the general expression

$$f_n^{(i)} = \frac{i}{n} e^{-\lambda nb} \frac{(\lambda nb)^{n-i}}{(n-i)!} \qquad (n \geqslant i). \tag{1.172}$$

Assuming (1.172) to hold for $n \leqslant i + m$ for some m, we obtain from (1.169)

$$f_{i+m+1}^{(i)} = \sum_{r=1}^{m+1} e^{-\lambda ib} \frac{(\lambda ib)^r}{r!} f_{m+1}^{(r)}$$

$$= \sum_{r=1}^{m+1} e^{-\lambda ib} \frac{(\lambda ib)^r}{r!} \frac{r}{m+1} e^{-\lambda(m+1)b} \frac{[\lambda(m+1)b]^{m+1-r}}{(m+1-r)!}$$

$$(1.173) \qquad = e^{-\lambda(i+m+1)b} \frac{\lambda ib}{(m+1)!} \sum_{r=0}^{m} \binom{m}{r} (\lambda ib)^r [\lambda(m+1)b]^{m-r}$$

$$= e^{-\lambda(i+m+1)b} \frac{\lambda ib}{(m+1)!} [\lambda(i+m+1)b]^m$$

$$= \frac{i}{i+m+1} e^{-\lambda(i+m+1)b} \frac{[\lambda(i+m+1)b]^{m+1}}{(m+1)!},$$

which proves (1.172) for $n = i + m + 1$. The required result therefore follows by induction.

Adding (1.172) over $n \geqslant i$, we obtain

$$\sum_{n=i}^{\infty} f_n^{(i)} = \sum_{i}^{\infty} \frac{i}{n} e^{-\lambda nb} \frac{(\lambda nb)^{n-i}}{(n-i)!}$$

$$= \sum_{i}^{\infty} \frac{n-(n-i)}{n} e^{-\lambda nb} \frac{(\lambda nb)^{n-i}}{(n-i)!}$$

$$(1.174) \qquad = \sum_{0}^{\infty} e^{-\lambda(n+i)b} \frac{[\lambda(n+i)b]^n}{n!}$$

$$- \lambda b \sum_{0}^{\infty} e^{-\lambda(n+i+1)b} \frac{[\lambda(n+i+1)b]^n}{n!}.$$

Now we have the identity

$$(1.175) \qquad \sum_{n=0}^{\infty} e^{-\lambda(x+nb)} \frac{[\lambda(x+nb)]^n}{n!} = \begin{cases} (1-\lambda b)^{-1} & \text{if } \lambda b < 1 \\ e^{-\lambda x(1-\zeta)}(1-\lambda b\zeta)^{-1} & \text{if } \lambda b > 1. \end{cases}$$

The case $\lambda b > 1$ corresponds to Jensen's formula, which holds for complex values of λb such that $|e^{-(\lambda b-1)}\lambda b| < 1$; here ζ is the least positive root of the equation $K(z) = z$, and $0 < \zeta < 1$ since $\lambda b > 1$ (see Complement 17). If $\lambda b = 1$, the series on the left-hand side of (1.175) can be easily proved to be divergent. Using (1.175) in (1.174), we obtain

$$(1.176) \qquad \sum_{i}^{\infty} f_n^{(i)} = \frac{1}{1-\lambda b} - \frac{\lambda b}{1-\lambda b} = 1,$$

for $\rho = \lambda b < 1$, whereas for $\rho > 1$,

$$\sum_i^\infty f_n^{(i)} = \frac{e^{-\lambda ib(1-\zeta)}}{1-\lambda b\zeta} - \frac{\lambda b e^{-\lambda(i+1)b(1-\zeta)}}{1-\lambda b\zeta} \tag{1.177}$$

$$= \frac{e^{-\lambda ib(1-\zeta)}}{1-\lambda b\zeta}[1-\lambda b e^{-\lambda b(1-\zeta)}] = \zeta^i$$

since $e^{-\lambda b(1-\zeta)} = \zeta$. When $\rho = 1$, we obtain $\sum_i^\infty f_n^{(i)} = 1$ from (1.177) since $\zeta \to 1$ as $\rho \to 1$. Therefore

$$Pr\{N_i < \infty\} = \begin{cases} 1 & \text{if } \rho \leqslant 1 \\ \zeta^i & \text{if } \rho > 1; \end{cases} \tag{1.178}$$

moreover, in the case $\rho \leqslant 1$, we have

$$E(N_i) = \sum_i^\infty n f_n^{(i)} = i \sum_i^\infty e^{-\lambda nb} \frac{(\lambda nb)^{n-i}}{(n-i)!}$$

$$= i \sum_i^\infty e^{-\lambda(n+i)b} \frac{[\lambda(n+i)b]^n}{n!} \tag{1.179}$$

$$= \begin{cases} i(1-\rho)^{-1} & \text{if } \rho < 1 \\ \infty & \text{if } \rho = 1. \end{cases}$$

Thus if $\rho > 1$ there is a positive probability that the busy period will continue indefinitely, whereas if $\rho \leqslant 1$ it will terminate eventually; however, the average number of customers served during a busy period will be finite or infinite depending on whether $\rho < 1$ or $\rho = 1$.

1.8 IMBEDDED MARKOV CHAINS

a. The Concept of Imbedded Chains

In the queueing systems studied in Sections 1.2 to 1.4, it was noted that the queue-length $Q(t)$ is a Markov process because the specification of the queue-length at time τ was adequate to predict its length at time $\tau + t$ on account of the Markovian property of the Poisson distribution. In the systems $M/E_k/1$ (Section 1.5) and $E_k/M/1$ (Section 1.6), $Q(t)$ is not Markovian, but its properties could be obtained from those of a second process $Q_1(t)$, which was Markovian. The difficulty of having to deal with a non-Markovian process was not overcome in the system $M/D/s$ (Section 1.7), and therefore we had to be content with deriving the limiting distributions. These remarks indicate that when the input and service time distributions assume general forms, the process $Q(t)$ is no longer

Markovian. The correct specification of the queueing system is then given by the vector process $[Q(t), u(t), v(t)]$, where $u(t)$ is the time which has elapsed since the last arrival, and $v(t)$ is the expended service time of the customer being served at time t. We can study this vector process, although the theory will be rather complicated, but it is still possible to do something about the process $Q(t)$ by making use of its "regeneration points."

A set S of time-instants is said to be a set of regeneration points for a stochastic process $X(t)$ if and only if, for all $t > t_0$ we have

$$\text{distr}\,[X(t) \mid X(t_0)] = \text{distr}\,[X(t) \mid X(\tau) \quad \text{for all} \quad \tau \leqslant t_0] \tag{1.180}$$

whenever t_0 is known to belong to S; this condition implies that the development of the process during $t > t_0$ is independent of the history of the process during $(0, t_0]$. For a Markov process, the whole range of t values is a set of regeneration points. If a process has a set of regeneration points, then it is called regenerative. Suppose that there exists a denumerable S-set of regeneration points $\{t_n, n = 0, 1, 2, \ldots\}$ such that $t_0 < t_1 < t_2 < \cdots$, and put $X_n = X(t_n)$; then it follows from the above definition that the sequence of random variables $\{X_n\}$ forms a Markov chain. This chain is said to be imbedded in the given process $X(t)$.

In a single server queueing system, the set of points at which the counter is free is clearly an S-set. As a second example, we have the set S_x consisting (for a given x) of those instants of time at which the customer at the counter has already been served for a period x. In the system $M/G/1$, with Poisson input and a general service time distribution, the instants at which the customers leave the system are points of regeneration. In the general case if there exists an increasing sequence $\{t_n\}$ of regeneration points such that the transition probabilities associated with $\{Q_{n+1} \mid Q_n\}$, where $Q_n = Q(t_n)$ can be calculated in a simple manner, then analysis of the imbedded Markov chain $\{Q_n\}$ will yield valuable information regarding the process $Q(t)$.

The concept of regeneration points is due to Palm (1943), and the technique of imbedded Markov chains is due to Kendall, who applied it to the systems $M/G/1$ (1951) and $GI/M/s$ (1954). Later, Wishart (1956) extended Kendall's analysis to the system $GI/E_k/1$, and Bailey (1954b) applied the technique to bulk queues. In these investigations the authors deal with queue-length; Lindley (1952) carried out the imbedded Markov chain analysis of waiting time, and his work was continued by Smith (1953).

In the remainder of this section we study the imbedded Markov chains associated with the systems $M/G/1$ and $GI/M/1$. Only an outline of the main results will be given here, since a detailed treatment by entirely different methods will be given in Chapter 4. Application to waiting times will be discussed in Section 1.10.

b. The System $M/G/1$

Suppose that customers arrive in a Poisson process at a rate λ, and that the service time has the distribution $dB(v)$ $(0 < v < \infty)$. Let the L.S.T. of this distribution be denoted by $\psi(\theta)$, so that

$$\psi(\theta) = \int_0^\infty e^{-\theta v}\, dB(v) \qquad [\mathrm{Re}\,(\theta) > 0]. \tag{1.181}$$

The mean service time is $b = -\psi'(0)$, which we assume to be finite. The traffic intensity is then $\rho = \lambda b < \infty$.

Let t_n denote the instant at which the nth customer leaves $(n = 0, 1, 2, \ldots;\ t_0 = 0)$; then the instants $t_n + 0$ are obviously points of regeneration of the queue-length process $Q(t)$. If we denote $Q_n = Q(t_n + 0)$, then $\{Q_n\}$ is a time-homogeneous Markov chain with an enumerable infinity of states; let its transition probabilities be denoted by

$$P_{ij}^{(n)} = Pr\{Q_n = j \mid Q_0 = i\} \qquad (i, j \geqslant 0, \quad n \geqslant 1). \tag{1.182}$$

The transition probabilities $P_{ij} \equiv P_{ij}^{(1)}$ of the first order are given by

$$P_{0j} = k_j, \qquad P_{ij} = k_{j-i+1}, \tag{1.183}$$

where

$$k_j = \int_0^\infty e^{-\lambda v} \frac{(\lambda v)^j}{j!}\, dB(v) \quad (j \geqslant 0), \qquad k_j = 0 \quad (j < 0), \tag{1.184}$$

that is, k_j is the probability of j arrivals during a service period of arbitrary duration. The transition probability matrix $P \equiv (P_{ij})$ is therefore given by

$$P \equiv \begin{array}{c|cccccc} i \backslash j & 0 & 1 & 2 & 3 & . & . \\ \hline 0 & k_0 & k_1 & k_2 & k_3 & . & . \\ 1 & k_0 & k_1 & k_2 & k_3 & . & . \\ 2 & 0 & k_0 & k_1 & k_2 & . & . \\ 3 & 0 & 0 & k_0 & k_1 & . & . \\ . & . & . & . & . & . & . \\ . & . & . & . & . & . & . \end{array} \tag{1.185}$$

The p.g.f. of the distribution $\{k_j\}$ is given by

$$K(z) = \sum_0^\infty k_j z^j = \int_0^\infty e^{-\lambda v + \lambda v z}\, dB(v) = \psi(\lambda - \lambda z) \qquad (|z| < 1), \tag{1.186}$$

and its mean is given by $K'(1) = -\lambda\psi'(0) = \rho$.

Since $k_j > 0$ for all j, the Markov chain $\{Q_n\}$ is irreducible and aperiodic. Furthermore, it can be shown that the chain is transient if $\rho > 1$, persistent null if $\rho = 1$, and persistent non-null (or ergodic) if $\rho < 1$ (see Complement 25). In the ergodic case the limiting probabilities

$$u_j = \lim_{n\to\infty} P_{ij}^{(n)} \qquad (u_j > 0, \quad \sum u_j = 1) \tag{1.187}$$

exist, and are the unique solution of the equations

$$u_j = \sum_{i=0}^\infty u_i P_{ij} \qquad (j = 0, 1, \ldots). \tag{1.188}$$

Thus $\{u_j\}$ is the unique stationary distribution of Q_n. To solve (1.188), let us write

$$\begin{aligned} u_0 &= k_0(u_0 + u_1) \\ u_j &= u_0 k_j + \sum_{i=1}^{j+1} u_i k_{j-i+1} \qquad (j \geqslant 1), \end{aligned} \tag{1.189}$$

and define the p.g.f. $U(z) = \sum_0^\infty u_j z^j$ $(|z| < 1)$. Then proceeding in the usual manner we obtain from these equations

$$\begin{aligned} U(z) &= u_0 \sum_0^\infty k_j z^j + \sum_0^\infty z^j \sum_{i=1}^{j+1} u_i k_{j-i+1} \\ &= u_0 K(z) + \sum_1^\infty u_i z^{i-1} K(z) \\ &= u_0 K(z) + \frac{K(z)}{z}[U(z) - u_0]; \end{aligned}$$

this gives $U(z) = u_0(1 - z)K(z)[K(z) - z]^{-1}$. The condition $U(1 - 0) = 1$ easily yields $u_0 = 1 - \rho$, so that we finally obtain

$$U(z) = \frac{(1 - \rho)(1 - z)K(z)}{K(z) - z}, \tag{1.190}$$

a result due to Kendall (1951).

From (1.190) we can obtain the limiting distribution of the waiting time. Let Q denote the length of the queue (in statistical equilibrium) left behind by a departing customer and W his waiting time. Let

$$\Phi(\theta) = \int_{0-}^\infty e^{-\theta x}\, dF(x) \qquad [\mathrm{Re}\,(\theta) > 0] \tag{1.191}$$

be the L.S.T. of W. Now, Q is the number of customers who arrived during the total time spent in the system by a departing customer, which is $W + v$, v being his service time. We have therefore

$$u_j = Pr\{Q = j\} = \int_0^\infty e^{-\lambda t} \frac{(\lambda t)^j}{j!} d_t Pr\{W + v \leqslant t\}, \tag{1.192}$$

from which we obtain

$$U(z) = \int_0^\infty e^{-\lambda t(1-z)} d_t Pr\{W + v \leqslant t\}. \tag{1.193}$$

However, the integral on the right-hand side of (1.193) is the L.S.T. of $W + v$ for $\theta = \lambda - \lambda z$, and since W and v are independent random variables, this transform is $\Phi(\lambda - \lambda z)\psi(\lambda - \lambda z) = \Phi(\lambda - \lambda z)K(z)$. Thus

$$U(z) = \Phi(\lambda - \lambda z)K(z),$$

which gives

$$\Phi(\theta) = \frac{U(1 - \theta/\lambda)}{K(1 - \theta/\lambda)} = \frac{(1 - \rho)\theta}{\theta - \lambda + \lambda\psi(\theta)}, \tag{1.194}$$

a result due to Pollaczek (1930) and Khintchine (1932).

From (1.190) and (1.194) we find the mean queue-length and the mean waiting time as

$$E(Q) = U'(1) = \rho + \frac{\lambda^2 E(v^2)}{2(1 - \rho)} \tag{1.195}$$

$$E(W) = -\Phi'(0) = \frac{\lambda E(v^2)}{2(1 - \rho)} \qquad (\rho < 1). \tag{1.196}$$

As an application of the above results, let us consider the queue $M/M/1$, for which

$$\begin{gathered} dB(v) = \mu e^{-\mu v}\, dv, \qquad \psi(\theta) = \frac{\mu}{\mu + \theta}, \qquad \rho = \frac{\lambda}{\mu} \\ K(z) = \mu(\mu + \lambda - \lambda z)^{-1} = (1 + \rho - \rho z)^{-1}. \end{gathered} \tag{1.197}$$

Substituting (1.197) in (1.190) and (1.194), we find that

$$U(z) = \frac{1 - \rho}{1 - \rho z}, \qquad \Phi(\theta) = \frac{(1 - \rho)(\mu + \theta)}{\theta + \mu - \lambda}; \tag{1.198}$$

these results are in agreement with those obtained in Section 1.2.

c. The System $GI/M/1$

This is a single server system in which the interarrival times have the distribution $dA(u)$ $(0 < u < \infty)$, whereas the service time distribution is $\mu e^{-\mu v}\, dv$ $(0 < v < \infty)$. Let $\psi(\theta)$ be the L.S.T. of $A(u)$ and $a = -\psi'(0)$ the mean interarrival time. The traffic intensity is then $\rho = (\mu a)^{-1}$. Let the successive customers arrive at the instants $t_0, t_1, t_2, \ldots$ ($t_0 = 0$); then the t_n are points of regeneration of the process $Q(t)$ and the Markov chain $\{Q_n\}$, where $Q_n = Q(t_n - 0)$ is imbedded in this process. Let the transition probabilities $P_{ij}^{(n)}$ of $\{Q_n\}$ be defined as in (1.182). Furthermore, let k_j be the probability that j customers will complete their service during an interarrival period of arbitrary duration, so that

$$k_j = \int_0^\infty e^{-\mu u} \frac{(\mu u)^j}{j!}\, dA(u) \qquad (j = 0, 1, 2, \ldots). \tag{1.199}$$

Then we have

$$P_{ij} = k_{i-j+1} \qquad (0 < j \leqslant i + 1, \quad i \geqslant 0) \tag{1.200}$$

$$\begin{aligned} P_{i0} &= \int_0^\infty dA(u) \int_0^u e^{-\mu v} \frac{\mu^{i+1} v^i}{i!}\, dv \\ &= \int_0^\infty dA(u) \left[1 - \sum_0^i e^{-\mu u} \frac{(\mu u)^r}{r!} \right] \\ &= 1 - \sum_0^i k_i = \alpha_i \qquad (i \geqslant 0), \end{aligned} \tag{1.201}$$

were $\alpha_i = k_{i+1} + k_{i+2} + \cdots$. Thus the transition probability matrix $P \equiv (P_{ij})$ is given by

$$P \equiv \begin{array}{c|cccccc} & 0 & 1 & 2 & 3 & \cdot & \cdot \\ \hline 0 & \alpha_0 & k_0 & 0 & 0 & 0 & \cdot \\ 1 & \alpha_1 & k_1 & k_0 & 0 & 0 & \cdot \\ 2 & \alpha_2 & k_2 & k_1 & k_0 & 0 & \cdot \\ \cdot & \cdot & \cdot & \cdot & \cdot & \cdot & \cdot \\ \cdot & \cdot & \cdot & \cdot & \cdot & \cdot & \cdot \end{array} \tag{1.202}$$

Since $k_j > 0$, the chain $\{Q_n\}$ is irreducible and aperiodic; it is ergodic if and only if $\rho < 1$ (see Complement 27). In the ergodic case the equations determining the stationary distribution (u_j) are

$$\begin{aligned} u_0 &= \sum_0^\infty \alpha_i u_i \\ u_j &= \sum_{i=j-1}^\infty u_i k_{i-j+1} \qquad (j \geqslant 1). \end{aligned} \tag{1.203}$$

To solve (1.203), consider the p.g.f. $K(z) = \sum_0^\infty k_j z^j = \psi(\mu - \mu z)$; we have $K'(1) = a\mu = \rho^{-1}$. We know that the equation

$$K(z) = z \tag{1.204}$$

has a root ζ such that $0 < \zeta < 1$ since $K'(1) > 1$ (see Complement 17).

We assert that a solution of (1.203) is given by

$$u_j = (1 - \zeta)\zeta^j \qquad (j \geqslant 0); \tag{1.205}$$

since the solution is known to be unique, it follows that the required stationary distribution is given by (1.205). To prove our assertion, we substitute (1.205) in (1.203) and find that

$$\begin{aligned}\sum_0^\infty \alpha_i u_i &= (1 - \zeta)\sum_0^\infty \alpha_i \zeta^i = (1 - \zeta)\sum_0^\infty \zeta^i \sum_{i+1}^\infty k_j \\ &= (1 - \zeta)\sum_1^\infty k_j \sum_0^{j-1} \zeta^i = \sum_0^\infty k_j(1 - \zeta^j) \\ &= 1 - K(\zeta) = 1 - \zeta = u_0,\end{aligned} \tag{1.206}$$

$$\begin{aligned}\sum_{i=j-1}^\infty u_i k_{i-j+1} &= (1 - \zeta)\sum_0^\infty \zeta^{i+j-1} k_j = (1 - \zeta)\zeta^{j-1}K(\zeta) \\ &= (1 - \zeta)\zeta^j = u_j,\end{aligned} \tag{1.207}$$

in agreement with (1.203).

The stationary distribution of the queue-length Q_n has thus the geometric form (1.205), irrespective of the form of the interarrival time distribution function $A(u)$; the value of the common ratio ζ, however, depends on the nature of this distribution, since $K(z)$ in the equation (1.204) involves $A(u)$. The stationary distribution of the waiting time of an arriving customer can also be found by using (1.205), since this waiting time W is the total service time of the customers present in the system before the arrival. Thus we obtain

$$F(0) = Pr\{W = 0\} = (1 - \zeta) \tag{1.208}$$

$$\begin{aligned}dF(x) &= Pr\{x < W < x + dx\} \\ &= (1 - \zeta)\sum_1^\infty \zeta^j e^{-\mu x} \frac{\mu^j}{(j-1)!} x^{j-1}\, dx \\ &= (1 - \zeta)\zeta\mu e^{-\mu x(1-\zeta)}\, dx \qquad (0 < x < \infty);\end{aligned} \tag{1.209}$$

the distribution of W in the range $(0 < x < \infty)$ is therefore a negative exponential, irrespective of the form of $A(u)$. This result is due to Smith (1953); it has been extended to the case of the many-server system $GI/M/s$ by Kendall (1954).

1.9 THE WAITING TIME IN THE SYSTEM $M/G/1$

a. The Process $W(t)$

The waiting time $W(t)$ in a queueing system is the total service time of all customers present in the system at time t. If the distribution of the queue-length $Q(t)$ can be determined, then the distribution of $W(t)$ can be easily obtained, as we saw in the case of the system $M/M/1$. However, this method fails in the general case where the process $Q(t)$ is non-Markovian, and its distribution cannot be obtained by simple methods. It is therefore necessary to investigate whether the distribution of waiting time can be determined directly. Takács (1955) showed that in the system with (nonhomogeneous) Poisson arrivals, the process $W(t)$ is Markovian and he established its forward Kolmogorov equation. In this section we

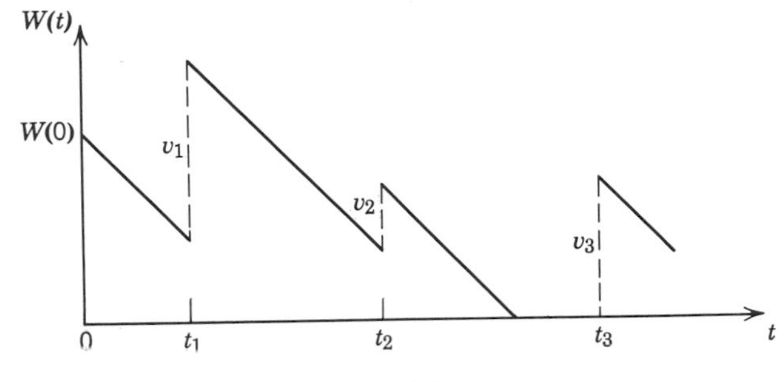

Figure 1.2

describe Takács' results for the system $M/G/1$, where the arrivals are Poisson (with parameter λ) and the service time distribution is $dB(v)$ $(0 < v < \infty)$.

Let $W(0) = u$ be the initial waiting time; for $t > 0$, $W(t)$ decreases at a unit rate until a customer arrives, and at this point it increases by an amount v, where v is the service time of this customer. After this $W(t)$ again decreases at a unit rate until the next customer arrives, and so on. If at any time t, $W(t) = 0$, then it remains zero until the next arrival occurs, say at $t + s$, and $W(t + s) = v$, where v is the service time of this customer. A typical realization of the process is shown in Figure 1.2.

Here $t_1, t_2, t_3, \ldots$ are the instants of arrival of the successive customers and $v_1, v_2, v_3, \ldots$ their service times. Clearly, if $t_n < t < t_{n+1}$, we have

$$(1.210)\qquad W(t) = \begin{cases} W(t_n) - (t - t_n) & \text{if } W(t_n) > t - t_n \\ 0 & \text{if } W(t_n) \leqslant t - t_n \end{cases}$$

and at $t = t_n$,

$$(1.211)\qquad W(t_n + 0) = W(t_n) + v_n.$$

Clearly, the t_n are points of discontinuity for the process $W(t)$; since $W(t_n - 0) = W(t_n)$ it follows that $W(t)$ is continuous to the left at these points. Since the instants t_n occur in a Poisson process and the v_n are mutually independent, it follows that $W(t)$ is a Markov process.

Now let $X(t)$ denote the total service time of customers who arrive during an interval $(0, t]$; then

$$X(t) = v_1 + v_2 + \cdots + v_{A(t)}, \tag{1.212}$$

where $A(t)$ is the number of customers who arrive during $(0, t]$; clearly, $X(t)$ is also a stochastic process. If the server is busy throughout $(0, t]$, then $W(t) = X(t) - t = Y(t)$ (say). In the general case, let us define a function $L(x)$ as follows:

$$L(x) = \begin{cases} 1 & \text{if } x \leqslant 0 \\ 0 & \text{if } x > 0; \end{cases} \tag{1.213}$$

then that part of the interval $(0, t]$ during which the server is idle is given by

$$\int_0^t L[W(s)]\, ds, \tag{1.214}$$

and $W(t)$ is given by the formula

$$W(t) = W(0) + Y(t) + \int_0^t L[W(s)]\, ds. \tag{1.215}$$

When $W(0) = 0$, this yields the important result

$$W(t) = \sup_{0 \leqslant \tau \leqslant t} [Y(t) - Y(\tau-)], \tag{1.216}$$

which is due to Reich (1958). For we have

$$\begin{aligned} W(t) &= W(\tau-) + Y(t) - Y(\tau-) + \int_{\tau-}^t L[W(s)]\, ds \\ &> Y(t) - Y(\tau-) \qquad (\tau \leqslant t). \end{aligned} \tag{1.217}$$

Furthermore, let $t_0 = \max [\tau \mid \tau \leqslant t, W(\tau-) = 0]$, so that t_0 is the last instant of time (before t) at which the server is idle; then

$$W(t) = Y(t) - Y(t_0-). \tag{1.218}$$

The result (1.216) now follows from (1.217) and (1.218). When $W(0) = u \geqslant 0$, we have the slightly more general result

$$W(t) = \max \left[\sup_{0 \leqslant \tau \leqslant t} [Y(t) - Y(\tau-)], u + Y(t) \right] \tag{1.219}$$

(see Section 7.9).

b. The Integro-Differential Equation of $W(t)$

The process $W(t)$ is easily seen to be time-homogeneous; it is of the "mixed" type, since its changes of state occur continuously as well as by jumps. Let us denote its transition distribution function (d.f.) by

$$F(x_0;\ x, t) = Pr\{W(t) \leqslant x \mid W(0) = x_0\} \qquad (t > 0, x, x_0 \geqslant 0), \tag{1.220}$$

$$F(x_0;\ x, 0) = \begin{cases} 0 & \text{if } x < x_0 \\ 1 & \text{if } x \geqslant x_0. \end{cases} \tag{1.221}$$

We shall sometimes write $F(x, t) \equiv F(x_0;\ x, t)$ for convenience. In order to derive the forward Kolmogorov equation of the process, we make the following assumptions regarding $F(x, t)$: (1) $F(x, t)$ is a continuous function of both x and t for all $x \geqslant 0$, $t \geqslant 0$; (2) $F(x, t)$ has a bounded partial derivative $\partial F/\partial x$; and (3) the function $G(x, t)$, where

$$G(x, t) = \int_0^x F(x - v, t)\, dB(v) \tag{1.222}$$

is continuous in x [it is continuous in t, since $F(x, t)$ is so]. Sufficient conditions for these assumptions to be valid are that the service time d.f. $B(v)$ is absolutely continuous and has a bounded derivative for all x [see Hasofer (1963)]. These conditions are indeed severe, and do not hold, for instance, in the system $M/D/1$, where the service time is a constant. However, the L.S.T. of $F(x, t)$ [see (1.224)] can be obtained directly from (1.215), and in Chapter 2 we shall invert this to obtain $F(x, t)$.

Now, considering the waiting time during the infinitesimal time interval $(t, t + dt]$, we obtain the relation

$$\begin{aligned} F(x, t + dt) &= F(x + dt, t)(1 - \lambda\, dt) \\ &\quad + \lambda\, dt \int_0^{x+dt} F(x + dt - v, t)\, dB(v) + o(dt), \end{aligned} \tag{1.223}$$

which can be written as

$$\begin{aligned} \frac{F(x, t + dt) - F(x, t)}{dt} &= \frac{F(x + dt, t) - F(x, t)}{dt} \\ &\quad - \lambda F(x + dt, t) + \lambda G(x + dt, t) + \frac{o(dt)}{dt}. \end{aligned} \tag{1.224}$$

Writing $x - dt$ for x and $t - dt$ for t, we obtain similarly

$$\begin{aligned} \frac{F(x, t - dt) - F(x, t)}{-dt} &= \frac{F(x - dt, t) - F(x, t)}{-dt} \\ &\quad - \lambda F(x, t - dt) + \lambda G(x, t - dt) + \frac{o(dt)}{dt}. \end{aligned} \tag{1.225}$$

Using our assumptions we find from (1.224) and (1.226) that the partial derivative $\partial F/\partial t$ exists and satisfies the equation

$$\frac{\partial F}{\partial t} - \frac{\partial F}{\partial x} = -\lambda F(x, t) + \lambda \int_0^x F(x - v, t)\, dB(v); \tag{1.226}$$

this integro-differential equation is thus the required forward Kolmogorov equation of the process.

Let us denote the Laplace transform of $F(x, t)$ by

$$\Phi(\theta, t) = \int_0^\infty e^{-\theta x} F(x, t)\, dx; \tag{1.227}$$

also, let

$$\psi(\theta) = \int_0^\infty e^{-\theta v}\, dB(v) \qquad [\operatorname{Re}(\theta) > 0] \tag{1.228}$$

be the L.S.T. of the service time d.f. $B(v)$. We have then

$$\int_0^\infty e^{-\theta x} \frac{\partial F}{\partial t}\, dx = \frac{\partial \Phi}{\partial t} \tag{1.229}$$

and

$$\begin{aligned} \int_0^\infty e^{-\theta x} \frac{\partial F}{\partial x}\, dx &= [e^{-\theta x} F(x, t)]_0^\infty + \theta \int_0^\infty e^{-\theta x} F(x, t)\, dx \\ &= -F(0, t) + \theta \Phi(\theta, t). \end{aligned} \tag{1.230}$$

Multiplying both sides of the equation (1.226) by $e^{-\theta x}$, integrating over $(0 \leqslant x < \infty)$, and using (1.229) and (1.230), we obtain

$$\begin{aligned} \frac{\partial \Phi}{\partial t} - [\theta \Phi(\theta, t) - F(0, t)] &= -\lambda \Phi(\theta, t) + \lambda \int_0^\infty e^{-\theta x}\, dx \int_0^x F(x - v, t)\, dB(v) \\ &= -\lambda \Phi(\theta, t) + \lambda \int_0^\infty dB(v) \int_v^\infty e^{-\theta x} F(x - v, t)\, dx \\ &= -\lambda \Phi(\theta, t) + \lambda \psi(\theta) \Phi(\theta, t), \end{aligned}$$

from which we find that $\Phi(\theta, t)$ satisfies the differential equation

$$\frac{\partial \Phi}{\partial t} - [\theta - \lambda + \lambda \psi(\theta)]\Phi(\theta, t) = -F(0, t). \tag{1.231}$$

This can also be obtained by proceeding as in (1.223) to (1.226). To solve (1.231), let us multiply both sides by $e^{-[\theta - \lambda + \lambda\psi(\theta)]t}$, and write it as

$$\frac{\partial}{\partial t} \{\Phi e^{-[\theta - \lambda + \lambda \psi(\theta)]t}\} = -F(0, t) e^{-[\theta - \lambda + \lambda \psi(\theta)]t};$$

integrating this we obtain

$$\Phi e^{-[\theta-\lambda+\lambda\psi(\theta)]t} = A - \int_0^t F(0, \tau)e^{-[\theta-\lambda+\lambda\psi(\theta)]\tau}\, d\tau, \tag{1.232}$$

where A is a constant. Putting $t = 0$ in (1.232), we find that

$$\begin{aligned} A = \Phi(\theta, 0) &= \int_0^\infty e^{-\theta x} F(x, 0)\, dx \\ &= \int_{x_0}^\infty e^{-\theta x}\, dx = \frac{e^{-\theta x_0}}{\theta} \qquad \text{[using (1.221)]}; \end{aligned} \tag{1.233}$$

substituting for A in (1.232), and simplifying, we obtain finally the solution of (1.231) as

$$\Phi(\theta, t) = \theta^{-1} e^{-\theta x_0 + [\theta-\lambda+\lambda\psi(\theta)]t} - \int_0^t F(0, t - \tau)e^{[\theta-\lambda+\lambda\psi(\theta)]\tau}\, d\tau. \tag{1.234}$$

The right-hand side of (1.234) contains the unknown probability $F(0, t)$; this may be obtained by finding the Laplace transform of $\Phi(\theta, t)$ with respect to t from (1.231) and proceeding as in Section 1.2a [Beněs (1957)].

The limiting behavior of $F(x, t)$ as $t \to \infty$ can be investigated by putting $\theta = i\omega$ (for ω real) in (1.235) and letting $t \to \infty$; in particular, when $\rho < 1$, this will lead to the Pollaczek-Khintchine formula (1.195), when $\rho = -\lambda\psi'(0)$ is the relative traffic intensity. In Chapter 2 we study the system $M/G/1$ in detail using different methods.

1.10 THE WAITING TIME IN THE SYSTEM $GI/G/1$

a. The Imbedded Markov Chain

Let $W(t)$ be the waiting time in the system $GI/G/1$. Except in the special case $M/G/1$, the process $W(t)$ is non-Markovian. However, as in $Q(t)$, important results concerning $W(t)$ can be obtained from an imbedded Markov chain analysis of the process. Such an analysis was carried out by Lindley (1952). In this section we give an outline of his main results; for a more detailed investigation see Chapter 4.

Let the successive customers arrive at the instants $t_0, t_1, t_2, \ldots$ ($t_0 = 0$), and put $u_n = t_{n+1} - t_n$ ($n = 0, 1, 2, \ldots$). Also let $v_0, v_1, v_2, \ldots$ be the service times of these customers. We assume that the random variables X_n, where $X_n = v_n - u_n$ ($n = 0, 1, 2, \ldots$), are mutually independent; this is implied by our assumption regarding the mutual independence of the random variables $u_0, u_1, u_2, \ldots, v_0, v_1, v_2, \ldots$, but the present assumption is actually a weaker one. We assume further that the X_n are identically distributed with the d.f.

$$K(x) = Pr\{X_n \leqslant x\} \qquad (-\infty < x < \infty). \tag{1.235}$$

We have $K(-\infty) = 0$, $K(+\infty) = 1$. This d.f. can be expressed in terms of the d.f.'s of the u_n and v_n. Finally, we assume that $0 < E|X_n| < \infty$.

Now, let $W_n = W(t_n - 0)$, so that W_n is the waiting time of the nth arrival. By considering $W(t)$ at $t = t_n - 0$, and $t = t_{n+1} - 0$, we obtain the recurrence relations

$$W_{n+1} = \begin{cases} W_n + v_n - u_n & \text{if} \quad W_n + v_n > u_n \\ 0 & \text{if} \quad W_n + v_n \leqslant u_n \qquad (n = 0, 1, 2, \ldots), \end{cases} \tag{1.236}$$

which show clearly that the sequence of random variables $\{W_n\}$ forms a Markov chain; this is a time-homogeneous process with a continuous infinity of states. Let its transition d.f. be denoted by

$$P_n(x_0; x) = Pr\{W_n \leqslant x \mid W_0 = x_0\} \qquad (n \geqslant 1) \tag{1.237}$$

$$P_0(x_0; x) = \begin{cases} 0 & \text{if} \quad x < x_0 \\ 1 & \text{if} \quad x \geqslant x_0 \qquad (x, x_0 \geqslant 0). \end{cases} \tag{1.238}$$

In particular, the d.f. $P(x_0; x) \equiv P_1(x_0; x)$ can be obtained from (1.236); thus

$$\begin{aligned} P(x_0; x) &= Pr\{W_{n+1} \leqslant x \mid W_n = x_0\} \\ &= Pr\{W_{n+1} = 0 \mid W_n = x_0\} + Pr\{0 < W_{n+1} \leqslant x \mid W_n = 0\} \\ &= Pr\{x_0 + v_n - u_n \leqslant 0\} + Pr\{0 < x_0 + v_n - u_n \leqslant x\} \\ &= Pr\{x_0 + v_n - u_n \leqslant x\} = K(x - x_0). \end{aligned} \tag{1.239}$$

The functions $P_n(x_0; x)$ satisfy the Chapman-Kolmogorov equations

$$P_{m+n}(x_0; x) = \int_{0-}^{\infty} d_y P_n(x_0; y) P_m(y; x) \qquad (m, n \geqslant 0). \tag{1.240}$$

In particular, when $m = 1$, these give

$$\begin{aligned} P_{n+1}(x_0; x) &= \int_{0-}^{\infty} d_y P_n(x_0; y) P(y; x) \\ &= \int_{0-}^{\infty} d_y P_n(x_0; y) K(x - y) \\ &= [P_n(x_0; y) K(x - y)]_{0-}^{\infty} - \int_{0-}^{\infty} P_n(x_0; y)\, dK(x - y) \\ &= -\int_{0-}^{\infty} P_n(x_0; y)\, dK(x - y) \qquad (n = 0, 1, \ldots); \end{aligned} \tag{1.241}$$

since $P_1(x_0; y)$ is known, $P_n(x_0; x)$ can be obtained successively for $n =$ 2, 3, . . . from (1.241).

The unconditional (absolute) d.f. of X_n is defined by

$$F_n(x) = Pr\{W_n \leqslant x\} \qquad (n = 0, 1, 2, \ldots); \tag{1.242}$$

in particular, $F_0(x)$, the d.f. of X_0, is called the initial d.f. If $F_0(x)$ and the $P_n(x_0; x)$ are known, $F_n(x)$ $(n \geqslant 1)$ can be obtained from the relation

$$F_n(x) = \int_{0-}^{\infty} dF_0(y) P_n(y; x) \qquad (n = 1, 2, \ldots). \tag{1.243}$$

b. The Stationary Distribution

Now suppose that the limit

$$F(x) = \lim_{n \to \infty} P_n(x_0; x) \tag{1.244}$$

exists, independently of the initial value x_0. Clearly, $F(x)$ is a nonnegative, monotone nondecreasing function, such that $F(x) = 0$ for $x < 0$, but it might happen that $F(x) \equiv 0$. If $F(\infty) = 1$, $F(x)$ is also the limit of $F_n(x)$ as $n \to \infty$, that is, $F(x)$ is the limiting d.f. of W_n. To prove this, consider (1.243); writing the integral on its right-hand side as

$$\int_{0-}^{A} dF_0(y) P_n(y; x) + \int_{A}^{\infty} dF_0(y) P_n(y; x), \qquad (A > 0), \tag{1.245}$$

we find that

$$\begin{aligned} &\int_{0}^{A} dF_0(y) P_n(y; x) \to F(x) F_0(A), \\ &\int_{A}^{\infty} dF_0(y) P_n(y; x) \leqslant \int_{A}^{\infty} dF_0(y) = 1 - F_0(A), \end{aligned} \tag{1.246}$$

and making A indefinitely large, that

$$F_n(x) = \int_{0-}^{\infty} dF_0(y) P_n(y; x) \to F(x) \qquad (x \geqslant 0), \tag{1.247}$$

as required. Proceeding similarly with (1.241), we find that $F(x)$ satisfies the integral equation

$$F(x) = -\int_{0-}^{\infty} F(y)\, dK(x - y) \qquad (x \geqslant 0); \tag{1.248}$$

in fact, $F(x)$ is the unique solution of this equation having the properties of a d.f. For, if possible, let there be a second solution $G(x)$, which is also a d.f. We have

$$\begin{aligned} F_{n+1}(x) &= \int_{0-}^{\infty} dF_n(y) P_1(y; x) \\ &= \int_{0-}^{\infty} dF_n(y) K(x-y) \qquad \text{using (1.239)} \\ &= -\int_{0-}^{\infty} F_n(y)\, dK(x-y). \end{aligned} \tag{1.249}$$

If now $G(x)$ is the initial d.f., then

$$\begin{aligned} F_1(x) &= -\int_{0-}^{\infty} F_0(y)\, dK(x-y) \\ &= -\int_{0}^{\infty} G(y)\, dK(x-y) = G(x), \end{aligned} \tag{1.250}$$

$$\begin{aligned} F_2(x) &= -\int_{0-}^{\infty} F_1(y)\, dK(x-y) \\ &= -\int_{0}^{\infty} G(y)\, dK(x-y) = G(x), \end{aligned} \tag{1.251}$$

and so on, $F_n(x) = G(x)$ for all n, and in the limit as $n \to \infty$, $F(x) = G(x)$. This proves the uniqueness of the solution of the integral equation (1.248). Incidentally, the preceding arguments also show that if the initial d.f. is given by $F_0(x) = F(x)$, then $F_n(x) = F(x)$ $(n \geqslant 1)$, so that the process may be said to be in statistical equilibrium.

It remains to prove that the limit (1.244) exists. In order to do this, let us write the recurrence relation (1.236) as

$$W_{n+1} = \max(0, W_n + X_n) \qquad (n = 0, 1, 2, \ldots); \tag{1.252}$$

from this we obtain successively

$$\begin{aligned} W_1 &= \max(0, W_0 + X_0), \\ W_2 &= \max(0, W_1 + X_1) = \max(0, X_1, X_1 + X_0 + W_0), \\ W_3 &= \max(0, W_2 + X_2) \\ &= \max(0, X_2, X_2 + X_1, X_2 + X_1 + X_0 + W_0), \\ &\cdots\cdots\cdots\cdots\cdots\cdots\cdots\cdots \\ W_n &= \max[0, X_{n-1} + X_{n-2} + \cdots + X_{n-r} \ (1 \leqslant r \leqslant n-1), \\ &\qquad X_{n-1} + X_{n-2} + \cdots + X_0 + W_0] \qquad (n \geqslant 1). \end{aligned} \tag{1.253}$$

Now let $S_0 = 0$, $S_n = X_0 + X_1 + \cdots + X_{n-1}$ $(n \geqslant 1)$; then since $X_{n-1} + X_{n-2} + \cdots + X_{n-r} = S_n - S_{n-r}$, we can write (1.253) as

$$(1.254) \qquad \begin{aligned} W_n &= \max\,[S_n - S_{n-r}\,(0 \leqslant r \leqslant n-1),\, W_0 + S_n] \\ &= \max\,[S_n - S_r\,(1 \leqslant r \leqslant n),\, W_0 + S_n], \end{aligned}$$

a result which may be compared with (1.219). Since $S_n - S_{n-r} = X_{n-1} + X_{n-2} + \cdots + X_{n-r}$, and the X_n are identically distributed, it follows that $S_n - S_{n-r}$ has the same distribution as S_r. Therefore we can write

$$(1.255) \qquad W_n \sim \max\,[S_r\,(0 \leqslant r \leqslant n-1),\, W_0 + S_n],$$

where, for two random variables X, Y, we write $X \sim Y$ if they have the same distribution. When $W_0 = 0$, (1.255) reduces to

$$(1.256) \qquad W_n \sim \max_{0 \leqslant r \leqslant n} S_r,$$

so that

$$(1.257) \qquad P_n(0; x) = Pr\{E_n\},$$

where the event $E_n = [S_r \leqslant x\,(0 \leqslant r \leqslant n)]$. Clearly, $E_{n+1} \subset E_n$ $(n = 0, 1, \ldots)$, so that the sequence of events $\{E_n\}$ is monotone decreasing, and therefore $E_n \rightarrow E_x$, where

$$(1.258) \qquad E_x = [S_r \leqslant x\,(r \geqslant 0)],$$

and

$$(1.259) \qquad F(x) = \lim_{n\rightarrow\infty} P_n(0; x) = Pr\{E_x\}.$$

The nature of this limit event E_x depends on the value of $\alpha = E(X_n)$. Three cases arise.

1. $\alpha < 0$. We have

$$(1.260) \qquad Pr\left\{\frac{S_n}{n} \rightarrow \alpha\right\} = 1$$

by the strong law of large numbers. Since $\alpha < 0$, for any $\epsilon > 0$ we can find an integer N such that

$$(1.261) \qquad Pr\{S_n \leqslant 0\,(n = N+1, N+2, \ldots)\} > 1 - \tfrac{1}{2}\epsilon;$$

for any $x \geqslant 0$, this gives

$$(1.262) \qquad \begin{aligned} &Pr\{S_n \leqslant x\,(n = N+1, N+2, \ldots)\} \\ &\qquad \geqslant Pr\{S_n \leqslant 0\,(n = N+1, N+2, \ldots)\} > 1 - \tfrac{1}{2}\epsilon. \end{aligned}$$

Moreover, considering the distribution of $S_1, S_2, \ldots, S_N$, we can find an $x \geqslant 0$ such that

$$(1.263) \qquad Pr\{S_n \leqslant x\,(n = 0, 1, \ldots, N)\} > 1 - \tfrac{1}{2}\epsilon.$$

From (1.262) and (1.263) we obtain

$$\begin{aligned} &Pr\{S_n > x \quad \text{for some } n\} \\ &\leqslant Pr\{S_n > x \quad \text{for some } n \leqslant N\} + Pr\{S_n > x \quad \text{for some } n > N\} \\ &\leqslant \tfrac{1}{2}\epsilon + \tfrac{1}{2}\epsilon = \epsilon, \end{aligned}$$

and therefore

$$Pr\{E\} = Pr\{S_n \leqslant x \ (n \geqslant 0)\} > 1 - \epsilon. \tag{1.264}$$

When $x \to \infty$, this gives $F(\infty) = 1$.

2. $\alpha > 0$. From (1.260) we see that for any given sequence $\{X_n\}$ we can almost always find an N such that $S_n > \frac{1}{2}n\alpha$ for $n > N$. For sufficiently large n and for all x, this gives $S_n > x$ for $n > N$ with probability one. This proves that $F(x) = Pr\{E\} = 0$ for all x.

3. $\alpha = 0$. Let us ignore the trivial case where $Pr\{X_n = 0\} = 1$. The arguments based on the strong law of large numbers do not yield any useful result in this case. However, from the fluctuation theory of sums of independent random variables, due to Chung and Fuchs (1951), we have the result

$$Pr\{|S_n - x| < \epsilon \text{ for any infinity of } n\} = 1 \tag{1.265}$$

for any x and any $\epsilon > 0$. Therefore for any x we can find an n such that $S_n > x$ with probability one, so that $F(x) = 0$ for all x. In the lattice case where the possible values of X_n are of the form kd, where $k = \cdots, -1, 0, 1, 2, \ldots$, and d is a constant, (1.265) holds only for $x = kd$, but we reach the same conclusion.

We have thus proved the existence of the limit (1.244) for $W_0 = 0$. Where $W_0 = x_0 \geqslant 0$ we find from (1.255) that

$$P_n(x_0; x) = Pr\{S_r \leqslant x \ (0 \leqslant r \leqslant n-1); \ S_n \leqslant x - x_0\}. \tag{1.266}$$

This shows that

$$P_n(x_0; x) \leqslant Pr\{S_r \leqslant x \ (0 \leqslant r \leqslant n-1)\} = P_{n-1}(0; x),$$

from which

$$\limsup_{n \to \infty} P_n(x_0, x) \leqslant F(x). \tag{1.267}$$

Furthermore, we have

$$P_n(x_0; x) \geqslant Pr\{S_r \leqslant x \ (0 \leqslant r \leqslant n-1)\} - Pr\{S_n > x - x_0\},$$

where, since $\alpha < 0$, our arguments show that $Pr\{S_n > x - x_0\} \to 0$ as $n \to \infty$; therefore

$$\liminf_{n \to \infty} P_n(x_0, x) \geqslant F(x). \tag{1.268}$$

It follows from (1.267) and (1.268) that $P_n(x_0; x) \to F(x)$ for $x \geqslant 0$.

These results may be summarized as follows. If $\alpha = E(X_n) \geqslant 0$, then the waiting time increases indefinitely, whereas if $\alpha < 0$, the waiting time has the d.f. $F(x)$ in the limit, where $F(x)$ is the unique solution of the equation (1.248) subject to the condition that it is a proper d.f. Let us also observe that if we assume the existence of finite mean interarrival time (say a) and mean service time (say b), then the condition $\alpha \geqslant 0$ gives $\rho \geqslant 1$, and $\alpha < 0$ gives $\rho < 1$.

The integral equation (1.248) is of the Wiener-Hopf type and can be solved by known methods. However, at least in the simpler cases, elementary methods are available to solve it. In Section 1.10c we outline an ad hoc method used by Lindley (1952) for $D/E_k/1$, and in Section 1.10d we give a direct solution due to Prabhu (1962) for $E_k/D/1$. For a detailed investigation see Smith (1953).

c. The System $D/E_k/1$

In this system the interarrival time is a constant (a say), and the service time has the distribution given by

$$dB(v) = e^{-k\mu v} \frac{(k\mu)^k}{(k-1)!} v^{k-1}\, dv \qquad (0 < v < \infty). \tag{1.269}$$

The random variables $X_n = v_n - u_n$ have the d.f.

$$\begin{aligned} K(x) &= Pr\{v_n - u_n \leqslant x\} = Pr\{v_n \leqslant x + a\} \\ &= \begin{cases} 0 & \text{if } -\infty < x < a \\ B(x+a) & \text{if } -a \leqslant x < \infty; \end{cases} \end{aligned} \tag{1.270}$$

we have $\alpha = E(X_n) = E(v_n - u_n) = \mu^{-1} - a = a(\rho - 1)$, where $\rho = (a\mu)^{-1}$ is the traffic intensity of the system. We assume that $\rho < 1$, so that the limiting d.f. $F(x)$ exists and satisfies the equation

$$F(x) = -\int_{0-}^{x+a} F(y)\, dB(x + a - y),$$

or

$$F(x - a) = \int_0^x F(x - v)\, dB(v) \qquad (x \geqslant a). \tag{1.271}$$

In order to solve this equation, Lindley (1952) postulates a solution of the type

$$F(x) = \sum_0^k c_i e^{\lambda_i x}, \tag{1.272}$$

where the c_i and λ_i are in general complex quantities and Re $(\lambda_i) \leqslant 0$.

To determine these quantities, substitute (1.272) in (1.271); we then find that

$$
\begin{aligned}
\sum_0^k c_i e^{\lambda_i(x-a)} &= \sum_0^k c_i \int_0^x e^{\lambda_i(x-v)}\, dB(v) \\
&= \sum_0^k c_i e^{\lambda_i x} \int_0^x e^{-(\lambda_i + k\mu)v} \frac{(k\mu)^k v^{k-1}}{(k-1)!}\, dv \\
&= \sum_0^k c_i e^{\lambda_i x} \frac{(k\mu)^k}{(k\mu+\lambda)^k} \\
&\quad - \sum_{s=0}^{k-1} \frac{x^{k-s-1}}{(k-s-1)!} e^{-k\mu x} \sum_{i=0}^k \frac{c_i}{(k\mu+\lambda_i)^{s+1}}.
\end{aligned} \tag{1.273}
$$

Equating coefficients of $e^{\lambda_i x}$ on both sides, we obtain

$$\left(\frac{k\mu}{k\mu+\lambda_i}\right)^k = e^{-\lambda_i a} \qquad (i = 0, 1, \ldots, k), \tag{1.274}$$

$$\sum_{i=0}^k \frac{c_i}{(k\mu+\lambda_i)^{s+1}} = 0 \qquad (s = 0, 1, \ldots, k-1). \tag{1.275}$$

Clearly, $\lambda_0 = 0$ satisfies (1.274); without loss of generality we take $c_0 = 1$, so that we can write (1.272) as

$$F(x) = 1 + \sum_1^k c_i e^{\lambda_i x}. \tag{1.276}$$

It can be proved that $\lambda_1, \lambda_2, \ldots, \lambda_k$ are distinct, with Re $(\lambda_i) < 0$ $(i = 1, 2, \ldots, k)$, and furthermore, that the constants $c_1, c_2, \ldots, c_k$ are uniquely determined by (1.275). The resulting expression for $F(x)$ in (1.276) is then seen to be real, and $F(x)$ is a proper d.f. Since it is known that (1.271) has a unique solution, it follows that (1.276) is the required solution.

d. The System $E_k/D/1$

We now consider the system $E_k/D/1$, in which the service time is a constant $(=b)$ say, and the interarrival time distribution is given by

$$dA(u) = e^{-\lambda u} \lambda^k u^{k-1} \frac{du}{(k-1)!} \qquad (0 < u < \infty), \tag{1.277}$$

where we have written λ instead of the usual $k\lambda$ for convenience. Here we have

$$K(x) = Pr\{X_n \leqslant x\} = 1 - A(b-x),$$

so that

$$dK(x) = \begin{cases} -dA(b-x) & \text{if} \quad -\infty < x \leqslant b \\ 0 & \text{if} \quad b < x < \infty; \end{cases} \tag{1.278}$$

and $\alpha = b - (k\lambda)^{-1} = (k\lambda)^{-1}(\rho - 1)$, where $\rho = \lambda b/k$ is the traffic intensity. We shall assume that $\rho < 1$. The integral equation (1.248) reduces in this case to

$$F(x) = \int_{\max(0,x-b)}^{\infty} F(y)\,dA(y + b - x); \tag{1.279}$$

this has been solved by Pollaczek (1959).

It is interesting to note that (1.279) is the same as the equation (1.165) for the limiting waiting time d.f. in the k-server system $M/D/k$; $F(x)$ itself has been obtained (using a different method) by Crommelin (1932) in the form

$$F(x) = \sum_{0}^{k-1} \alpha_r \sum_{s=0}^{n} e^{\lambda(x-sb)} \frac{[-\lambda(x - sb)]^{r+ks}}{(r + ks)!} \tag{1.280}$$

[cf. equation (1.162)]. Here the α_r are expressed in terms of the limiting queue-length distribution. However, since this interpretation is not possible for the α_r in the present case of the system $E_k/D/1$, it seems worthwhile to derive a solution of the type (1.280) directly from (1.279); this was obtained by Prabhu (1962) as follows. (An integral equation similar to (1.279) also occurs in the theory of finite dams; see Chapter 7.)

Substituting (1.277) in (1.279) we obtain

$$F(x) = \int_{\max(0,x-b)}^{\infty} F(y)e^{-\lambda(b-x+y)}\, \frac{\lambda^k(b - x + y)^{k-1}\,dy}{(k - 1)!}, \tag{1.281}$$

or putting $G(x) = F(x)e^{-\lambda x}$, $\mu = e^{-\lambda b}$,

$$G(x) = \mu \int_{\max(0,x-b)}^{\infty} G(y)\frac{\lambda^k(b - x + y)^{k-1}\,dy}{(k - 1)!}. \tag{1.282}$$

This can be written

(1.283)

$$G(x) = \begin{cases} \displaystyle\sum_{0}^{k-1} \alpha_r \frac{(-\lambda x)^r}{r!} & (0 \leqslant x < b) \\ \displaystyle\sum_{0}^{k-1} \alpha_r \frac{(-\lambda x)^r}{r!} + \mu(-\lambda)^k \int_0^{x-b} G(y)\frac{(x - b - y)^{k-1}}{(k - 1)!}\,dy & (x \geqslant b), \end{cases}$$

where

(1.284)

$$\alpha_r = \mu \int_0^{\infty} G(y)\lambda^{k-1-r}(b + y)^{k-1-r}\frac{dy}{(k - 1 - r)!} \qquad (r = 0, 1, \ldots, k - 1).$$

For $b \leqslant x < 2b$, we obtain from (1.283),

(1.285)

$$\begin{aligned}G(x) &= \sum_0^{k-1} \alpha_r \frac{(-\lambda x)^r}{r!} + \mu(-\lambda)^k \int_0^{x-b} \sum_0^{k-1} \alpha_r \frac{(-\lambda y)^r (x-b-y)^{k-1}}{r!\,(k-1)!}\,dy \\ &= \sum_0^{k-1} \alpha_r \frac{(-\lambda x)^r}{r!} + \mu \sum_0^{k-1} \alpha_r \frac{[-\lambda(x-b)]^{r+k}}{(r+k)!} \qquad (b \leqslant x < 2b).\end{aligned}$$

Proceeding in this manner we obtain

$$(1.286) \quad G(x) = \sum_0^{k-1} \alpha_r \sum_{s=0}^{n} \mu^s \frac{[-\lambda(x-sb)]^{r+sk}}{(r+sk)!} \qquad (nb \leqslant x < nb+b).$$

To complete the proof, assume (1.286) to be true for $n = 1, 2, \ldots, n$; then for $nb + b \leqslant x < nb + 2b$ we obtain

(1.287)

$$\begin{aligned}G(x) &= \sum_0^{k-1} \alpha_r \frac{(-\lambda x)^r}{r!} \\ &\quad + \mu(-\lambda)^k \left[\sum_{m=0}^{n-1} \int_{mb}^{mb+b} + \int_{nb}^{x-b} G(y) \frac{(x-b-y)^{k-1}\,dy}{(k-1)!}\right] \\ &= \sum_0^{k-1} \alpha_r \frac{(-\lambda x)^r}{r!} \\ &\quad + \sum_0^{k-1} \alpha_r \sum_{s=0}^{n} \int_{sb}^{x-b} \mu^{s+1}(-\lambda)^{r+sk+k} \frac{(x-sb)^{r+sk}(x-b-y)^{k-1}}{(r+sk)!\,(k-1)!}\,dy \\ &= \sum_0^{k-1} \alpha_r \frac{(-\lambda x)^r}{r!} + \sum_0^{k-1} \alpha_r \sum_{s=0}^{n} \mu^{s+1} \frac{[-\lambda(x-sb-b)]^{r+sk+k}}{(r+sk+k)!} \\ &= \sum_0^{k-1} \alpha_r \sum_{s=0}^{n+1} \mu^s \frac{[-\lambda(x-sb)]^{r+sk}}{(r+sk)!} \qquad (nb+b \leqslant x < nb+2b),\end{aligned}$$

which establishes (1.286) for $n + 1$. To evaluate the unknown constants $\alpha_r(0, 1, \ldots, k-1)$ we note that

(1.288)

$$\begin{aligned}\alpha_p &= \mu \sum_{m=0}^{\infty} \int_{mb}^{mb+b} G(y) \frac{\lambda^{k-1-p}(b+y)^{k-1-p}\,dy}{(k-1-p)!} \\ &= \sum_0^{k-1} \alpha_r \sum_{s=0}^{\infty} \int_{sb}^{\infty} \mu^{s+1}(-\lambda)^{r+sk+k-1-p} \frac{(y-sb)^{r+sk}(b+y)^{k-1-p}}{(r+sk)!\,(k-1-p)!}\,dy \\ &= \sum_0^{k-1} d_{pr}\alpha_r \qquad (p = 0, 1, \ldots, k-1),\end{aligned}$$

where

$$(1.289)\quad d_{pr} = \sum_{s=0}^{\infty} \int_{sb}^{\infty} \mu^{s+1}(-\lambda)^{r+sk+k-1-p} \frac{(y-sb)^{r+sk}(b+y)^{k-1-p}}{(r+sk)!\,(k-1-p)!}\, dy$$

$$(p, r = 0, 1, \ldots, k-1).$$

It can be proved that the quantities d_{pr} are finite. The α_r thus satisfy the system of linear equations (1.288); we shall assume that these have a unique solution, a necessary and sufficient condition for which is that the matrix $\|D - I\|$, where $D = \|d_{pr}\|$, is of rank $k-1$. Substituting for $G(x)$ in (1.286) we obtain (1.280); the solution of (1.279) is therefore complete.

COMPLEMENTS AND PROBLEMS

Section 1.2

1. Prove the identities

$$(1)\qquad \int_0^t g_i(t-\tau)k_0(\tau)\, d\tau + g_i(t) = \rho^{-i}k_i(t) \qquad (i > 0)$$

$$(2)\qquad \int_0^t g_i(t-\tau)k_j(\tau)\, d\tau = \rho^{-i}k_{i+j}(t) \qquad (i > 0, j > 0).$$

2. Show that the solution of the differential equation (1.20), subject to the boundary condition $G(z, 0) = z^i$ is given by

$$(3)\qquad G(z, t) = z^i K(z, t) - \mu \frac{1-z}{z} \int_0^t P_{i0}(t-\tau)K(z, \tau)\, d\tau,$$

where $K(z, t)$ is the p.g.f. of $X(t)$, given by (1.37). A direct inversion of (3) gives

$$(4)\qquad Pr\{Q(t) \leqslant j \mid Q(0) = i\} = K_{j-i}(t) - \mu \int_0^t P_{i0}(t-\tau)k_{j+1}(\tau)\, d\tau.$$

Now from (1.62) and (1.65) we obtain

$$(5)\qquad P_{i0}(t) = \frac{1}{\mu} \sum_{i+1}^{\infty} g_\nu(t).$$

Using this, we can write the second term on the right-hand side of (4) as

$$(6)\qquad \sum_{i+1}^{\infty} \int_0^t g_\nu(t-\tau)k_{j+1}(\tau)\, d\tau = \sum_{i+1}^{\infty} \rho^{-\nu}k_{\nu+j+1}(t) \qquad \text{[from (2)]}$$

$$= \rho^{j+1}K_{-j-i-2}(t).$$

Substituting (6) in (4) we obtain (1.44).

3. From (1.29) show that

$$(7)\quad P'_{ij}(t) = -(\lambda+\mu)k_{j-i}(t) + \mu k_{j-i+1}(t) + \lambda k_{j-i-1}(t) + \rho^{-i}\mu[k_{j+i+2}(t) - 2k_{j+i+1}(t) + k_{j+i}(t)]$$

[Bailey (1954)]. This result was first given by Ledermann and Reuter (1954).

4. Integrating (7) over $(0, t)$, show that

$$(8) \qquad P_{ij}(t) = k_{j-i}(t) + \rho^{-i}\mu \int_0^t [k_{j+i+2}(\tau) - 2k_{j+i+1}(\tau) + k_{j+i}(\tau)]\, d\tau.$$

When $\rho = 1$, this yields (1.47) [Bailey (1957)].

5. *The modified process.* Consider the modified process which ceases as soon as the total number of customers falls to zero. Prove that the difference-differential equations of this process are

$$(9) \qquad \begin{aligned} P'_{i0}(t) &= \mu P_{i1}(t) \\ P'_{i1}(t) &= -(\lambda + \mu)P_{i1}(t) + \mu P_{i2}(t) \\ P'_{ij}(t) &= -(\lambda + \mu)P_{ij}(t) + \lambda P_{ij-1}(t) + \mu P_{ij+1}(t) \qquad (j \geqslant 2). \end{aligned}$$

The transform $G^*(z, \theta)$ in this case is given by

$$(10) \qquad G^*(z, \theta) = \frac{z^{i+1} - (1 - z)(\mu - \lambda z)P^*_{i0}(\theta)}{\lambda(z - \xi)(\eta - z)},$$

where $P^*_{i0}(\theta) = \xi^i/\theta$ [Bailey (1954)]. Note that the $P_{ij}(t)$ here is our ${}^0P_{ij}(t)$ $(j \geqslant 1)$, and $P_{i0}(t) = G_i(t)$. By inverting (10), Bailey establishes the results (1.63) and (1.65).

6. *First passage times.* Let

$$(11) \qquad T_{ij} = \inf\{t \mid Q(t) = j,\ Q(0) = i\}$$

be the first passage time of the process $Q(t)$ from the state i to the state j, and $f_{ij}(t)$ its frequency function. Show that the Laplace transform of $f_{ij}(t)$ is given by

$$(12) \qquad f^*_{ij}(\theta) = \int_0^\infty e^{-\theta t} f_{ij}(t)\, dt = \begin{cases} \xi^{i-j} & \text{if } j < i \\ \dfrac{\lambda(\xi^{i+1} - \eta^{i+1}) - \mu(\xi^i - \eta^i)}{\lambda(\xi^{j+1} - \eta^{j+1}) - \mu(\xi^j - \eta^j)} & \text{if } j > i \end{cases}$$

[Bailey (1957)].

7. *Extension of Champernowne's methods.* Using the combinatorial arguments of Section 1.2c, show that

$$(13) \qquad Pr\{T_i > t \mid Q(0) = i,\ A(t) = a,\ D(t) = b\} = 1 - \frac{a!\, b!}{(b - i)!\, (a + i)!}$$

and hence that

$$(14) \qquad {}^0P^{(b)}_{ij}(t) = Pr\{Q(t) = j;\quad T_i > t;\quad D(t) = b \mid Q(0) = i\}$$
$$= e^{-(\lambda+\mu)t}\lambda^{b+j-i}\mu^b t^{2b+j-i}\left[\frac{1}{b!\,(b + j - i)!} - \frac{1}{(b - i)!\,(b + j)!}\right].$$

It follows that the joint distribution of the duration of the busy period T_i and the number $N(T_i)$ of customers served during this period is given by

$$\begin{aligned} dG_i^{(n)}(t) &= Pr\{t < T_i < t + dt;\, N(T_i) = n\} \\ &= {}^0P_{i1}^{(n-1)}(t)\mu\, dt \\ &= ie^{-(\lambda+\mu)t}\frac{\mu^n\lambda^{n-i}}{n!\,(n-i)!}t^{2n-i-1}\,dt \qquad (n \geqslant i). \end{aligned} \tag{15}$$

Adding (15) over $n = i, i + 1, \ldots$, we obtain the distribution of T_i. On the other hand, integrating (15) over $0 \leqslant t < \infty$ we obtain the distribution of the number of customers served; thus

$$\begin{aligned} Pr\{N(T_i) = n\} &= \int_0^\infty dG_i^{(n)}(t) \\ &= \frac{i}{n}\binom{-n}{n-i}\alpha^n(-\beta)^{n-i} \qquad (n \geqslant i), \end{aligned} \tag{16}$$

where $\alpha = (1 + \rho)^{-1}$, $\beta = 1 - \alpha$.

8. Establish the relations

$$dG_i^{(n)}(t) = \sum_{r=1}^{n-i}\int_0^t e^{-(\lambda+\mu)\tau}\frac{\lambda^r\mu^i\tau^{r+i-1}}{r!\,(i-1)!}\,dG_r^{(n-i)}(t-\tau) \qquad (n \geqslant i+1) \tag{17}$$

$$dG_i^{(i)}(t) = e^{-(\lambda+\mu)t}\frac{\mu^i t^{i-1}}{(i-1)!}\,dt \qquad (i \geqslant 1). \tag{18}$$

Hence obtain the result (15) for $dG_i^{(n)}(t)$.

9. If Q denotes the queue-length in statistical equilibrium, show that $E(Q) = \rho(1 - \rho)^{-1}$. For the number Q' actually waiting to be served, we have

$$\begin{aligned} &Pr\{Q' = 0\} = 1 - \rho^2, \qquad Pr\{Q' = j\} = (1 - \rho)\rho^{j+1} \qquad (j \geqslant 1), \\ &E(Q') = \rho^2(1 - \rho)^{-1}. \end{aligned} \tag{19}$$

Furthermore, show that the mean waiting time is given by

$$E(W) = \frac{\rho}{\mu(1-\rho)} \qquad (\rho < 1). \tag{20}$$

10. *The nonhomogeneous process.* If λ and μ are functions of t, the process $Q(t)$ is nonhomogeneous. For an analysis of this process see Clarke (1956).

Section 1.3

11. Show that the probability that all servers will be busy is given by

$$\sum_s^\infty u_j = \frac{u_s}{1-\rho}; \tag{21}$$

this is Erlang's *loss formula*. Furthermore, show that

(*a*) the probability that at least one customer will be waiting is

$$= \sum_1^\infty v_j = \rho u_s(1 - \rho)^{-1};$$

(*b*) the mean number of waiting customers, if any, is

$$= \sum_{1}^{\infty} jv_j \Big/ \sum_{1}^{\infty} v_j = (1 - \rho)^{-1};$$

and

(c) the mean waiting time of queued up customers is

$$= \frac{\int_{0+}^{\infty} x\, dF(x)}{\int_{0+}^{\infty} dF(x)} = (s\mu - \lambda)^{-1}.$$

All these formulas hold in the limit as $t \to \infty$ and it is assumed that $\rho < 1$.

12. Show that for the number R of busy servers we have

$$Pr\{R = j\} = \begin{cases} \dfrac{u_0}{j!}\left(\dfrac{\lambda}{\mu}\right)^j & (0 \leqslant j \leqslant s - 1) \\ u_s/(1 - \rho) & (j = s), \end{cases} \tag{22}$$

$$E(R) = \frac{\lambda}{\mu}.$$

13. *Finite number of customers.* Show that if the population contains a finite number ($N \geqslant s$) of customers, the limiting distribution of the queue-length is given by

$$u_j = \begin{cases} u_0 \dbinom{N}{j}\left(\dfrac{\lambda}{\mu}\right)^j & (0 \leqslant j \leqslant s) \\ \dfrac{u_0}{s!}\dbinom{N}{j}\left(\dfrac{\lambda}{\mu}\right)^j \dfrac{j!}{s^{j-s}} & (s \leqslant j \leqslant N), \end{cases} \tag{23}$$

where u_0 is determined so that $u_0 + u_1 + \cdots + u_N = 1$. These results were obtained by Fry (1928) for a telephone traffic model, and later by Palm (1947) for the machine interference problem.

14. *Loss systems.* If an arriving customer who finds all servers busy leaves the system instead of waiting for service, we have a loss system. In such a system, let $Q(t)$ be the number of busy servers at time t; $Q(t) \leqslant s$ with probability one.

(*a*) If the population of customers is infinite, show that the limiting distribution of $Q(t)$ is given by

$$u_j = \frac{\dfrac{1}{j!}\left(\dfrac{\lambda}{\mu}\right)^j}{\sum_0 \dfrac{1}{j!}\left(\dfrac{\lambda}{\mu}\right)^j} \qquad (0 \leqslant j \leqslant s), \tag{24}$$

a result due to Erlang (1917). In particular, the probability that all servers will be busy is given by

$$u_s = \frac{\dfrac{1}{s!}\left(\dfrac{\lambda}{\mu}\right)^s}{1 + \left(\dfrac{\lambda}{\mu}\right) + \dfrac{1}{2!}\left(\dfrac{\lambda}{\mu}\right)^2 + \cdots + \dfrac{1}{s!}\left(\dfrac{\lambda}{\mu}\right)^s}, \tag{25}$$

which is called *Erlang's loss formula.*

(*b*) If the population contains a finite number N of customers, then

$$u_j = \frac{\dbinom{N}{j}\left(\dfrac{\lambda}{\mu}\right)^j}{\sum_0^s \dbinom{N}{j}\left(\dfrac{\lambda}{\mu}\right)^j} \qquad (0 \leqslant j \leqslant s) \tag{26}$$

(the *Engset distribution*).

15. *Systems with finite waiting room capacity.* If the system can accommodate a maximum number $N\,(\geqslant s)$ of customers at any given time, show that the limiting queue-length distribution is given by (1.83) with

$$u_0 = \left[\sum_0^{s-1} \frac{1}{j!}\left(\frac{\lambda}{\mu}\right)^j + \frac{1}{s!}\left(\frac{\lambda}{\mu}\right)^s \frac{1 - \rho^{N-s+1}}{1 - \rho}\right]^{-1}. \tag{27}$$

In particular, when $s = 1$, we have

$$u_j = \frac{(1 - \rho)\rho^j}{1 - \rho^{N+1}} \qquad (0 \leqslant j \leqslant N), \tag{28}$$

so that the limiting distribution in this case is a truncated geometric distribution.

16. *The case of variable input.* The system $M/M/s$ where the parameter λ is a function of t has been considered by Kolmogorov (1931).

Section 1.5

17. *A result from branching process theory.* Let $K(z) = \sum_0^\infty k_j z^j$ be a p.g.f., and assume that $k_0 > 0$, $0 < K'(1) = \alpha < \infty$. Then the equation $z = K(z)$ has a root ζ such that $0 < \zeta < 1$ if and only if $\alpha > 1$ [see Feller (1957)].

To prove this, consider the function

$$f(z) = K(z)/z = k_0/z + k_1 + k_2 z + \cdots (0 < z \leqslant 1).$$

We have $f(+0) = \infty$, $f(1) = 1$. Moreover, $f''(z) = 2k_0/z^3 + 2k_3 + 6k_4 z + \cdots > 0$. Thus $f'(z)$ is a monotone increasing function and vanishes at most once in $(0 < z < 1)$, which happens if and only if $f'(1) = \alpha - 1 > 0$. If $f'(z) = 0$ at $z = z_0\,(0 < z_0 < 1)$, then $f(z)$ is monotone decreasing in $(0 < z < z_0)$ and monotone increasing in $(z_0 < z \leqslant 1)$. Since $f(1) = 1$ and $f(z_0) < 1$, there exists exactly one value ζ such that $f(\zeta) = 1$, $0 < \zeta < 1$.

18. The limiting probabilities u_j satisfy the system of equations (1.119) with $P'_{ij}(t) = 0$, viz.,

$$k\mu u_1 = \lambda u_0$$
$$k\mu u_{j+1} = (\lambda + k\mu)u_j \qquad (1 \leqslant j \leqslant k) \tag{29}$$
$$k\mu u_{j+1} = (\lambda + k\mu)u_j - \lambda u_{j-k} \qquad (j \geqslant k).$$

Solving these equations successively for $j = 0, 1, \ldots, k-1$, we obtain

$$u_j = u_0 \frac{\rho}{k}\left(1 + \frac{\rho}{k}\right)^{j-1} \qquad (1 \leqslant j \leqslant k). \tag{30}$$

It is clear that $u_0 = 1 - \rho$. Summing (29) over $0, 1, \ldots, j (j \geqslant k)$ and simplifying, we obtain

$$u_j = \frac{\rho}{k}(u_{j-k} + u_{j-k+1} + \cdots + u_{j-1}). \tag{31}$$

The solution of (31) is $u_j = \sum_1^k c_i m_i^{\,j}$, where $m_1, m_2, \ldots, m_k$ are the roots of the equation

$$m^k = \frac{\rho}{k}(1 + m + m^2 + \cdots + m^{k-1}). \tag{32}$$

We can choose the constants $c_1, c_2, \ldots, c_k$ so that

$$\sum_1^k c_i m_i^{\,j} = u_j \qquad (0 \leqslant j \leqslant k-1), \tag{33}$$

where the u_j are given by (30); these equations yield a unique solution for the c_i [Erlang (1920)]. Note that the substitution $m = z^{-1}$ reduced (32) to the equation (1.123).

19. *A more general phase-type service.* Suppose that instead of demanding a fixed number k of phases, a customer demands a random number N of phases, with probability $c_n = Pr\{N = n\}$ $(n \geqslant 1)$, the service time for each phase having a negative exponential distribution. Obtain the transform $G^*(z, \theta)$ of the number of phases in this system [Luchak (1958)].

Section 1.6

20. Show that the probability that a customer who joins the system finds j customers in front of him is given by w_j, where

$$w_j = (1 - \zeta)\zeta^j \quad (j \geqslant 0), \qquad \zeta = \zeta_0^{\,k}. \tag{34}$$

Hence prove that the limiting distribution of the waiting time of a customer who joins the system is given by

$$dF(0) = 1 - \zeta, \qquad dF(x) = (1 - \zeta)\zeta\mu e^{-\mu x(1-\zeta)}\, dx \qquad (0 < x < \infty) \tag{35}$$

[Jackson and Nickols (1956)]. Note that ζ is the least positive root of the equation

$$x = \left(\frac{k\lambda}{k\lambda + \mu - \mu x}\right)^k. \tag{36}$$

Section 1.7

21. Show that the probability of not having to wait is given by

$$F(0) = v_{s-1} = (s - \lambda b) \prod_{1}^{s-1} (1 - z_j)^{-1}. \tag{37}$$

22. Show that (1.152) can be written as

$$U(z) = (s - \lambda b) \prod_{1}^{s-1} \left(\frac{z - z_i}{1 - z_i}\right) \frac{1 - z}{1 - z^s e^{\lambda b(1-z)}}\ ; \tag{38}$$

and hence obtain the mean and variance of the queue-length in statistical equilibrium [cf. Bailey (1954b)].

23. From (1.169) show that the p.g.f. of N_i is given by $\sum_{i}^{\infty} f_n^{(i)} z^n = \xi^i$, where $\xi = \xi(z)$ satisfies the functional equation $\xi = ze^{-\lambda b(1-\xi)}$.

Section 1.8

24. Show that in the system $GI/G/1$, the event $A = \{W_n = 0\}$ is a recurrent event in Feller's (1957) terminology and that A is transient, persistent null, or persistent non-null depending on whether $\alpha > 0$, $\alpha = 0$, or $\alpha < 0$. In the case $\alpha = 1$ obtain the mean recurrence time of A [Lindley (1952)].

25. Show that the recurrence time distribution of the state 0 of the Markov chain $\{Q_n\}$ in the system $M/G/1$ is given by

$$f_{00}^{(n)} = \frac{1}{n} k_{n-1}^{(n)} \qquad (n \geqslant 1) \tag{39}$$

where $k_j^{(n)}$ is the coefficient of z^j in the expansion of $[K(z)]^n$. Hence, if

$$A = \sum_{1}^{\infty} \frac{1}{n} k_{n-1}^{(n)}, \qquad B = \sum_{1}^{\infty} k_{n-1}^{(n)}, \tag{40}$$

then $\{Q_n\}$ is transient if $A < 1$, persistent null if $A = 1$, $B = \infty$, and persistent non-null if $A = 1$, $B < \infty$. Note that this classification does not assume that $\rho < \infty$.

26. Show that in the special case $M/E_k/1$, the formula (1.190) can be written as

$$U(z) = \prod_{i=1}^{k} \left(\frac{z_i - 1}{z_i - z}\right) \tag{41}$$

where $z_1, z_2, \ldots, z_k$ are the roots (other than zero) of the equation

$$z(k + \rho - \rho z)^k = k^k \tag{42}$$

and it is known that $|z_i| > 1$ $(i = 1, 2, \ldots, k)$.

27. Show that for the Markov chain $\{Q_n\}$ in the system $GI/M/1$, the p.g.f. of the recurrence time of the state 0 is given by

$$\sum_{1}^{\infty} f_{00}^{(n)} z^n = \frac{z - \xi}{1 - \xi}, \tag{43}$$

where $\xi \equiv \xi(z)$ satisfies the functional equation $\xi = zK(\xi)$. Hence prove that the chain is transient if $\rho > 1$, persistent null if $\rho = 1$, and persistent non-null if $\rho < 1$. Obtain the mean recurrence time in the case $\rho < 1$.

Section 1.9

28. *The modified process.* Let z be the first zero in $t \geqslant 0$ of $W(t)$ and define

$$Z(t) = \begin{cases} W(t) & \text{for } t \leqslant z \\ 0 & \text{for } t > z. \end{cases} \tag{44}$$

Show that the forward Kolmogorov equation of this modified process $Z(t)$ is

$$\frac{\partial F}{\partial t} - \frac{\partial F}{\partial x} = -\lambda F(x, t) + \lambda \int_0^x F(x - v, t)\, dB(v) + \lambda F(0, t)[1 - B(x)]. \tag{45}$$

[Beneš (1957).]

Section 1.10

29. *The system $D/M/1$.* Show that in the system $D/M/1$,

$$P_n(0, x) = 1 - \sum_{r=1}^{n} e^{-\mu(x+ra)} \frac{\mu^{r-1}}{(r-1)!} (x + ra)^{r-2}(x + a) \qquad (n \geqslant 1). \tag{46}$$

Hence, using (1.175), prove that the limiting d.f. $F(x)$ is given by

$$F(x) = 1 - \zeta e^{-\mu(1-\zeta)x} \qquad (x \geqslant 0), \tag{47}$$

where ζ is the least positive root of the equation $z = e^{-\mu a(1-z)}$, and it is known that $0 < \zeta < 1$ since $\rho^{-1} = \mu a > 1$. This is a special case of Smith's result (1.209).

30. In the case $M/G/1$, define a function $F^*(x)$ by putting

$$F^*(x) = -\int_0^\infty F(y)\, dK(x - y) \qquad (-\infty < x < \infty). \tag{48}$$

The characteristic function of $F^*(x)$ is given by

$$\int_{-\infty}^{\infty} e^{i\theta x}\, dF^*(x) = \Phi(\theta)\psi(\theta) \frac{\lambda}{\lambda + i\theta}, \tag{49}$$

where $\Phi(\theta)$, $\psi(\theta)$ are the characteristic functions of $F(x)$ and $B(x)$ respectively. Now, $F^*(x) = F(x)$ for $x \geqslant 0$; show that $F^*(x) = ce^{\lambda x}$ for $x < 0$, where c is a constant. Hence prove the result

$$\Phi(\theta) = \frac{ci\theta}{\lambda + i\theta - \lambda\psi(\theta)}, \tag{50}$$

which is equivalent to the Pollaczek-Khintchine formula (1.194) [Lindley (1952)].

31. When $k = 1$, show that Lindley's procedure gives the result (47) for the system $D/M/1$.

REFERENCES

Bailey, N. T. J. (1954a). A continuous time treatment of a simple queue using generating functions. *J. Roy. Stat. Soc.*, **B16,** 288–291.

Bailey, N. T. J. (1954b). On queueing processes with bulk service. *J. Roy. Stat. Soc.*, **B16,** 80–87.

Bailey, N. T. J. (1957). Some further results in the non-equilibrium theory of a simple queue. *J. Roy. Stat. Soc.*, **B19,** 326–333.

Beněs, V. E. (1957). On queues with Poisson arrivals. *Ann. Math. Statist.*, **28,** 670–677.

Brockmeyer, E. et. al. (1948). *The Life and Works of A. K. Erlang.* The Copenhagen Telephone Company.

Borel, E. (1942). Sur l'emploi du théorème de Bernoulli pour faciliter le calcul d'une infinité de coefficients. Application au problème de l'attente à un guichet. *Comptes Rendus Acad. Sci.*, Paris, **214,** 452–456.

Chung, K. L., and W. H. J. Fuchs (1951). Four papers on probability. *Mem. Amer. Math. Soc.*, No. 6, 1–12.

Champernowne, D. G. (1956). An elementary method of solution of the queueing problem with a single server and constant parameters. *J. Roy. Stat. Soc.*, **B18,** 125–128.

Clarke, A. B. (1956). A waiting line process of Markov type. *Ann. Math. Statist.*, **27,** 452–459.

Crommelin, C. D. (1932). Delay probability formulas when the holding times are constant. *P. O. Elect. Engrs. J.*, **25,** 41–50.

Erlang, A. K. (1909, 1917, 1920). See the survey by A. Jensen (1948).

Feller, W. (1957). *An Introduction to Probability Theory and its Applications*, 2nd edition. John Wiley, New York.

Fry, T. C. (1928). *Probability and its Engineering Uses.* D. Van Nostrand, New York.

Hasofer, A. M. (1963). On the integrability, continuity, and differentiability of a family of functions introduced by L. Takács. *Ann. Math. Statist.*, **34,** 1045–1049.

Jackson, R. R. P., and D. G. Nickols (1956). Some equilibrium results for the queueing process $E_k/M/1$. *J. Roy. Stat. Soc.*, **B18,** 275–279.

Jensen, A. (1948). An elucidation of A. K. Erlang's statistical works through the theory of stochastic process. See Brockmeyer et al. (1948), 23–100.

Kendall, David G. (1951). Some problems in the theory of queues. *J. Roy. Stat. Soc.*, **B13,** 151–185.

Kendall, David G. (1954). Stochastic processes occurring in the theory of queues and their analysis by the method of the imbedded Markov chain. *Ann. Math. Statist.*, **24,** 338–354.

Khintchine, A. Y. (1932). See the reference to his book below.

Khintchine, A. Y. (1960). *Mathematical Methods in the Theory of Queueing.* Charles Griffin, London.

Kolmogorov, A. N. (1931). Sur le problème d'attente. *Matem. Sbornik*, **38,** 101–106.

Ledermann, W., and G. E. H. Reuter (1954). Spectral theory for the differential equations of simple birth and death processes. *Phil. Trans.*, **A246,** 321–369.

Lindley, D. V. (1952). The theory of queues with a single server. *Proc. Cam. Phil. Soc.*, **48,** 277–289.

Luchak, G. (1958). The continuous time solution of the equations of the single channel queue with a general class of service time distributions by the method of generating functions. *J. Roy. Stat. Soc.*, **B20,** 176–181.

Molina, E. C. (1927). Application of the theory of probability to telephone trunking problems. *Bell. Syst. Tech. J.*, **6,** 461–494.

Palm, C. (1943). Intensitätsschwankungen in Fernsprechverkehr. *Ericsson Technics*, **44,** 1–189.

Palm, C. (1947). The distribution of repairmen in servicing automatic machines (in Swedish). Industritidningen Norden, **75,** 75–80.

Pollaczek, F. (1930). See reference to more recent work below.

Pollaczek, F. (1957). Problèmes Stochastiques posés par le Phénomène de formation d'une Queue d'Attente à un Guichet et par des Phénomènes Apparentés. *Mémorial de Sci. Math.* (Paris) No. 136.

Pollaczek, F. (1959). Application de la théorie des probabilités posées par l'encombrement des réseaux téléphoniques. *Ann. Télécommun.*, **14,** 165–183.

Pollaczek, F. (1963). *Théorie Analytique des Problèmes Stochastiques relatifs à un Groupe de lignes Téléphoniques avec Dispostif d'Attente.* Gauthier-Villars, Paris.

Prabhu, N. U. (1962). Elementary methods for some waiting time problems. *Opns. Res.*, **10,** 559–566.

Reich, Edgar (1958). On the integro-differential equation of Takács I. *Ann. Math. Statist.*, **29,** 563–570.

Saaty, T. L. (1960). Time dependent solution of the many server Poisson queue. *Opns. Res.*, **8,** 755–772.

Smith, W. L. (1953). On the distribution of queueing times. *Proc. Cam. Phil. Soc.*, **49,** 449–461.

Takács, Lajos (1955). Investigation of waiting time problems by reduction to Markov processes. *Acta Math.* (Budapest), **6,** 101–129.

Tanner, J. C. (1953). A problem of interference between two queues. *Biometrika*, **40,** 58–69.

Tanner, J. C. (1961). A derivation of the Borel distribution. *Biometrika*, **48,** 222–224.

Vaulot, E. (1924). Application de calcul des probabilités à l'exploitation téléphonique. *Revue Générale de l'Electricité*, **16,** 411–418.

Wishart, D. M. G. (1956). A queueing system with χ^2 service time distribution. *Ann. Math. Statist.*, **27,** 768–779.

Chapter 2

Transient Behavior of the Systems $M/G/1$ and $GI/M/1$

2.1 INTRODUCTION

In this chapter we study the two single server systems $M/G/1$ and $GI/M/1$. It has been observed that the stochastic processes occurring in a queueing system are in general non-Markovian. However, in the two cases studied here we shall find that it is possible to obtain the properties of the underlying processes in a straightforward manner.

We first consider the system $M/G/1$, in which

1. The customers arrive "at random," that is, the interarrival times have the negative exponential distribution $\lambda e^{-\lambda t}\,dt$ $(0 < t < \infty)$, whereas the number $A(t)$ of customers arriving during a time interval $(0, t]$ has the Poisson distribution

$$Pr\{A(t) = n\} = e^{-\lambda t}\frac{(\lambda t)^n}{n!} \qquad (n = 0, 1, \ldots). \tag{2.1}$$

2. The queue discipline is "first come, first served."
3. There is only one counter and the service time has the distribution $dB(t)$ $(0 < t < \infty)$. Let $\psi(\theta) = \int_0^\infty e^{-\theta t}\,dB(t)$ $[\mathrm{Re}\,(\theta) > 0]$ be the Laplace-Stieltjes transform (L.S.T.) of $B(t)$. We assume that the mean service time is finite, so that $0 < b = -\psi'(0) < \infty$, and the relative traffic intensity is $\rho = \lambda b$ $(0 < \rho < \infty)$.

Let $W(t)$ be the waiting time; as observed already, $W(t)$ is a Markov process. Furthermore, let $Q(t)$ be the queue-length at time t, that is, the number of customers (including the one at the counter, if any) present in the system; except in the case $M/M/1$, $Q(t)$ is non-Markovian. We also define the random variables

(2.2) $$T(x) = \inf\,[t \mid W(t) = 0,\ W(0) = x],$$

(2.3) $$T_i = \inf\,[t \mid Q(t) = 0,\ Q(0) = i];$$

these denote the busy periods initiated by a waiting time x and a queue-length i, respectively. For $i = 1$, T_i reduces to the conventionally defined busy period.

In Section 2.2 the joint distribution of the number of customers served during the busy period $T(x)$ and the length of $T(x)$ is derived. This yields results regarding the conventionally defined busy period T_1. In Section 2.3 the probability of finding an empty queue at any given time is obtained; more generally, the transition distribution function (d.f.) of $W(t)$ is obtained in Section 2.4. The queue-length distribution is discussed in Sections 2.5 and 2.6. The limiting behavior of the system is studied in Section 2.7, and finally in Section 2.8 some particular cases are considered.

2.2 THE BUSY PERIOD

a. A Fundamental Result

Let $X(t)$ be the total service time of customers arriving in a time interval $(0, t]$; clearly, $X(t) = v_1 + v_2 + \cdots + v_{A(t)}$, where $A(t)$ is the number of arrivals during $(0, t]$, and has the Poisson distribution (2.1), whereas $v_1, v_2, \ldots$ are mutually independent random variables with the distribution $dB(v)$. It follows that $X(t)$ has the compound Poisson distribution given by

(2.4) $$K(x, t) = Pr\{X(t) \leqslant x\} = \sum_{n=0}^{\infty} e^{-\lambda t} \frac{(\lambda t)^n}{n!} B_n(x),$$

where $B_n(x)$ is the n-fold convolution of $B(x)$ with itself $(n \geqslant 1)$, and $B_0(x) = 0$ if $x < 0$, and $= 1$ if $x \geqslant 0$. The L.S.T. of $X(t)$ is given by

(2.5) $$\begin{aligned} E\{e^{-\theta X(t)}\} &= \int_{0-}^{\infty} e^{-\theta x}\, d_x K(x, t) \\ &= \sum_{n=0}^{\infty} e^{-\lambda t} \frac{(\lambda t)^n}{n!} \int_{0-}^{\infty} e^{-\theta x}\, dB_n(x) \\ &= \sum_{n=0}^{\infty} e^{-\lambda t} \frac{(\lambda t)^n}{n!} [\psi(\theta)]^n \\ &= e^{-\lambda t + \lambda t \psi(\theta)}. \end{aligned}$$

We may consider $X(t)$ as the accumulated "service potential" (or "load") which is steadily exhausted by the server at unit rate per unit time except when it is zero. Thus the busy period $T(x)$ defined by (2.2) can be expressed as

$$T(x) = \inf [t \mid x + X(t) - t \leqslant 0]. \tag{2.6}$$

Also, let $N(x)$ be the number of customers served during $T(x)$, excluding those present initially [we shall call $N(x)$ the number of "new" customers]. Let the joint distribution of $T(x)$ and $N(x)$ be denoted by

$$G_n(x, t) = Pr\{T(x) \leqslant t;\ N(x) = n\}. \tag{2.7}$$

We have

$$\begin{aligned} dG_0(x, t) &= \begin{cases} e^{-\lambda t} & (t = x) \\ 0 & (t \neq x) \end{cases} \\ G_0(x, t) &= e^{-\lambda t} B_0(t - x), \end{aligned} \tag{2.8}$$

since if no new customers arrive during $(0, t]$, then the waiting time reduces to zero at time x. For $n \geqslant 1$, at least one new customer must arrive during $(0, x]$, as otherwise the waiting time will reduce to zero at $x < t$; let the first new customer arrive at time τ, where τ has the distribution $\lambda e^{-\lambda\tau}\, d\tau$ $(0 < \tau < x]$. If v is the service time of this customer, then the waiting time $W(\tau + 0) = x - \tau + v$, where v has the distribution $dB(v)$. During the remaining interval $(\tau, t]$, $n - 1$ customers must be served; thus we have that

(2.9)
$$\begin{aligned} dG_n(x, t) &= \int_{\tau=0}^{x} \int_{v=0}^{t-x} \lambda e^{-\lambda\tau}\, dG_{n-1}(x - \tau + v, t - \tau)\, d\tau\, dB(v) \qquad (t \geqslant x) \\ &= 0 \qquad (t < x). \end{aligned}$$

This gives us a recurrence relation for $G_n(x, t)$; from (2.8) and (2.9) we can obtain $G_n(x, t)$ for $n \geqslant 1$. Thus, substituting (2.8) in (2.9) with $n = 1$, we obtain

$$\begin{aligned} dG_1(x, t) &= \int_{\tau=0}^{x} \int_{v=0}^{t-x} \lambda e^{-\lambda\tau} e^{-\lambda(t-\tau)}\, dB_0(t - x - v)\, dB(v)\, d\tau \\ &= e^{-\lambda t} \lambda x\, dB_1(t - x). \end{aligned} \tag{2.10}$$

In order to proceed in this manner, we note that the identity

$$\begin{aligned} \frac{1}{m + n} \frac{d}{d\theta} [\psi(\theta)]^{m+n} &= [\psi(\theta)]^{m+n-1} \psi'(\theta) \\ &= \frac{1}{m} [\psi(\theta)]^n \frac{d}{d\theta} [\psi(\theta)]^m \end{aligned}$$

is equivalent to the relation

$$\int_0^\infty e^{-\theta x}\left[\frac{x}{m+n}\, dB_{m+n}(x) - \int_0^x \frac{v}{m}\, dB_m(v)\, dB_n(x-v)\right] = 0$$

for all $\theta > 0$, and this implies the important result

$$\int_0^x v\, dB_m(v)\, dB_n(x-v) = \frac{mx}{m+n}\, dB_{m+n}(x). \tag{2.11}$$

Substituting (2.10) in (2.9) with $n = 2$ and using (2.11), we obtain

(2.12)

$$\begin{aligned} dG_2(x, t) &= \int_{\tau=0}^{x} \int_{v=0}^{t-x} \lambda e^{-\lambda\tau} e^{-\lambda(t-\tau)} \lambda(x - \tau + v)\, d\tau\, dB_1(t - x - v)\, dB(v) \\ &= \lambda^2 e^{-\lambda t} \int_{v=0}^{t-x} (\tfrac{1}{2}x^2 + vx)\, dB(v)\, dB_1(t - x - v) \\ &= e^{-\lambda t} \frac{\lambda^2 tx}{2}\, dB_2(t - x). \end{aligned}$$

The results (2.8), (2.10), and (2.12) suggest the general expression

$$\begin{aligned} G_n(x, t) &= \int_{\tau=x}^{t} e^{-\lambda\tau} \frac{(\lambda\tau)^{n-1}}{n!} \lambda x\, dB_n(\tau - x) \qquad (t \geqslant x) \\ &= 0 \qquad (t < x) \end{aligned} \tag{2.13}$$

for ($n = 0, 1, \ldots$). To prove that it is indeed so, let us assume (2.13) to be valid for $n = 0, 1, \ldots, n-1$; then the recurrence relation (2.9) gives

$$dG_n(x, t) = \int_{\tau=0}^{x} \lambda e^{-\lambda\tau} e^{-\lambda(t-\tau)} \frac{[\lambda(t-\tau)]^{n-2}}{(n-1)!}\, d\tau.$$

$$\begin{aligned} &\int_{v=0}^{t=x} \lambda(x - \tau + v)\, dB_{n-1}(t - x - v)\, dB(v) \\ &= \lambda^n e^{-\lambda t} \int_{\tau=0}^{x} \frac{(t-\tau)^{n-2}}{(n-1)!}\, d\tau \left(\frac{t-x}{n} + x - \tau\right) dB_n(t - x) \\ &= \lambda^n e^{-\lambda t}\, dB_n(t - x) \int_{t-x}^{t} \tau^{n-2}\left[\tau - \frac{n-1}{n}(t - x)\right] d\tau \\ &= e^{-\lambda t} \frac{(\lambda t)^{n-1}}{n!} \lambda x\, dB_n(t - x) \end{aligned} \tag{2.14}$$

which is in agreement with (2.11). The fundamental result (2.13) leads to several useful results, as shown in the following sections.

b. The Distribution of $T(x)$

From (2.13) we see that the d.f. $T(x)$ is given by

$$G(x, t) = Pr\{T(x) \leqslant t\} = \sum_{n=0}^{\infty} G_n(x, t) \tag{2.15}$$

$$= \int_{\tau=x}^{t} \sum_{n=0}^{\infty} e^{-\lambda\tau} \frac{(\lambda\tau)^{n-1}}{n!} \lambda x \, dB_n(\tau - x).$$

To obtain the L.S.T. of $T(x)$ we proceed as follows. The argument used in deriving the recurrence relation (2.9) also gives the relation

$$T(x) = x + T[X(x)]. \tag{2.16}$$

Since $X(t)$ is a process with stationary independent increments, it is obvious that we must have

$$E[e^{-\theta T(x)}] = [e^{-\theta T(1)}]^x = e^{-x\eta(\theta)} \qquad \text{(say);} \tag{2.17}$$

the relation (2.16) then gives

$$e^{-x\eta(\theta)} = E[e^{-\theta T(x)}] = E[e^{-\theta x \ \eta(\theta)X(x)}]$$

$$= e^{-\theta x - \lambda x + \lambda x \psi(\eta)},$$

where we have used (2.5). Hence we see that $\eta(\theta)$ satisfies the functional equation

$$\eta(\theta) = \theta + \lambda - \lambda\psi(\eta). \tag{2.18}$$

The required root of (2.17) is such that $\eta(\infty) = \infty$ [from (2.17)], and we shall show that this root is unique. It suffices to prove this for real positive values of θ, because $\eta(\theta)$ can then be extended to θ such that Re $(\theta) \geqslant 0$. Putting $\eta(\theta) = x$ in (2.18), we obtain

$$\eta^{-1}(x) = \lambda\psi(x) - \lambda + x, \tag{2.19}$$

where $\eta^{-1}(x)$ is the inverse function of η. Now consider the function

$$f(x) = \lambda\psi(x) - \lambda + x \qquad (x \geqslant 0). \tag{2.20}$$

We have $f(0) = 0$, $f(\infty) = \infty$, and $f'(x) = \lambda\psi'(x) + 1$, $f''(x) = \lambda\psi''(x) = \lambda \int_0^{\infty} e^{-xv} v^2 \, dB(v) > 0$. Hence it follows that $f(x)$ is positive and monotone increasing for $x > x_0$, where x_0 is the largest positive root of $f(x) = 0$, and $x_0 = 0$ or > 0 depending on whether $f'(0) = \lambda\psi'(0) + 1 = 1 - \rho \geqslant 0$ or < 0. Thus for a given $\theta \geqslant 0$ there is a unique x such that $f(x) = \theta$ in the range $x > x_0$, and from (2.19) it is clear that $x = \eta(\theta)$. Furthermore, as $\theta \to 0+$, $x \to x_0$. Thus the L.S.T. (2.17) of the busy period $T(x)$ is uniquely determined by (2.18) and tends to $e^{-x\eta(+0)}$. Hence

$$Pr\{T(x) < \infty\} = \lim_{\theta \to 0+} E[e^{-\theta T(x)}] = \begin{cases} 1 & \text{if } \rho \leqslant 1 \\ e^{-x\eta_0} & \text{if } \rho > 1, \end{cases} \tag{2.21}$$

where η_0 is the largest positive root of the equation $f(x) = 0$, that is,

$$x = \lambda - \lambda\psi(x). \tag{2.22}$$

c. The Busy Period T_1

Let $t = 0$ be an epoch just before commencement of service, and $Q(0) = i$. Then $W(0) = x$ is the cumulative service time of the i customers in the system. It follows that the joint distribution of the length of the busy period T_i and the number $N(T_i)$ of customers served (including those initially present) is given by

(2.23)

$$\begin{aligned} Pr\{T_i \leqslant t, N(T_i) = n\} &= \int_{x=0}^{t} dB_i(x) G_{n-i}(x, t) \\ &= \int_{x=0}^{t} dB_i(x) \int_{\tau=x}^{t} e^{-\lambda\tau} \frac{(\lambda\tau)^{n-i-1}}{(n-i)!} \lambda x \, dB_{n-i}(\tau - x) \\ &= \int_{\tau=0}^{t} e^{-\lambda\tau} \frac{(\lambda\tau)^{n-i-1}}{(n-i)!} \int_{x=0}^{\tau} \lambda x \, dB_i(x) \, dB_{n-i}(\tau - x) \\ &= \int_{\tau=0}^{t} e^{-\lambda\tau} \frac{i(\lambda\tau)^{n-i}}{n(n-i)!} dB_n(\tau), \end{aligned}$$

where we have again used the identity (2.11).

When $i = 1$, we have T_1, the busy period as conventionally defined, that is, the one initiated by a single customer. From (2.23) we find that the d.f. of T_1 is given by

$$G(t) = Pr\{T_1 \leqslant t\} = \sum_{n=1}^{\infty} \int_{\tau=0}^{t} e^{-\lambda\tau} \frac{(\lambda\tau)^{n-1}}{n!} dB_n(\tau), \tag{2.24}$$

and for the distribution $\{f_n\}$ of $N(T_1)$, the number of customers served during T_1 we have

$$f_n = Pr\{N(T_1) = n\} = \int_{t=0}^{\infty} e^{-\lambda t} \frac{(\lambda t)^{n-1}}{n!} dB_n(t) \qquad (n \geqslant 1). \tag{2.25}$$

From (2.17) and (2.23) we see that the L.S.T. of T_1 is given by

$$\Gamma(\theta) = E(e^{-\theta T_1}) = \int_0^\infty dB(x)e^{-x\eta(\theta)} = \psi(\eta), \tag{2.26}$$

where $\Gamma(\theta)$ satisfies the functional equation

$$\Gamma(\theta) = \psi(\theta + \lambda - \lambda\Gamma); \tag{2.27}$$

we have, further, that

$$Pr\{T_1 < \infty\} = \begin{cases} 1 & \text{if} \quad \rho \leqslant 1 \\ \zeta & \text{if} \quad \rho > 1, \end{cases} \tag{2.28}$$

where ζ is the smallest positive root of the equation

$$\zeta = \psi(\lambda - \lambda\zeta). \tag{2.29}$$

To obtain the probability generating function (p.g.f.) of $N(T_1)$, we proceed as follows. If $Q(0) = 1$, then at the end of the initial customer's service time v, $Q(v) = A(v)$, where $A(v)$ is the number of arrivals during $(0, v]$ and has the Poisson distribution (2.1). Hence we obtain the relation

$$N(T_1) = 1 + N[T_{A(v)}]. \tag{2.30}$$

Clearly, $E[z^{N(T_i)}] = E[z^{N(T_1)}]^i = \xi^i$ (say); then the last relation gives

$$\begin{aligned} \xi &= E[z^{N(T_1)}] = E[z\xi^{A(v)}] \\ &= z\sum_{n=0}^{\infty}\int_{v=0}^{\infty} \xi^n e^{-\lambda v}\frac{(\lambda v)^n}{n!}\,dB(v) \\ &= z\int_{v=0}^{\infty} e^{-\lambda v+\lambda v\xi}\,dB(v) = z\psi(\lambda - \lambda\xi). \end{aligned}$$

Thus ξ satisfies the functional equation

$$\xi = z\psi(\lambda - \lambda\xi); \tag{2.31}$$

proceeding as in (2.18) we can prove that there is a unique root $\xi(z)$ of (2.31) such that $\xi(0) = 0$. Obviously, $Pr\{N(T_1) < \infty\} = Pr\{T_1 < \infty\}$.

2.3 THE PROBABILITY OF AN EMPTY QUEUE

Let

$$F(x; y, t) = Pr\{W(t) \leqslant y \mid W(0) = x\} \qquad t \geqslant 0, x \geqslant 0, y \geqslant \max(0, x - t) \tag{2.32}$$

denote the transition d.f. of the waiting time $W(t)$. In particular,

$$F(x; 0, t) = Pr\{W(t) = 0 \mid W(0) = x\} \qquad (t \geqslant x \geqslant 0) \tag{2.33}$$

is the probability that the queue is empty (the server is idle) at time t. Let $N(t)$ be the number of customers served during $(0, t]$, and $F_n(x; 0, t)$ the joint probability

$$F_n(x; 0, t) = Pr\{W(t) = 0;\ N(t) = n \mid W(0) = x\}. \tag{2.34}$$

We have

$$F_0(x; 0, t) = \begin{cases} e^{-\lambda t} & (t \geqslant x) \\ 0 & (t < x), \end{cases} \tag{2.35}$$

and for $n \geqslant 1$,

$$\begin{aligned} F_n(x; 0, t) = &\int_{\tau=0}^{x}\int_{v=0}^{t-x} \lambda e^{-\lambda\tau} F_{n-1}(x - \tau + v; 0, t - \tau)\, d\tau\, dB(v) \\ &+ \int_{\tau=x}^{t}\int_{v=0}^{t-\tau} \lambda e^{-\lambda\tau} F_{n-1}(v; 0, t - \tau)\, d\tau\, dB(v), \end{aligned} \tag{2.36}$$

where we argue as in (2.9), but now the first new customer may arrive in the interval $(x, t]$. Substituting (2.35) in (2.36) with $n = 1$, we obtain

$$\begin{aligned} F_1(x; 0, t) &= \left(\int_{\tau=0}^{x}\int_{v=0}^{t-x} + \int_{\tau=x}^{t}\int_{v=0}^{t-\tau}\right) \lambda e^{-\lambda t}\, d\tau\, dB(v) \\ &= \int_{v=0}^{t-x}\int_{\tau=0}^{t-v} \lambda e^{-\lambda t}\, d\tau\, dB(v) \\ &= \lambda e^{-\lambda t} \int_{v=0}^{t-x} (t - v)\, dB(v). \end{aligned} \tag{2.37}$$

Similarly, substituting (2.37) in (2.36) with $n = 2$ and using (2.11), we obtain

$$\begin{aligned} F_2(x; 0, t) &= \left(\int_{\tau=0}^{x}\int_{v=0}^{t-x}\int_{w=0}^{t-x-v} + \int_{\tau=x}^{t}\int_{v=0}^{t-\tau}\int_{w=0}^{t-\tau-v}\right) \\ &\qquad \times \lambda^2 e^{-\lambda t}\, d\tau (t - \tau - w)\, dB(v)\, dB(w) \\ &= \left(\int_{\tau=0}^{x}\int_{v=0}^{t-x}\int_{w=v}^{t-x} + \int_{\tau=x}^{t}\int_{v=0}^{t-\tau}\int_{w=v}^{t-\tau}\right) \\ &\qquad \times \lambda^2 e^{-\lambda t}\, d\tau (v + t - \tau - w)\, dB(v)\, dB(w - v) \\ &= \left(\int_{w=0}^{t-x}\int_{\tau=0}^{x}\int_{v=0}^{w} + \int_{w=0}^{t-x}\int_{\tau=x}^{t-w}\int_{v=0}^{w}\right) \\ &\qquad \times \lambda^2 e^{-\lambda t}\, d\tau (v + t - \tau - w)\, dB(v)\, dB(w - v) \\ &= \lambda^2 e^{-\lambda t} \int_{w=0}^{t-x}\int_{\tau=0}^{t-w} d\tau \int_{v=0}^{w} (v + \tau)\, dB(v)\, dB(w - v) \\ &= \lambda^2 e^{-\lambda t} \int_{w=0}^{t-x} dB_2(w) \int_{\tau=0}^{t-w} (\tau + \tfrac{1}{2}w)\, d\tau \\ &= e^{-\lambda t} \frac{\lambda^2 t}{2} \int_{w=0}^{t-x} (t - w)\, dB_2(w). \end{aligned} \tag{2.38}$$

By induction it follows as in (2.14), that

$$F_n(x; 0, t) = e^{-\lambda t}\frac{(\lambda t)^{n-1}}{n!}\int_{v=0}^{t-x}\lambda(t-v)\,dB_n(v) \qquad (n \geqslant 0). \tag{2.39}$$

It follows that

$$\begin{aligned} F(x; 0, t) &= \sum_{n=0}^{\infty} F_n(x; 0, t) \\ &= \sum_{n=0}^{\infty} e^{-\lambda t}\frac{(\lambda t)^{n-1}}{n!}\int_{v=0}^{t-x}\lambda(t-v)\,dB_n(v). \end{aligned} \tag{2.40}$$

We can also write

$$\begin{aligned} F(x; 0, t)\,dt &= e^{-\lambda t}\,dt + \sum_{n=1}^{\infty} e^{-\lambda t}\frac{(\lambda t)^{n-1}}{n!}\int_{u=x}^{t-}\lambda u[-d_u B_n(t-u)]\,dt \\ &= e^{-\lambda t}\,dt + \sum_{n=1}^{\infty} e^{-\lambda t}\frac{(\lambda t)^{n-1}}{n!}\int_{u=x}^{t-}\lambda u\, d_t B_n(t-u)\,du \\ &= e^{-\lambda t}\,dt + \int_{u-x}^{t-} dG(u, t)\,du. \end{aligned} \tag{2.41}$$

Using (2.41) we obtain the Laplace transform of $F(x; 0, t)$ as

$$\begin{aligned} F^*(x; 0, \theta) &= \int_{t=x}^{\infty} e^{-\theta t}F(x; 0, t)\,dt \\ &= \int_{u=x}^{\infty} du \int_{t=u+}^{\infty} e^{-\theta t}\,dG(u, t) + \int_{t=x}^{\infty} e^{-(\theta+\lambda)t}\,dt \\ &= \int_{u=x-}^{\infty} du e^{-u\eta(\theta)} = \frac{e^{-x\eta(\theta)}}{\eta(\theta)}. \end{aligned} \tag{2.42}$$

2.4 THE TRANSITION D.F. OF $W(t)$

We are now in a position to obtain the transition d.f. $F(x; y, t)$ for $y \geqslant 0$. Clearly, $F(x; y, t) = K(t + y - x, t)$ for $0 \leqslant t \leqslant x$, $y \geqslant x - t$; therefore it remains to obtain $F(x; y, t)$ for $0 \leqslant x < t$, $y \geqslant 0$. Let us denote the Laplace transform of $F(x; y, t)$ by

$$\Phi(x; \theta, t) = \int_0^{\infty} e^{-\theta y}F(x; y, t)\,dy \qquad [\mathrm{Re}\,(\theta) > 0]; \tag{2.43}$$

then we have

(2.44)

$$\Phi(x; \theta, t) = \theta^{-1}e^{-\lambda t+\lambda t\psi(\theta)+\theta(t-x)} - \int_0^{t-x} F(x; 0, t-\tau)e^{-\lambda\tau+\lambda\tau\psi(\theta)+\theta\tau}d\tau$$

[see equation (1.235)]. Let us recall, however, that (2.44) was obtained from the integro-differential equation for $F(x; y, t)$, which itself was established under rather restrictive conditions. The following is a direct derivation of (2.44).

From equation (1.216), we have

$$W(t) = W(0) + Y(t) + \int_0^t \zeta(\tau)\, d\tau, \tag{2.45}$$

where $Y(t) = X(t) - t$, and the random variable $\zeta(t)$ is defined as follows:

$$\zeta(t) = \begin{cases} 1 & \text{if } W(t) = 0 \\ 0 & \text{if } W(t) > 0. \end{cases} \tag{2.46}$$

Let $I(t) = \int_0^t \zeta(\tau)\, d\tau$; $I(t)$ is that part of the interval $[0, t]$ during which $W(t) = 0$. We have $dI(t) = \zeta(t)\, dt$ and

$$e^{-\theta I(t)} = 1 - \theta \int_0^t e^{-\theta I(\tau)}\, dI(\tau) = 1 - \theta \int_0^t e^{-\theta I(\tau)} \zeta(\tau)\, d\tau.$$

However, when $\zeta(t) \neq 0$, $W(t) = 0$, and $I(t) = -W(0) - Y(t)$, and therefore

$$e^{-\theta I(t)} = 1 - \theta \int_0^t e^{\theta W(0) + \theta Y(\tau)} \zeta(\tau)\, d\tau. \tag{2.47}$$

It follows that

$$\begin{aligned} e^{-\theta W(t)} &= e^{-\theta[W(0) + Y(t) + I(t)]} \\ &= e^{-\theta W(0) - \theta Y(t)} - \theta \int_0^t e^{-\theta[Y(t) - Y(\tau)]} \zeta(\tau)\, d\tau. \end{aligned} \tag{2.48}$$

Now let $W(0) = x \geqslant 0$, and take expectation of both sides of (2.48); then, noting that $\zeta(\tau)$ is determined by $Y(t)$ $(t \leqslant \tau)$ and $Y(t) - Y(\tau)$ is independent of $Y(\tau)$, we obtain

$$\begin{aligned} \theta\Phi(x; \theta, t) &= e^{-\theta x} E[e^{-\theta Y(t)}] \\ &\quad - \theta \int_0^t E\{e^{-\theta[Y(t) - Y(\tau)]}\} E[\zeta(\tau)]\, d\tau. \end{aligned} \tag{2.49}$$

Finally, since

$$\begin{aligned} E[e^{-\theta Y(t)}] &= e^{\theta t} E[e^{-\theta X(t)}] = e^{\theta t + \lambda t[1 - \psi(\theta)]} \\ E\{e^{-\theta[Y(t) - Y(\tau)]}\} &= E\{e^{-\theta Y(t - \tau)}\} = e^{\theta(t - \tau) + \lambda(t - \tau)[1 - \psi(\theta)]} \\ E[\zeta(t)] &= Pr\{W(t) = 0 \mid W(0) = x\} = F(x; 0, t), \end{aligned} \tag{2.50}$$

the result (2.44) follows for $\theta \geqslant 0$.

We now attempt to invert the transform (2.44). Here $F(x; y, t)$ is the inverse transform of $\Phi(x; \theta, t)$. To obtain the inverse of the right-hand side of (2.44) we note that

$$\int_{x-t}^{\infty} e^{-\theta y} K(t + y - x, t)\, dy = \theta^{-1} e^{-\lambda t + \lambda t \psi(\theta) + \theta(t-x)}, \tag{2.51}$$

and

$$\int_{y=-\tau}^{\infty} e^{-\theta y}\, d_y K(\tau + y, \tau) = e^{-\lambda\tau + \lambda\tau\psi(\theta) + \theta\tau} \tag{2.52}$$

on account of (2.5). Thus (2.44) yields the relation

$$\begin{aligned} \int_0^{\infty} e^{-\theta y} F(x; y, t)\, dy &= \int_{x-t}^{\infty} e^{-\theta y} K(t + y - x, t)\, dy \\ &\quad - \int_{\tau=0}^{t-x} d\tau \int_{y=-\tau}^{\infty} e^{-\theta y} F(x; 0, t - \tau)\, d_y K(\tau + y, \tau) \\ &= \int_{x-t}^{\infty} e^{-\theta y} K(t + y - x, t)\, dy - \left(\int_{y=0}^{\infty} \int_{\tau=0}^{t-x} + \int_{y=x-t}^{0-} \int_{\tau=-y}^{t-x} \right) \\ &\quad \times e^{-\theta y}\, dy F(x; 0, t - \tau)\, dK(\tau + y, \tau), \end{aligned} \tag{2.53}$$

where we have written

$$\begin{aligned} dK(t + y, t) &= d_x K(x, t)\big|_{x=t+y} \\ &= \sum_{n=0}^{\infty} e^{-\lambda t} \frac{(\lambda t)^n}{n!}\, d_t B_n(t + y). \end{aligned} \tag{2.54}$$

Thus (2.53) yields the relation

$$F(x; y, t) = K(t + y - x, t) - \int_{\tau=0}^{t-x} F(x; 0, t - \tau)\, dK(\tau + y, \tau) \tag{2.55}$$

for $y \geqslant 0$, provided, however, that we are able to prove the identity

$$K(t + y - x, t) = \int_{\tau=-y}^{t-x} F(x; 0, t - \tau)\, dK(\tau + y, \tau)$$

for $x - t \leqslant y < 0$, or $0 < -y \leqslant t - x$. Thus we have to show that

$$K(t - y - x, t) = \int_{\tau=y}^{t-x} F(x; 0, t - \tau)\, dK(\tau - y, \tau) \qquad (0 < y \leqslant t - x). \tag{2.56}$$

In order to do this, we consider the process $Z(t) = x + X(t) - t$, which is a time-homogeneous Markov process with the transition d.f.

$$P(x; y, t) = Pr\{Z(t) \leqslant y \mid Z(0) = x\} = K(t + y - x, t). \tag{2.57}$$

Consider a path from u (>0) to $-y$ (<0) in this process; clearly, such a path should pass through 0, and the first passage time to 0 is $T(u)$ on account of (2.6). Hence a direct enumeration of all such paths gives

$$d_y P(u; -y, t) = \int_{\tau=u-}^{t-y} dG(u, \tau)\, d_y P(0; -y, t - \tau). \tag{2.58}$$

Integrating this over $x \leqslant u \leqslant t - y$, we obtain

$$\begin{aligned} \int_{u=x}^{t-y} d_y P(u; -y, t)\, du & \\ &= \int_{u=x}^{t-y} du \Big[e^{-\lambda u}\, d_y P(0; -y, t - u) \\ &\quad + \int_{\tau=u+}^{t-y} dG(u, \tau)\, d_y P(0; -y, t - \tau) \Big] \\ &= \int_{\tau=x}^{t-y} d_y P(0; -y, t - \tau) \Big[e^{-\lambda \tau}\, d\tau + \int_{u=x}^{\tau-} dG(u, \tau)\, du \Big] \\ &= \int_{\tau=x}^{t-y} d_y P(0; -y, t - \tau) F(x; 0, \tau)\, d\tau, \end{aligned} \tag{2.59}$$

using (2.41). Substituting for $P(x; y, t)$ from (2.57) in this we obtain

$$\int_{u=x}^{t-y} d_y K(t - y - u, t)\, du = \int_{\tau=y}^{t-x} F(x; 0, t - \tau)\, d_y K(\tau - y, \tau)\, d\tau,$$

that is,

(2.60)

$$dy \int_{u=x}^{t-y} d_u K(t - y - u, t) = -dy \int_{\tau=y}^{t-x} F(x; 0, t - \tau)\, dK(\tau - y, \tau),$$

which gives (2.56).

We have thus established the identity (2.56), and since the probability $F(x; 0, t)$ has already been determined in Section 2.3, our inversion of the transform in (2.44) is valid, and (2.55) gives the transition d.f. $F(x; y, t)$ of the waiting time $W(t)$ for $0 \leqslant x < t$, $y \geqslant 0$; obviously, it is also valid for $0 \leqslant t \leqslant x$, $y \geqslant x - t$.

Putting $y = 0$ in (2.55), we obtain the relation

$$F(x; 0, t) + \int_{\tau=0}^{t-x} F(x; 0, t - \tau)\, dK(\tau, \tau) = K(t - x, t), \tag{2.61}$$

which may be considered as an integral equation for $F(x; 0, t)$. A direct solution of (2.61) appears to be difficult in comparison with the method used in Section 2.3 to obtain $F(x; 0, t)$.

On taking transforms with respect to t in (2.44) and using (2.42), we obtain

$$\begin{aligned}\Phi^*(x; \theta, s) &= \int_0^\infty e^{-st}\Phi(x; \theta, t)\, dt \\ &= \theta^{-1}e^{-\theta x}\int_{t=0}^\infty e^{-[s-\theta+\lambda-\lambda\psi(\theta)]t}\, dt \\ &\quad - \int_{\tau=0}^\infty e^{-[\lambda-\lambda\psi(\theta)-\theta]\tau}\, d\tau \int_{t=\tau}^\infty e^{-st}F(x; 0, t - \tau)\, dt \\ &= \frac{\theta^{-1}e^{-\theta x} - e^{-x\eta(s)}/\eta(s)}{s - \theta + \lambda - \lambda\psi(\theta)}\end{aligned} \tag{2.62}$$

for $R(s) > \theta - \lambda + \lambda\psi(\theta)$.

2.5 TRANSITION PROBABILITIES OF $Q(t)$

We define the transition probabilities of the queue-length $Q(t)$ as follows:

$$P_{ij}(t) = Pr\{Q(t) = j \mid Q(0) = i\} \qquad (i \geqslant 0, j \geqslant 0). \tag{2.63}$$

We have

$$P_{00}(t) = F(0; 0, t), \tag{2.64}$$

and if $t = 0$ is an epoch of commencement of service, then

$$P_{i0}(t) = \int_{x=0}^{t} dB_i(x)F(x; 0, t) \qquad (i \geqslant 1). \tag{2.65}$$

If $t = 0$ is not such an epoch, $B_i(x)$ in (2.65) has to be replaced by $B_i'(x)$, the d.f. of $v_1' + v_2 + \cdots + v_i$, where v_1' is the unexpended service time of the customer being served at $t = 0$. Let us consider the first case, and note that (2.65) reduces to (2.64) when $i = 0$ because of the definition of

$B_0(x)$. Substituting for $F(x; 0, t)$ from (2.40) in (2.65), we obtain

$$
\begin{aligned}
P_{i0}(t) &= \int_{x=0}^{t} dB_i(x) \int_{u=0}^{t-x} \sum_{n=0}^{\infty} e^{-\lambda t} \frac{(\lambda t)^{n-1}}{n!} \lambda(x+u)[-d_u B_n(t-x-u)] \\
&= \int_{u=0}^{t} \sum_{n=0}^{\infty} e^{-\lambda t} \frac{(\lambda t)^{n-1}}{n!} \int_{x=0}^{t-u} \lambda(x+u)\, dB_i(x)[-d_u B_n(t-u-x)] \\
&= \int_{u=0}^{t} \sum_{n=0}^{\infty} e^{-\lambda t} \frac{(\lambda t)^{n-1}}{n!} \lambda \left[\frac{i(t-u)}{n+i} + u \right] [-d_u B_{n+i}(t-u)],
\end{aligned}
$$

where we have used the identity (2.11). After some simplification this gives for $i \geqslant 0$,

$$
P_{i0}(t) = \sum_{n=i}^{\infty} e^{-\lambda t} \frac{(\lambda t)^{n-i-1}}{(n-i)!} \lambda \int_0^t \left[t - \left(1 - \frac{i}{n}\right) v \right] dB_n(v). \tag{2.66}
$$

From (2.65) we see that the Laplace transform of $P_{i0}(t)$ is given by

$$
\begin{aligned}
P_{i0}^*(\theta) &= \int_0^{\infty} e^{-\theta t} P_{i0}(t)\, dt = \int_{x=0}^{\infty} dB_i(x) F^*(x; 0, \theta) \\
&= \int_{x=0}^{\infty} dB_i(x) \frac{e^{-x\eta(\theta)}}{\eta(\theta)} = \frac{[\psi(\eta)]^i}{\eta(\theta)}.
\end{aligned}
\tag{2.67}
$$

We shall now obtain $P_{ij}(t)$ for $i \geqslant 0$, $j \geqslant 1$. Consider the customer being served at time t; we have two possibilities concerning this customer.

1. This customer belongs to the initial group of i customers. Let him be the $(\nu + 1)$st customer of this group $(0 \leqslant \nu \leqslant i - 1)$; then during $(0, t]$, ν departures and $j - i + \nu$ arrivals must have occurred, the probability of which is

$$
\sum_{\nu=\max(0, i-j)}^{i-1} C_\nu(t) e^{-\lambda t} \frac{(\lambda t)^{j-i+\nu}}{(j-i+\nu)!}, \tag{2.68}
$$

where

$$
C_n(t) = B_n(t) - B_{n+1}(t) \qquad (n \geqslant 0).
$$

2. The customer being served at time t does not belong to the initial group. Let τ be the arrival epoch of this customer $(0 < \tau < t)$, and his waiting time $W(\tau - 0) = y$; then his service must have commenced at time $\tau + y$, and must continue at least until time t. Moreover, during $(\tau, t]$, $j - 1$ customers must have arrived. The probability of this second case is therefore

$$
\begin{aligned}
\int_{\tau=0}^{t} \int_{y=0}^{t-\tau} \int_{x=0}^{\tau+y} &\lambda\, d\tau\, dB_i(x)\, d_y F(x; y, \tau)[1 - B(t - \tau - y)] \\
&\times e^{-\lambda(t-\tau)} \frac{[\lambda(t-\tau)]^{j-1}}{(j-1)!}.
\end{aligned}
\tag{2.69}
$$

It follows that

$$P_{ij}(t) = \sum_{\nu=\max(0,i-j)}^{i-1} C_\nu(t)e^{-\lambda t}\frac{(\lambda t)^{j-i+\nu}}{(j-i+\nu)!}$$

$$(2.70)\qquad + \int_{\tau=0}^{t}\int_{y=0}^{t-\tau}\int_{x=0}^{\tau+y} \lambda\, d\tau\, dB_i(x)\, d_yF(x;\, y, \tau)[1 - B(t-\tau-y)]$$

$$\times\, e^{-\lambda(t-\tau)}\frac{[\lambda(t-\tau)]^{j-1}}{(j-1)!}$$

for $i \geqslant 1, j \geqslant 1$. For $i = 0$, the first possibility does not arise, and

$$(2.71)\qquad P_{0j}(t) = \int_{\tau=0}^{t}\int_{y=0}^{t-\tau} \lambda\, d\tau\, d_yF(0;\, y, \tau)[1 - B(t-\tau-y)] \times e^{-\lambda(t-\tau)}\frac{[\lambda(t-\tau)]^{j-1}}{(j-1)!} \qquad (j \geqslant 1).$$

We have thus obtained the transition probabilities $P_{ij}(t)$ for $i \geqslant 0, j \geqslant 0$. In (2.70) we have assumed that $t = 0$ is an epoch of commencement of service; otherwise $B_i(x)$ has to be replaced by $B_i'(x)$.

Let us now define the transform

$$(2.72)\qquad P_i^*(\theta, \omega) = \int_{t=0}^{\infty}\sum_{j=1}^{\infty} e^{-\theta t}P_{ij}(t)\omega^j\, dt \qquad [\text{Re}\,(\theta) > 0, |\omega| < 1].$$

From (2.70) we obtain $P_i^*(\theta, \omega) = I_1 + I_2$, where

$$I_1 = \sum_{j=1}^{\infty}\sum_{\nu=\max(0,i-j)}^{i-1}\int_0^\infty e^{-\theta t}C_\nu(t)e^{-\lambda t}\frac{(\lambda t)^{j-i+\nu}}{(j-i+\nu)!}\omega^j\, dt$$

$$= \sum_{\nu=0}^{i-1}\sum_{j=i-\nu}^{\infty}\int_0^\infty e^{-\theta t}C_\nu(t)e^{-\lambda t}\frac{(\lambda t)^{j-i+\nu}}{(j-i+\nu)!}\omega^j\, dt$$

$$(2.73)\qquad = \sum_{\nu=0}^{i-1}\omega^{i-\nu}\int_0^\infty C_\nu(t)e^{-\theta t-\lambda t(1-\omega)}\, dt$$

$$= \sum_{\nu=0}^{i-1}\omega^{i-\nu}[\psi(\theta+\lambda-\lambda\omega)]^\nu\,\frac{1-\psi(\theta+\lambda-\lambda\omega)}{\theta+\lambda-\lambda\omega}$$

$$= \omega\,\frac{1-\psi(\theta+\lambda-\lambda\omega)}{\theta+\lambda-\lambda\omega}\,\frac{\omega^i - [\psi(\theta+\lambda-\lambda\omega)]^i}{\omega-\psi(\theta+\lambda-\omega\lambda)},$$

and

$$I_2 = \omega \int_{t=0}^{\infty} \int_{\tau=0}^{t} \int_{y=0}^{t-\tau} \int_{x=0}^{\tau+y} \lambda\, d\tau\, dB_i(x)\, d_yF(x; y, \tau)[1 - B(t - \tau - y)] \times e^{-\lambda(t-\tau)(1-\omega)-\theta t}\, dt$$

$$= \omega \int_{\tau=0}^{\infty} \lambda\, d\tau \left[\int_{x=0}^{\tau} \int_{y=0}^{\infty} + \int_{x=\tau}^{\infty} \int_{y=x-\tau}^{\infty} dB_i(x)\, d_yF(x; y, \tau) \right] \times \int_{t=\tau+y}^{\infty} [1 - B(t - \tau - y)] e^{-\theta t - \lambda(t-\tau)(1-\omega)}\, dt$$

$$= \omega \frac{1 - \psi(\theta + \lambda - \lambda\omega)}{\theta + \lambda - \lambda\omega} \int_{\tau=0}^{\infty} e^{-\theta\tau} \lambda\, d\tau \times \int_{x=0}^{\infty} (\theta + \lambda - \lambda\omega)\, dB_i(x) \Phi(x; \theta + \lambda - \lambda\omega, \tau)$$

$$(2.74) \quad = \omega \frac{1 - \psi(\theta + \lambda - \lambda\omega)}{\theta + \lambda - \lambda\omega} \int_{\tau=0}^{\infty} e^{-\theta\tau} \lambda\, d\tau \int_{x=0}^{\infty} dB_i(x) \times \Big\{ \exp[-\lambda\tau + \lambda\tau\psi(\theta + \lambda - \lambda\omega) + (\theta + \lambda - \lambda\omega)(\tau - x)] - (\theta + \lambda - \lambda\omega) \int_{s=0}^{\tau} F(x; 0, \tau - s) \times \exp[-\lambda s + \lambda s\psi(\theta + \lambda - \lambda\omega) + (\theta + \lambda - \lambda\omega)s]\, ds \Big\}$$

$$= \omega \frac{1 - \psi(\theta + \lambda - \lambda\omega)}{\theta + \lambda - \lambda\omega} \left\{ \frac{[\psi(\theta + \lambda - \lambda\omega)]^i}{\omega - \psi(\theta + \lambda - \lambda\omega)} - (\theta + \lambda - \lambda\omega) \int_{x=0}^{\infty} dB_i(x) \int_{s=0}^{\infty} e^{-\lambda\omega s + \lambda s\psi(\theta+\lambda-\lambda\omega)}\, ds \times \int_{\tau=s}^{\infty} e^{-\theta(\tau-s)} \lambda F(x; 0, \tau - s)\, d\tau \right\}$$

$$= \omega \frac{1 - \psi(\theta + \lambda - \lambda\omega)}{\theta + \lambda - \lambda\omega} \left\{ \frac{[\psi(\theta + \lambda - \lambda\omega)]^i}{\omega - \psi(\theta + \lambda - \lambda\omega)} - \frac{\theta + \lambda - \lambda\omega}{\eta(\theta)} \cdot \frac{[\psi(\eta)]^i}{\omega - \psi(\theta + \lambda - \lambda\omega)} \right\}.$$

From (2.73) and (2.74) we obtain

$$(2.75) \quad P_i^*(\theta, \omega) = \omega \frac{1 - \psi(\theta + \lambda - \lambda\omega)}{\omega - \psi(\theta + \lambda - \lambda\omega)} \left[\frac{\omega^i}{\theta + \lambda - \lambda\omega} - \frac{[\psi(\eta)]^i}{\eta(\theta)} \right].$$

Similarly, for $i = 0$ we obtain

$$(2.76)\quad P_0^*(\theta, \omega) = \lambda\omega \frac{1 - \psi(\theta + \lambda - \lambda\omega)}{\omega - \psi(\theta + \lambda - \lambda\omega)} \cdot \frac{\omega - \psi(\eta)}{(\theta + \lambda - \lambda\omega)\eta(\theta)}.$$

2.6 ZERO-AVOIDING TRANSITIONS OF $Q(t)$

Let us consider $A(t)$, the number of arrivals during $(0, t]$, which is a Poisson process with the distribution (2.1), and the renewal process $\{V_n\}$, $V_n = v_1 + v_2 + \cdots + v_n$, where v_n is the service time of the nth customer $(n \geqslant 1)$. Furthermore, let $D(t) = \max [n \mid V_n \leqslant t]$, so that $Pr\{D(t) = n\} = B_n(t) - B_{n+1}(t) = C_n(t)$ $(n \geqslant 0)$. It is clear that the busy period T_i defined in (2.3) can be expressed as

$$(2.77)\qquad T_i = \inf [t \mid i + A(t) - D(t) \leqslant 0],$$

and furthermore, that the times of termination of busy periods are points of regeneration of the non-Markovian process $i + A(t) - D(t)$. Moreover, as long as the busy period T_i is in progress, $Q(t)$ coincides with this process.

Let $G_i(t) = Pr\{T_i \leqslant t\}$; in particular, $G_1(t) = G(t)$, which has already been obtained in Section 2.2 (equation 2.24). For $i \geqslant 1$ we have from (2.23),

$$(2.78)\qquad G_i(t) = \sum_{n=i}^{\infty} \int_{\tau=0}^{t} e^{-\lambda\tau} \frac{(\lambda\tau)^{n-i}}{(n-i)!} \, i \, dB_n(\tau).$$

As a generalization of (2.78) let us define

$$(2.79)\quad {}^0P_{ij}(t) = Pr\{Q(t) = j, T_i > t \mid Q(0) = i\} \qquad (i \geqslant 1, j \geqslant 1);$$

this is the probability of a queue-length j at time t, given that the server has been busy throughout the interval $(0, t]$. Here we have assumed that $t = 0$ is an epoch of commencement of service. We may call ${}^0P_{ij}(t)$ the zero-avoiding transition probabilities of $Q(t)$; to obtain these we need the following result:

$$Pr\{i + A(t) - D(t) = j, T_i > t;\ D(t) = n\} = e^{-\lambda t} \frac{(\lambda t)^{n+j-i}}{(n+j-i)!} C_n(t)$$

$$(2.80)\qquad - \sum_{m=i}^{n} \int_0^t Pr\{\tau < T_i < \tau + d\tau;\ D(\tau) = m\} e^{-\lambda(t-\tau)}$$

$$\times \frac{[\lambda(t-\tau)]^{n-m+j}}{(n-m+j)!} C_{n-m}(t-\tau).$$

To prove (2.80), we note that

$$e^{-\lambda t}\frac{(\lambda t)^{n+j-i}}{(n+j-i)!}C_n(t) = Pr\{i + A(t) - D(t) = j;\ D(t) = n\}$$

$$\begin{aligned}(2.81)\qquad &= Pr\{i + A(t) - D(t) = j,\ T_i > t;\ D(t) = n\}\\ &\quad + Pr\{i + A(t) - D(t) = j,\ T_i \leqslant t;\ D(t) = n\}.\end{aligned}$$

The first term on the right-hand side of (2.81) is the required probability, whereas the second term can be written as

$$\begin{aligned}&\sum_{m=i}^{n}\int_0^t Pr\{\tau < T_i < \tau + d\tau;\ D(\tau) = m\}\\ &\quad\times Pr\{i + A(t) - D(t) = j;\ D(t) = n \mid T_i = \tau,\ D(\tau) = m\}\\ &= \sum_{m=i}^{n}\int_0^t Pr\{\tau < T_i < \tau + d\tau;\ D(\tau) = m\}\\ (2.82)\qquad &\quad\times Pr\{i + A(t) - D(t) = j;\ D(t)\\ &\qquad\qquad = n \mid i + A(\tau) - D(\tau) = 0,\ D(\tau) = m\}\\ &= \sum_{m=i}^{n}\int_0^t Pr\{\tau < T_i < \tau + d\tau;\ D(\tau) = m\}\\ &\quad\times Pr\{A(t-\tau) - D(t-\tau) = j;\ D(t-\tau) = n - m\}\\ &= \sum_{m=i}^{n}\int_0^t Pr\{\tau < T_i < \tau + d\tau;\ D(\tau) = m\}\\ &\quad\times e^{-\lambda(t-\tau)}\frac{[\lambda(t-\tau)]^{n-m+j}}{(n-m+j)!}C_{n-m}(t-\tau).\end{aligned}$$

The required result now follows from (2.81) and (2.82).

As already observed, if $T_i > t$, the queue-length $Q(t) = i + A(t) - D(t)$. Hence, using (2.80), we obtain

$$\begin{aligned}{}^0P_{ij}(t) &= Pr\{i + A(t) - D(t) = j,\ T_i > t\}\\ &= \sum_{n=0}^{\infty} e^{-\lambda t}\frac{(\lambda t)^{n+j-i}}{(n+j-i)!}C_n(t)\\ &\quad - \sum_{n=i}^{\infty}\sum_{m=i}^{n}\int_0^t Pr\{\tau < T_i < \tau + d\tau;\ D(\tau) = m\}\\ &\quad\times e^{-\lambda(t-\tau)}\frac{[\lambda(t-\tau)]^{n-m+j}}{(n-m+j)!}C_{n-m}(t-\tau).\end{aligned}$$

The second term in the last expression is

$$\sum_{m=i}^{\infty}\sum_{n=0}^{\infty}\int_0^t Pr\{\tau < T_i < \tau + d\tau;\, D(\tau) = m\} e^{-\lambda(t-\tau)} \frac{[\lambda(t-\tau)]^{n+j}}{(n+j)!} C_n(t-\tau)$$

$$= \sum_{n=0}^{\infty}\int_0^t dG_i(\tau) e^{-\lambda(t-\tau)} \frac{[\lambda(t-\tau)]^{n+j}}{(n+j)!} C_n(t-\tau)$$

$$= \sum_{n=0}^{\infty}\int_0^t dG_i(\tau) e^{-\lambda(t-\tau)} \frac{[\lambda(t-\tau)]^{n+j}}{(n+j)!} C_n(t-\tau).$$

Hence

$$ {}^0P_{ij}(t) = \sum_{n=0}^{\infty} e^{-\lambda t} \frac{(\lambda t)^{n+j-i}}{(n+j-i)!} C_n(t) - \sum_{n=0}^{\infty}\int_0^t dG_i(\tau) e^{-\lambda(t-\tau)} \frac{[\lambda(t-\tau)]^{n+j}}{(n+j)!} C_n(t-\tau). \tag{2.83}$$

2.7 LIMITING DISTRIBUTIONS

a. Limiting Distribution of $W(t)$

In this section we study the limiting behavior of the queueing system as $t \to \infty$. We first note that if $W(0) = 0$, then from equation (1.217),

$$W(t) = \sup_{0 \leqslant \tau \leqslant t} [X(\tau) - \tau]. \tag{2.84}$$

Now if we define the first passage time $U(y)$ as

$$U(y) = \inf\, [t \mid X(t) - t > y], \tag{2.85}$$

then

$$\begin{aligned} F(0; y, t) &= Pr\{X(\tau) - \tau \leqslant y \qquad (0 \leqslant \tau \leqslant t)\} \\ &= 1 - Pr\{U(y) \leqslant t\}. \end{aligned} \tag{2.86}$$

Thus $F(0; y, t)$ is a monotone nonincreasing function of t, so that $\lim_{t\to\infty} F(0; y, t)$ exists; let us denote this limit by $F^*(y)$. From (2.42) we find that

$$\begin{aligned} F^*(0) &= \lim_{t\to\infty} F(0; 0, t) \\ &= \lim_{\theta\to 0} \theta F^*(0; 0, \theta) = \lim_{\theta\to 0+} \frac{\theta}{\eta(\theta)} \\ &= \begin{cases} 0 & \text{if } \rho > 1 \\ [\eta'(0+)]^{-1} & \text{if } \rho \leqslant 1, \end{cases} \end{aligned} \tag{2.87}$$

since $\eta(0+) = 0$ or $\eta_0\,(> 0)$ depending on whether $\rho \leqslant 1$ or $\rho > 1$ on account of (2.21). Now, on differentiating (2.18) and putting $\theta = 0$, we obtain

$$\eta'(0+)\{1 + \lambda\psi'[\eta(0+)]\} = 1, \tag{2.88}$$

which gives $\eta'(0+) = (1 - \rho)^{-1}$ if $\rho < 1$ and $\eta'(0+) = \infty$ if $\rho = 1$. Hence (2.87) yields the result

$$F^*(0) = \begin{cases} 0 & \text{if } \rho \geqslant 1 \\ 1 - \rho & \text{if } \rho < 1. \end{cases} \tag{2.89}$$

Furthermore, because of our assumption, the transform $\Phi(0; \theta, t) \to \Phi^*(\theta)$ as $t \to \infty$, where

$$\begin{aligned} \Phi^*(\theta) &= \lim_{s\to 0} s\Phi^*(0; \theta, s) \\ &= \lim_{s\to 0} s \frac{\theta^{-1} - [\eta(s)]^{-1}}{s - \theta + \lambda - \lambda\psi(\theta)} \\ &= \begin{cases} 0 & \text{if } \rho \geqslant 1 \\ \dfrac{1 - \rho}{\theta - \lambda + \lambda\psi(\theta)} & \text{if } \rho < 1. \end{cases} \end{aligned} \tag{2.90}$$

We shall now extend these results to the general case where $W(0) = x \geqslant 0$. We have, as a slight generalization of (2.84),

$$W_x(t) = \max \{ \sup_{0\leqslant\tau\leqslant t} [X(\tau) - \tau], x + X(t) - t\}, \tag{2.91}$$

[see equation (1.220)], where the suffix x in $W_x(t)$ denotes the initial value $W(0) = x$. From (2.91) we find that

$$W_x(t) \geqslant \sup_{0\leqslant\tau\leqslant t} [X(\tau) - \tau] = W_0(t), \tag{2.92}$$

so that

$$F(x; y, t) \leqslant F(0; y, t). \tag{2.93}$$

From this it follows at once that $\lim_{t\to\infty} F(x; y, t) = 0$ if $\rho \geqslant 1$. In the case $\rho < 1$, (2.93) gives

$$\limsup_{t\to\infty} F(x; y, t) \leqslant F^*(y). \tag{2.94}$$

On the other hand, we have

$$\begin{aligned} F(x; y, t) &= Pr\{W(t) \leqslant y; T(x) > t \mid W(0) = x\} \\ &\quad + Pr\{W(t) \leqslant y; T(x) \leqslant t \mid W(0) = x\} \\ &\geqslant Pr\{W(t) \leqslant y; T(x) \leqslant t \mid W(0) = x\} \\ &= \int_{\tau=x}^{t} dG(x, \tau)F(0; y, t - \tau). \end{aligned} \tag{2.95}$$

Now, let $t_1 < t$ and write the last integral as $I_1 + I_2$, where

$$I_1 = \int_{\tau=x}^{t_1} dG(x, \tau)F(0; y, t - \tau),$$

(2.96)

$$I_2 = \int_{\tau=t_1}^{t} dG(x, \tau)F(0; y, t - \tau).$$

In these integrals, let first t and then $t_1 \to \infty$; then

$$I_1 \to \int_0^{t_1} dG(x, \tau)F^*(y) \to F^*(y)\int_0^{\infty} dG(x, \tau) = F^*(y), \tag{2.97}$$

and

$$|I_2| \leqslant \int_{\tau=t_1}^{t} dG(x, \tau) \to 0 \tag{2.98}$$

since $G(x, \infty) = Pr\{T(x) < \infty\} = 1$ if $\rho < 1$. From (2.95), (2.97), and (2.98) we obtain

$$\liminf_{t\to\infty} F(x; y, t) \geqslant F^*(y). \tag{2.99}$$

From (2.94) and (2.99) it follows that

$$\lim_{t\to\infty} F(x; y, t) = F^*(y) \tag{2.100}$$

independently of the initial value x.

To summarize: if $\rho \geqslant 1$, the waiting time accumulates indefinitely with probability one, whereas if $\rho < 1$, the waiting time has the limiting distribution $F^*(y)$ independently of the initial value $W(0) = x$, where $F^*(y)$ has the Laplace transform

$$\int_{0-}^{\infty} e^{-\theta y}F^*(y)\, dy = \frac{1 - \rho}{\theta - \lambda + \lambda\psi(\theta)}, \tag{2.101}$$

[cf. equation (1.196)]. We now invert this transform and obtain $F^*(y)$; a more direct procedure is to obtain $F^*(y)$ by letting $t \to \infty$ in the expression (2.49) for $F(x; y, t)$.

Let v be the service time, and let us assume that the abscissa of convergence of the L.S.T.

$$\psi(\theta) = E(e^{-\theta v}) = \int_0^{\infty} e^{-\theta v}\, dB(v)$$

is $\sigma < 0$. Thus $\psi(\theta) < \infty$ for $\theta > \sigma$, and since $B(v)$ is monotonic, $\psi(\theta)$ has a singularity at $\theta = \sigma$; more specifically, $\psi(\theta) \to \infty$ as $\theta \to \sigma$. Now consider the function $f(\theta) = \lambda - \lambda\psi(\theta) - \theta$ $(\theta \geqslant \sigma)$. Since $f''(\theta) = -\lambda\psi''(\theta) = -\lambda E(e^{-\theta v}v^2) < 0$ and $f(\theta) \to -\infty$ as $\theta \to \infty$ and as $\theta \to \sigma$, $f(\theta)$ is a concave function. Therefore $f(\theta)$ has a maximum θ', at which $f'(\theta') = \lambda E(e^{-\theta' v}v) - 1 = 0$, so that if $f'(0) = \rho - 1 \neq 0$, then $\theta' \neq 0$.

Since $f(0) = 0$ and $f(\theta') > f(0)$, there exists a unique value θ_0 such that $f(\theta_0) = 0$; moreover, $\theta_0 \gtrless 0$ depending on whether $\rho \gtrless 1$, and $\theta_0 = 0$ if $\rho = 1$. Let us consider the case $\rho < 1$; here $f(\theta) > 0$ for $\sigma < \theta_0 < \theta < 0$, and we can write

$$
\begin{aligned}
\frac{1}{\lambda - \lambda\psi(\theta) - \theta} &= \int_0^\infty e^{-[\lambda - \lambda\psi(\theta) - \theta]t}\, dt \\
&= \int_{t=0}^\infty dt \int_{x=0}^\infty e^{-\theta(x-t)}\, d_x K(x, t) \\
&= \int_{t=0}^\infty dt \int_{y=-t}^\infty e^{-\theta y}\, d_y K(t + y, t) \qquad (2.102)\\
&= \int_{y=0-}^\infty e^{-\theta y}\, dy \int_{t=0}^\infty dK(t + y, t) \\
&\quad + \int_{y=0+}^\infty e^{\theta y}\, dy \int_{t=y}^\infty dK(t - y, t),
\end{aligned}
$$

where we recall that

$$dK(t + y, t) = \sum_0^\infty e^{-\lambda t} \frac{(\lambda t)^n}{n!}\, dB_n(t + y) \qquad (-\infty < y < \infty).$$

Differentiating (2.17) and putting $\theta = 0$, we obtain

$$E[T(x)] = xe^{-x\eta(0+)}\eta'(0+) = x(1 - \rho)^{-1} \qquad \text{if} \quad \rho < 1,$$

so that

$$\int_{t=x}^\infty dK(t - x, t) = (1 - \rho)^{-1} \qquad \text{if} \quad \rho < 1, x > 0. \tag{2.103}$$

Substituting (2.103) in (2.102), we obtain

$$\frac{1}{\lambda - \lambda\psi(\theta) - \theta} = \int_{y=0+}^\infty e^{-\theta y}\, dy \int_{t=0}^\infty dK(t + y, t) - \frac{1}{\theta(1 - \rho)}. \tag{2.104}$$

We now have

$$
\begin{aligned}
\int_{0+}^\infty e^{-\theta y}[1 - F^*(y)]\, dy &= \frac{1}{\theta} + \frac{1 - \rho}{\lambda - \lambda\psi(\theta) - \theta} \qquad (2.105)\\
&= (1 - \rho)\int_{y=0}^\infty e^{-\theta y}\, dy \int_{t=0}^\infty dK(t + y, t),
\end{aligned}
$$

from (2.104). This is true for $\theta_0 < \theta < 0$, and hence for all θ. Thus we have

$$F^*(y) = 1 - (1 - \rho)\int_{t=0}^\infty dK(t + y, t) \qquad (y > 0). \tag{2.106}$$

b. Limiting Distribution of $Q(t)$

Since the transition probabilities of $Q(t)$ have been expressed in terms of $F(x; y, t)$, and the limiting behavior of $F(x; y, t)$ as $t \to \infty$ has already been investigated, it is easy to obtain the limiting distribution of $Q(t)$. We study the case $Q(0) = 0$; the procedure in the general case $Q(0) = i > 0$ is similar.

We have

$$P_{00}(t) = F(0; 0, t) \to \begin{cases} 0 & \text{if} \quad \rho \geqslant 1 \\ 1 - \rho & \text{if} \quad \rho < 1. \end{cases} \tag{2.107}$$

Let $t_1 < t$ and write $P_{0j}(t) = I_1 + I_2$, where

$$I_1 = \int_{\tau=0}^{t_1} \int_{y=0-}^{\tau} \lambda\, d\tau\, d_y F(0; y, t - \tau)[1 - B(\tau - y)] e^{-\lambda\tau} \frac{(\lambda\tau)^{j-1}}{(j-1)!} \tag{2.108}$$

$$\begin{aligned} I_2 &= \int_{\tau=t_1}^{t} \int_{y=0-}^{\tau} \lambda\, d\tau\, d_y F(0; y, t - \tau)[1 - B(\tau - y)] e^{-\lambda\tau} \frac{(\lambda\tau)^{j-1}}{(j-1!)} \\ &= \int_{\tau=t_1}^{t} d\tau\, e^{-\lambda\tau} \frac{\lambda^j \tau^{j-1}}{(j-1)!} \\ &\quad \times \left[F(0; \tau, t - \tau) + \int_{0-}^{\tau} F(0; y, t - \tau)\, dB(\tau - y) \right] \end{aligned} \tag{2.109}$$

In these, let first t and then $t_1 \to \infty$; then

$$I_1 \to \begin{cases} 0 & \text{if} \quad \rho \geqslant 1 \\ \displaystyle\int_{\tau=0}^{\infty} \int_{y=0-}^{\tau} \lambda\, d\tau\, dF^*(y)[1 - B(\tau - y)] e^{-\lambda\tau} \frac{(\lambda\tau)^{j-1}}{(j-1)!} & \text{if} \quad \rho < 1, \end{cases} \tag{2.110}$$

and

$$\begin{aligned} |I_2| &\leqslant \int_{t_1}^{t} d\tau\, e^{-\lambda\tau} \frac{\lambda^j \tau^{j-1}}{(j-1)!} |1 - B(\tau)| \\ &\leqslant 2 \int_{t_1}^{t} e^{-\lambda\tau} \frac{\lambda^j \tau^{j-1}}{(j-1)!} d\tau \to 0, \end{aligned} \tag{2.111}$$

since the integral of $e^{-\lambda\tau}\lambda^j\tau^{j-1}/(j-1)!$ over $(0, \infty)$ is convergent. From (2.108) to (2.111) we find that

$$P_{0j}(t) \to \begin{cases} 0 & \text{if} \quad \rho \geqslant 1 \\ \displaystyle\int_{t=0}^{\infty} \int_{y=0-}^{t} dF^*(y)[1 - B(t - y)] e^{-\lambda t} \frac{\lambda^j t^{j-1}}{(j-1)!} dt & \text{if} \quad \rho < 1. \end{cases} \tag{2.112}$$

In the general case where $Q(0) = i \geqslant 0$, a similar procedure gives the same limits as in (2.112), independently of the initial value i. Let us denote $\lim_{t\to\infty} P_{ij}(t) = P_j^*$ and $P^*(\omega) = \sum_0^\infty P_j^* \omega^j$ ($|\omega| < 1$); then from (2.101) we obtain

$$
\begin{aligned}
P^*(\omega) &= P_0^* + \sum_{j=1}^{\infty} P_j^* \omega^j \\
&= (1-\rho) + \omega \int_{t=0}^{\infty} \int_{y=0-}^{t} dF^*(y)[1 - B(t-y)] e^{-\lambda t + \lambda t \omega} \lambda \, dt \\
&= (1-\rho) + \lambda\omega(\lambda - \lambda\omega)\Phi^*(\lambda - \lambda\omega) \frac{1 - \psi(\lambda - \lambda\omega)}{\lambda - \lambda\omega} \qquad (2.113) \\
&= (1-\rho)\left[1 + \lambda\omega \frac{1 - \psi(\lambda - \lambda\omega)}{(\lambda - \lambda\omega) - \lambda + \lambda\psi(\lambda - \lambda\omega)}\right] \\
&= \frac{(1-\rho)(1-\omega)\psi(\lambda - \lambda\omega)}{\psi(\lambda - \lambda\omega) - \omega},
\end{aligned}
$$

a result due to Kendall (1951).

2.8 SPECIAL CASES

a. The System $M/D/1$

We shall now study the special case $M/D/1$ in which the service time is a constant b, so that

$$B(v) = 0 \quad (v < b), \qquad \text{and} \qquad = 1 \quad (v \geqslant b), \tag{2.114}$$

and in general, for $n \geqslant 1$,

$$B_n(v) = 0 \quad (v < nb), \qquad \text{and} \qquad = 1 \quad (v \geqslant nb). \tag{2.115}$$

The d.f. of the service potential $X(t)$ is given by

$$K(x, t) = \sum_{n=0}^{[x/b]} e^{-\lambda t} \frac{(\lambda t)^n}{n!}, \tag{2.116}$$

where $[x/b]$ is the greatest integer contained in x/b. This expression indicates that the distribution of $X(t)$ consists of discrete probabilities $k(x, t) = e^{-\lambda t}(\lambda t)^n/n!$ at the points $x = nb$ ($n = 0, 1, 2, \ldots$).

For the distribution of the busy period $T(x)$ we have

$$
dG(x, t) = \begin{cases} e^{-\lambda(x+nb)} \dfrac{\lambda^n}{n!} x(x+nb)^{n-1} & \text{if } t = x + nb, \quad n = 0, 1, 2, \ldots \\ 0 & \text{otherwise;} \end{cases}
$$

thus the possible values of $T(x)$ in this system are $x + nb$ ($n = 0, 1, 2, \ldots$), and for these values we may write $dG(x, t) = g(x, t)$, where

$$g(x, t) = \frac{x}{t} k(t - x, t). \tag{2.117}$$

The joint distribution of T_i and $N(T_i)$ can be obtained from (2.23) by substituting (2.115) and is found to agree with the result obtained in Section 1.7b.

The probability of finding an empty counter at time t is given by

$$\begin{aligned} F(x; 0, t) &= \sum_{n=0}^{\infty} e^{-\lambda t} \frac{(\lambda t)^{n-1}}{n!} \int_0^{t-x} \lambda(t - v)\, dB_n(v) \\ &= \sum_{0}^{N(x)} e^{-\lambda t} \frac{\lambda^n t^{n-1}}{n!} (t - nb), \end{aligned} \tag{2.118}$$

where $N(x) = [(t - x)/b]$. The transition d.f. of $W(t)$ is given by

$$\begin{aligned} F(x; y, t) = &\sum_{0}^{N(x-y)} e^{-\lambda t} \frac{(\lambda t)^n}{n!} \\ &- \sum_{m=0}^{N(x-y)} e^{-\lambda(mb-y)} \frac{\lambda^m}{m!} (mb - y)^m F(x; 0, t + y - mb). \end{aligned} \tag{2.119}$$

The second term on the right-hand side of (2.119) is

$$\begin{aligned} &= \sum_{m=0}^{N(x-y)} e^{-\lambda(mb-y)} \frac{\lambda^m}{m!} (mb - y)^m \\ &\quad \times \sum_{n=0}^{N(x-y)-m} e^{-\lambda(t+y-mb)} \frac{\lambda^n}{n!} (t + y - mb)^{n-1}(t + y - mb - nb) \\ &= \sum_{m=0}^{N} \sum_{n=m}^{N} e^{-\lambda t} \frac{\lambda^n}{n!} \binom{n}{m} (mb - y)^m (t + y - mb)^{n-m-1}(t + y - nb) \\ &= \sum_{n=0}^{N} \sum_{m=0}^{n} e^{-\lambda t} \frac{\lambda^n}{n!} \binom{n}{m} (mb - y)^m (t + y - mb)^{n-m-1}(t + y - nb). \end{aligned}$$

We can therefore write (2.119) as

$$\begin{aligned} F(x; y, t) = &\sum_{n=0}^{N(x-y)} e^{-\lambda t} \frac{\lambda^n}{n!} \Big[t^n - (t + y - nb) \\ &\times \sum_{m=0}^{n} \binom{n}{m} (mb - y)^m (t + y - mb)^{n-m-1} \Big]. \end{aligned} \tag{2.120}$$

For the queue-length $Q(t)$ we have first,

$$
\begin{aligned}
P_{i0}(t) &= \sum_{n=i}^{\infty} e^{-\lambda t} \frac{(\lambda t)^{n-i-1}}{(n-i)!} \lambda \int_0^t \left[t - \left(1 - \frac{i}{n}\right) v \right] dB_n(v) \\
&= \sum_{n=i}^{N(0)} e^{-\lambda t} \frac{(\lambda t)^{n-i-1}}{(n-i)!} \lambda (t - nb + ib) \qquad (2.121) \\
&= \sum_{n=0}^{N(0)-i} e^{-\lambda t} \frac{(\lambda t)^{n-1}}{n!} \lambda (t - nb).
\end{aligned}
$$

More generally, $P_{ij}(t)$ can be obtained by using the expression (2.120) for $F(x; y, t)$, but the resulting expression is rather complicated.

The limiting d.f. of $W(t)$ is given by

$$
F^*(y) = 1 - (1-\rho) \sum_{n=m+1}^{\infty} e^{-\lambda(nb-y)} \frac{\lambda^n}{n!} (nb - y)^n \qquad \left(m = \left[\frac{y}{b} \right] \right), \tag{2.122}
$$

and the limiting probabilities of $Q(t)$ by

$$
\begin{aligned}
P_0^* &= 1 - \rho \\
P_j^* &= \int_{y=0-}^{\infty} \int_{t=y}^{y+b} dF^*(y) e^{-\lambda t} \frac{\lambda^j t^{j-1}}{(j-1)!} dt \\
&= \int_0^{\infty} dy F^*(y) \left[e^{-\lambda y} \frac{\lambda^j y^{j-1}}{(j-1)!} - e^{-\lambda(y+b)} \frac{\lambda^j (y+b)^{j-1}}{(j-1)!} \right] \\
&= \int_0^b e^{-\lambda y} \frac{\lambda^j y^{j-1}}{(j-1)!} dy - (1-\rho) \int_0^{\infty} dy \qquad (2.123) \\
&\quad \times \left[e^{-\lambda y} \frac{\lambda^j y^{j-1}}{(j-1)!} - e^{-\lambda(y+b)} \frac{\lambda^j (y+b)^{j-1}}{(j-1)!} \right] \int_{t=0}^{\infty} dK(t+y, y) \\
&= \sum_{j}^{\infty} e^{-\rho} \frac{\rho^n}{n!} - (1-\rho) \sum_{0}^{\infty} e^{-n\rho} \left[\frac{(n\rho)^{n+j}}{(n+j)!} - \frac{(n\rho)^{n+j-1}}{(n+j-1)!} \right]
\end{aligned}
$$

for $j \geqslant 1$. In these results $\rho = \lambda b$ is the relative traffic intensity, and in (2.122) and (2.123) we have assumed that $\rho < 1$.

b. The System $M/M/1$

The queue-length process $Q(t)$ is Markovian in this case and has already been studied in Section 1.2. Here we derive results for the waiting time process $W(t)$. We have $dB(t) = \mu e^{-\mu t}\, dt$ $(0 < t < \infty)$, so that

$$
dB_n(t) = e^{-\mu t} \mu^n \frac{t^{n-1}}{(n-1)!} dt \qquad (n \geqslant 1). \tag{2.124}
$$

The distribution of $X(t)$ is therefore given by

$$K(0, t) = e^{-\lambda t}$$

$$(2.125)\qquad \begin{aligned} d_xK(x, t) &= \sum_{n=1}^{\infty} e^{-\lambda t}\frac{(\lambda t)^n}{n!}\, e^{-\mu x}\mu^n \frac{x^{n-1}}{(n-1)!}\, dx \\ &= e^{-\lambda t-\mu x}\sum_{0}^{\infty}\frac{(\lambda\mu)^{n+1}t^{n+1}x^n}{n!\,(n+1)!}\, dx \\ &= e^{-\lambda t-\mu x}\sqrt{\lambda\mu t/x}\, I_1(2\sqrt{\lambda\mu t x})\, dx, \end{aligned}$$

where $I_1(x)$ is the modified Bessel function of index j. Thus $X(t)$ has a discontinuity at $x = 0$ and has a continuous distribution in the range $0 < x < \infty$, with the frequency function (fr.f.) $k(x, t)$, where

$$(2.126)\qquad k(x, t) = e^{-\lambda t-\mu x}\sqrt{\lambda\mu t/x}\, I_1(2\sqrt{\lambda\mu t x}).$$

For the distribution of the busy period $T(x)$ we have

$$dG(x, t) = e^{-\lambda x} \qquad \text{if} \quad t = x,$$

$$(2.127)\qquad dG(x, t) = e^{-\lambda t-\mu x}x\sqrt{\frac{\lambda\mu}{t(t-x)}}\, I_1(2\sqrt{\lambda\mu t(t-x)})\, dt \qquad \text{if} \quad t > x;$$

thus in the range $x < t < \infty$, $T(x)$ has a fr.f. $g(x, t)$, where

$$(2.128)\qquad g(x, t) = \frac{x}{t}\, k(t-x, t).$$

Since $\psi(\theta) = \mu(\mu+\theta)^{-1}$, the functional equation (2.18) reduces to

$$\eta^2 - \eta(\theta + \lambda - \mu) - \mu\theta = 0,$$

so that the desired root is

$$(2.129)\qquad \eta \equiv \eta(\theta) = \frac{(\theta+\lambda-\mu) + \sqrt{(\theta+\lambda-\mu)^2 + 4\theta\mu}}{2},$$

where the square root is taken so that its real part is positive. We have

$$(2.130)\qquad \begin{aligned} \eta(0+) &= \frac{(\lambda-\mu) + |\lambda-\mu|}{2} \\ &= \begin{cases} \lambda-\mu & \text{if} \quad \rho > 1 \\ 0 & \text{if} \quad \rho \leqslant 1. \end{cases} \end{aligned}$$

Thus the L.S.T. of the distribution of $T(x)$ is $e^{-x\eta(\theta)}$, where $\eta(\theta)$ is given by (2.129) and

$$(2.131)\qquad Pr\{T(x) < \infty\} = \begin{cases} 1 & \text{if} \quad \rho \leqslant 1 \\ e^{-(\lambda-\mu)x} & \text{if} \quad \rho > 1. \end{cases}$$

Note that (2.129) can be written as

$$\eta = \frac{(\theta + \lambda + \mu) + \sqrt{(\theta + \lambda + \mu)^2 - 4\lambda\mu}}{2} - \mu \tag{2.132}$$
$$= \mu(\xi^{-1} - 1),$$

where

$$\xi \equiv \xi(\theta) = \frac{(\theta + \lambda + \mu) - \sqrt{(\theta + \lambda + \mu)^2 - 4\lambda\mu}}{2\lambda} \tag{2.133}$$

[cf. equation (1.25)]. This is the root $\Gamma(\theta)$ of the equation (2.27).

The joint distribution of the length of the busy period T_i and the number $N(T_i)$ of customers served during T_i is given by

$$Pr\{t < T_i < t + dt;\ N(T_i) = n\} = e^{-(\lambda+\mu)t} \frac{i\lambda^{n-i}\mu^n t^{2n-i-1}}{n(n-i)!\,(n-1)!}\,dt; \tag{2.134}$$

the distribution of T_i found from this agrees with equation (1.65). From (2.25) the distribution $\{f_n\}$ of $N(T_1)$ is found to be

$$\begin{aligned} f_n &= \int_0^\infty e^{-\lambda t}\frac{(\lambda t)^{n-1}}{n!}\, e^{-\mu t}\mu^n \frac{t^{n-1}}{(n-1)!}\,dt \\ &= \frac{\lambda^{n-1}\mu^n}{n!\,(n-1)!}\int_0^\infty e^{-(\lambda+\mu)t} t^{2n-2}\,dt \\ &= \frac{\lambda^{n-1}\mu^n}{(\lambda+\mu)^{2n-1}}\frac{(2n-2)!}{n!\,(n-1)!} \\ &= \frac{1}{2n-1}\binom{2n-1}{n-1}\frac{\lambda^{n-1}\mu^n}{(\lambda+\mu)^{2n-1}} \qquad (n \geqslant 1). \end{aligned} \tag{2.135}$$

The p.g.f. of $N(T_1)$ is $\xi(z)$, where

$$\xi \equiv \xi(z) = \frac{(\lambda + \mu) - \sqrt{(\lambda + \mu)^2 - 4\lambda\mu z}}{2\lambda}. \tag{2.136}$$

The probability that the system is empty at time t is given by

$$\begin{aligned} F(x; 0, t) &= e^{-\lambda t} + \sum_{n=1}^\infty e^{-\lambda t}\frac{(\lambda t)^{n-1}}{n!}\int_0^{t-x} \lambda(t - v)\mu^n e^{-\mu v}\frac{v^{n-1}}{(n-1)!}\,dv \\ &= e^{-\lambda t} + \int_0^{t-x} \frac{t-v}{t} k(v, t)\,dv \\ &= e^{-\lambda t} + \int_x^t g(v, t)\,dv \qquad (t \geqslant x). \end{aligned} \tag{2.137}$$

Since $dK(\tau + x, \tau) = k(\tau + x, \tau)\,d\tau$, we can write the transition d.f. of the waiting time $W(t)$ as

$$F(x; y, t) = K(t + y - x, t) - \int_0^{t-x} F(x; 0, t - \tau)k(\tau + y, \tau)\,d\tau,$$

from which, for $y > 0$, we find that

$$\frac{\partial}{\partial y} F(x; y, t) = k(t + y - x, t) - \int_0^{t-x} F(x; 0, t - \tau)k_1(\tau + y, \tau)\,d\tau,$$

where, for $x > 0$,

$$k_1(x, t) = \frac{\partial}{\partial x} k(x, t) = -\mu k(x, t) - \frac{1}{2x} k(x, t) - e^{-\lambda t - \mu x}\left(\frac{\lambda\mu t}{x}\right) I_1'(2\sqrt{\lambda\mu t x}). \tag{2.138}$$

Thus $W(t)$ has a discontinuity at the origin, whereas in the range $0 < y < \infty$ it has a continuous distribution with the transition fr.f. $f(x; y, t)$ given by

$$f(x; y, t) = k(t + y - x, t) - \int_0^{t-x} F(x; 0, t - \tau)k_1(\tau + y, \tau)\,d\tau. \tag{2.139}$$

c. The System $M/E_k/1$

Here $dB(t) = e^{-k\mu t}(k\mu)^k t^{k-1}\,dt/(k-1)!$; proceeding as in the case of $M/M/1$, we can obtain the distributions of the busy period and waiting time, but the expressions are complicated. The queue-length distribution can be obtained directly by considering $Q_1(t)$, the number of phases in the system; in Section 1.5 we saw that $Q_1(t)$ is a Markov process. To characterize this process, let us denote by $A(t)$ the number of phases which arrive in the system during $(0, t]$, and $D(t)$ the number of those which complete their service during this period. Then since each customer introduces k phases into the system, we see that the possible values of $A(t)$ are $0, k, 2k, \ldots$, and that $Pr\{A(t) = nk\} = e^{-\lambda t}(\lambda t)^n/n!$ $(n = 0, 1, 2, \ldots)$. The p.g.f. of $A(t)$ is therefore given by

$$E[z^{A(t)}] = \sum_{n=0}^{\infty} e^{-\lambda t}\frac{(\lambda t)^n}{n!} z^{nk} = e^{-\lambda t(1-z^k)}; \tag{2.140}$$

$A(t)$ is thus a multiple Poisson process. On the other hand, $D(t)$ is a simple Poisson process, with the p.g.f.

$$E[z^{D(t)}] = e^{-k\mu t(1-z)}. \tag{2.141}$$

Now consider the basic process $X(t) = A(t) - D(t)$; this is a Markov process, for which

$$E[z^{X(t)}] = E[z^{A(t)}]E\left[\left(\frac{1}{z}\right)^{D(t)}\right]$$

$$= \exp\{[\lambda z^k - (\lambda + k\mu) + k\mu(1/z)]t.\} \tag{2.142}$$

The distribution of $X(t)$ is given by

$$\begin{aligned} k_j(t) &= Pr\{X(t) = j\} = Pr\{A(t) - D(t) = j\} \\ &= \sum_{n=0}^{\infty} Pr\{A(t) = nk\} Pr\{D(t) = nk - j\} \\ &= \sum_{n=0}^{\infty} e^{-\lambda t} \frac{(\lambda t)^n}{n!} e^{-k\mu t} \frac{(k\mu t)^{nk-j}}{(nk-j)!} \\ &= e^{-(\lambda+k\mu)t} \left(\frac{\rho}{k}\right)^{j/(k+1)} I_{-j}^{(k)}(2\lambda^{1/(k+1)}(k\mu)^{k/(k+1)}t), \end{aligned} \tag{2.143}$$

where

$$I_j^{(k)}(x) = \sum_{n=0}^{\infty} \frac{(x/2)^{j+nk+n}}{n!\,(j+nk)!}. \tag{2.144}$$

This function was introduced by Luchak (1956), who studied its properties; when $k = 1$, it reduces to the Bessel function $I_j(x)$.

As in the case of $M/M/1$, we have the formula

$$Q_1(t) = \max\{\sup_{0 \leqslant \tau \leqslant t} [X(t) - X(\tau)],\ i + X(t)\}, \tag{2.145}$$

where $Q_1(0) = i$ (see Section 7.9). Proceeding as in Section 1.2, we find that

$$\begin{aligned} P_{i0}(t) &= Pr\{Q_1(t) = 0 \mid Q_1(0) = i\} \\ &= \frac{1}{k\mu} \sum_{\nu=i+1}^{\infty} g_\nu(t), \end{aligned} \tag{2.146}$$

where $g_i(t)$ is the fr.f. of T_i, the first passage time of $Q_1(t)$ from $i\,(> 0)$ to 0. To obtain $g_i(t)$, we consider the probability

$$g_i^{(n)}(t)\,dt = Pr\{t < T_i < t + dt;\ D(T_i) = n\} \qquad (n \geqslant i). \tag{2.147}$$

By a reasoning similar to the one used for the case $M/D/1$ (Section 1.7), we find that

$$g_i^{(i)}(t) = e^{-(\lambda+k\mu)t} \frac{(k\mu)^i t^{i-1}}{(i-1)!} \tag{2.148}$$

$$\begin{aligned} g_i^{(n)}(t) = \sum_{r=1}^{[(n-i)/k]} \int_0^t e^{-k\mu\tau}(k\mu)^i \frac{\tau^{i-1}}{(i-1)!}\,d\tau \\ \times e^{-\lambda\tau} \frac{(\lambda\tau)^r}{r!} g_{rk}^{(n-i)}(t-\tau) \qquad (n > i). \end{aligned} \tag{2.149}$$

From the recurrence relation (2.149) we find by induction that

$$g_i^{(i+nk)}(t) = \begin{cases} e^{-(\lambda+k\mu)t} \dfrac{i\lambda^n (k\mu)^{i+nk}}{n!\,(i+nk)!} t^{i+nk+n-1} & (n = 0, 1, 2, \ldots) \\ 0 \quad \text{otherwise.} \end{cases} \tag{2.150}$$

The fr.f. of T_i is $g_i(t) = \sum_{n=0}^{\infty} g_i^{(i+nk)}(t)$, and from (2.143) and (2.150) it follows that

$$g_i(t) = \frac{i}{t}\, k_{-i}(t). \tag{2.151}$$

Substituting (2.151) in (2.146) we obtain $P_{i0}(t)$. To obtain the transition probabilities $P_{ij}(t)$ of $Q_1(t)$ for $j \geqslant 1$, we note that the generating function $G(z, t) = \sum_0^{\infty} P_{ij}(t)z^j$ satisfies the differential equation

$$\frac{\partial G}{\partial t} - \left[\lambda z^k - (\lambda + k\mu) + k\mu \frac{1}{z}\right] = -k\mu \frac{1 - z}{z} P_{i0}(t) \tag{2.152}$$

[see equation (1.212)]. We now solve this equation in a slightly different manner. Multiplying both sides of (2.152) by the factor

$$\exp - \left[\lambda z^k - (\lambda + k\mu) + k\mu \frac{1}{z}\right] t,$$

we write it as

$$\frac{\partial}{\partial t}\left[G \exp\left\{-\left[\lambda z^k - (\lambda + k\mu) + k\mu \frac{1}{z}\right] t\right\}\right]$$
$$= -k\mu \frac{1 - z}{z} P_{i0}(t) \exp\left\{-\left[\lambda z^k - (\lambda + k\mu) + k\mu \frac{1}{z}\right] t\right\};$$

integrating this over $(0, t)$ we obtain

$$G \exp\left\{-\left[\lambda z^k - (\lambda + k\mu) + k\mu \frac{1}{z}\right] t\right\} \tag{2.153}$$
$$= A - k\mu \frac{1 - z}{z} \int_0^t P_{i0}(\tau) \exp\left\{-\left[\lambda z^k - (\lambda + k\mu) + k\mu \frac{1}{z}\right] \tau\right\} d\tau,$$

where $A = G(z, 0) = z^i$. Substituting for A in (2.153) and simplifying, we find that

$$G(z, t) = z^i \exp\left\{\left[\lambda z^k - (\lambda + k\mu) + k\mu \frac{1}{z}\right] t\right\} \tag{2.154}$$
$$- k\mu \frac{1 - z}{z} \int_0^t P_{i0}(t - \tau) \exp\left\{\left[\lambda z^k - (\lambda + k\mu) + k\mu \frac{1}{z}\right] \tau\right\} d\tau.$$

Proceeding as in Section 2.4, and remembering that if $U(z) = \sum_{-\infty}^{\infty} u_j z^j$, then $U(z)(1 - z)^{-1} = \sum_{-\infty}^{\infty} z^j \sum_{-\infty}^{j} u_\nu$, we obtain the result

$$Pr\{Q_1(t) \leqslant j \mid Q_1(0) = i\} = K_{j-i}(t) - k\mu \int_0^t P_{i0}(t - \tau) k_{j+1}(\tau)\, d\tau, \tag{2.155}$$

when $K_\nu(t) = \sum_{-\infty}^{\nu} k_j(t)$. Since $P_{i0}(t)$ has already been determined, this result is complete.

2.9 THE QUEUE $GI/M/1$

We now investigate the system $GI/M/1$, in which (1) the interarrival times have the distribution $dB(t)$, (2) the service time distribution is the negative exponential $\lambda e^{-\lambda t}\,dt$ $(0 < t < \infty)$, and (3) there is only one counter, and the queue discipline is "first come, first served." As before, we assume that $0 < b < \int_0^\infty t\,dB(t) < \infty$, so that $0 < \rho_2 = (\lambda b)^{-1} < \infty$, where ρ_2 is the relative traffic intensity.

If in the queueing system just described we interchange the interarrival and service time distributions, we obtain the system $M/G/1$, that is, the system in which the customers arrive in a Poisson process with mean λt, and the service time distribution is $dB(t)$. This latter system may be called the dual of the first; between these two systems several interesting duality relationships exist, as we shall discover in the following sections. For ready reference we note below some of the results derived in the preceding sections concerning $M/G/1$. The basic stochastic process in this system is the compound Poisson process $X(t)$, with the d.f.

$$K(x, t) = Pr\{X(t) \leqslant x\} = \sum_{n=0}^{\infty} e^{-\lambda t}\frac{(\lambda t)^n}{n!}B_n(x). \tag{2.156}$$

For the first passage time $T(x) = \inf\,[t \mid x + X(t) - t \leqslant 0]$ $(x > 0)$, we have

$$G(x, t) = Pr\{T(x) \leqslant t\} = \int_{\tau=x}^{t}\sum_{n=0}^{\infty} e^{-\lambda\tau}\frac{(\lambda\tau)^{n-1}}{n!}\lambda x\,dB_n(\tau - x), \tag{2.157}$$

and

$$E[e^{-\theta T(x)}] = \int_0^\infty e^{-\theta t}\,d_tG(x, t) = e^{-x\eta(\theta)}, \tag{2.158}$$

where $\eta(\theta)$ satisfies the functional equation $\eta(\theta) = \theta + \lambda - \lambda\psi(\eta)$, $\psi(\theta)$ being the L.S.T. of $dB(t)$. Furthermore,

$$F(x; y, t) = Pr\{\sup_{0\leqslant\tau\leqslant t}[X(\tau) - \tau] \leqslant y;\quad x + X(t) - t \leqslant y\}$$

$$= \begin{cases} \displaystyle\sum_{n=0}^{\infty} e^{-\lambda t}\frac{(\lambda t)^{n-1}}{n!}\int_{v=0}^{t-x}\lambda(t - v)\,dB_n(v) & (y = 0) \\ \displaystyle K(t + y - x) - \int_{\tau=0}^{t-x} F(x; 0, t - \tau)\,dK(\tau + y, \tau) & (y \geqslant 0). \end{cases} \tag{2.159}$$

We note the important relation

$$(2.160) \qquad F(x; 0, t)\, dt = e^{-\lambda t}\, dt + \int_{u=x+}^{t} dG(u, t)\, du \qquad (t \geqslant x)$$

and the Laplace transform

$$(2.161) \qquad F^*(x; 0, \theta) = \int_0^\infty e^{-\theta t} F(x; 0, t)\, dt = e^{-x\eta(\theta)}/\eta(\theta).$$

Finally, we remark that

$$(2.162) \qquad \lim_{t\to\infty} F(x; 0, t) = \begin{cases} 1 - \rho_2^{-1} & \text{if} \quad \rho_2 > 1 \\ 0 & \text{if} \quad \rho_2 \leqslant 1, \end{cases}$$

and more generally,

$$(2.163) \quad \lim_{t\to\infty} F(x; y, t) = \begin{cases} 1 - (1 - \rho_2^{-1}) \displaystyle\int_0^\infty dK(t + y, t) & \text{if} \quad \rho_2 > 1 \\ 0 & \text{if} \quad \rho_2 \leqslant 1. \end{cases}$$

2.10 THE WAITING TIME PROCESS $Y(t)$

a. Definition of $Y(t)$

The waiting time in a queueing system is usually defined as the time a customer would have to wait for the commencement of his service. From the point of view of a potential customer, this definition serves as an adequate description of the system and leads to useful results in several particular cases (as we have seen in the system $M/G/1$). However, we propose to define the waiting time as the time the customer at the counter has already spent in the system. We shall show that in $GI/M/1$ this definition leads to explicit results concerning the busy and idle periods, queue-length, and the conventionally defined waiting time.

The proposed definition of the waiting time $Y(t)$ is as follows. If at time t the counter is unoccupied, we put $Y(t) = 0$; otherwise, we define $Y(t)$ as the time which has elapsed since the arrival of the customer being served at time t. If, at any instant, $Y(t) > 0$, it increases at a unit rate as long as the customer at the counter continues to be served, but when his service is completed, $Y(t)$ decreases by an amount u, where u is the interval of time between his arrival and that of the customer who had followed him. More specifically, if $t = t_n$ is the epoch of departure of the nth customer, we have the relations

$$(2.164) \qquad Y(t_n + 0) = \begin{cases} Y(t_n - 0) - u_{n+1} & \text{if} \quad Y(t_n - 0) > u_{n+1} \\ 0 & \text{if} \quad 0 < Y(t_n - 0) \leqslant u_{n+1}, \end{cases}$$

where u_{n+1} is the interval of time between the nth and $(n + 1)$st arrivals.

Thus the process $Y(t)$ has discontinuities at the points t_n $(n = 1, 2, \ldots)$; we define $Y(t_n) = Y(t_n - 0)$, so that $Y(t)$ is continuous to the left at t_n. Moreover, if at any instant $Y(t) = 0$, it continues to be zero till the next arrival. A typical realization of $Y(t)$ is shown in Figure 2.1.

It is clear that at points t such that $Y(t) > 0$ the process is Markovian, but it loses the Markov property at points t such that $Y(t) = 0$ (except in the special case $M/M/1$). We do not therefore seek to establish any integro-differential equation for its transition d.f.; our methods are based on renewal theory and yield explicit results.

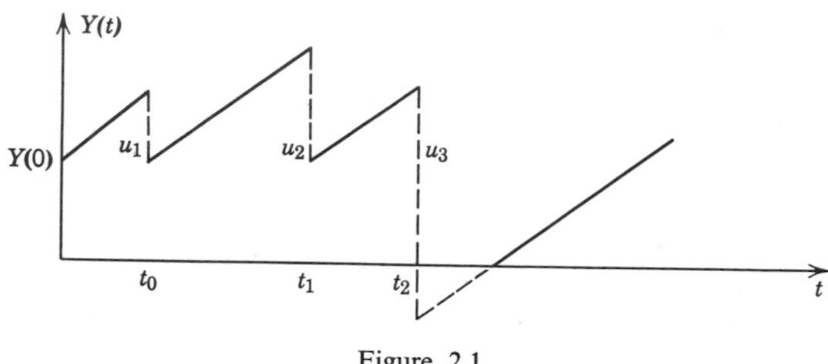

Figure 2.1

b. The Zero-Avoiding Transitions of $Y(t)$

We consider first the Markovian part of the process $Y(t)$. Let

$$S(y) = \inf\,[t > 0 \mid Y(t) = 0,\ Y(0) = y] \tag{2.165}$$

$$H(y, t) = Pr\{S(y) \leqslant t\}. \tag{2.166}$$

We have

$$\begin{aligned} S(y) &= \inf\,[t > 0 \mid y + t - X(t) < 0] \\ &= \inf\,[t > 0 \mid X(t) - t > y], \end{aligned} \tag{2.167}$$

where $X(t)$ is the total decrease in $Y(t)$ in the time interval $(0, t]$ and has the distribution (2.156). Hence, using (2.159), we obtain

$$\begin{aligned} Pr\{S(y) > t\} &= Pr\{\sup_{0 \leqslant \tau \leqslant t} [X(\tau) - \tau] \leqslant y\} \\ &= Pr\{W(t) \leqslant y \mid W(0) = 0\} = F(0; y, t), \end{aligned}$$

so that

$$H(y, t) = 1 - F(0; y, t). \tag{2.168}$$

Clearly, $S(y)$ is the first passage time from y to 0 of the process $Y(t)$. The zero-avoiding transition probabilities of $Y(t)$ are therefore given by

$$
\begin{aligned}
Pr\{Y(t) \geqslant x;\, S(y) > t \mid Y(0) = y\} & \\
&= Pr\{\inf_{0\leqslant\tau\leqslant t} [y + \tau - X(\tau)] \geqslant 0;\, y + t - X(t) \geqslant x\} \\
&= Pr\{\sup_{0\leqslant\tau\leqslant t} [X(\tau) - \tau] \leqslant y;\, x + X(t) - t \leqslant y\} \\
&= F(x;\, y, t) \qquad (x > 0,\, y \geqslant 0).
\end{aligned}
\tag{2.169}
$$

c. The Renewal Process $\{\zeta_n\}$

Let Z be the time interval between the commencement of two successive busy periods (the busy cycle). We have

$$
\begin{aligned}
Pr\{Z \leqslant z\} = \int_{\tau=0}^{z} \int_{x=0}^{\tau} & -d_x Pr\{Y(\tau) \geqslant x, \\
& S(0) > \tau \mid Y(0) = 0\}\lambda\, d\tau[B(x + z - \tau) - B(x)],
\end{aligned}
\tag{2.170}
$$

since, at the commencement of a busy period $Y(0) = 0$, and if at its termination $Y(\tau) = x > 0$, there must be a departure at time τ and the next arrival must occur at time t where $x < t \leqslant x + z - \tau$. Now from (2.160) we have

$$
-d_x F(x;\, 0, t)\, dt = d_t G(x, t)\, dx. \tag{2.171}
$$

Using (2.169) and (2.171) in (2.170) we obtain

$$
\begin{aligned}
Pr\{Z \leqslant z\} &= \int_{\tau=0}^{z} \int_{x=0}^{\tau} -\lambda\, d_x F(x;\, 0, \tau)\, d\tau\{B(x + z - \tau) - B(x)\} \\
&= \int_{x=0}^{z} \int_{\tau=x}^{z} \lambda\, d_\tau G(x, \tau)\{B(x + z - \tau) - B(x)\}\, dx.
\end{aligned}
\tag{2.172}
$$

The L.S.T. of the distribution of Z is given by

$$
\begin{aligned}
\phi(\theta) &= E(e^{-\theta Z}) \\
&= \int_{z=0}^{\infty} \int_{x=0}^{z} \int_{\tau=x}^{z} \lambda\, dx e^{-\theta z}\, d_\tau G(x, \tau)\, d_z B(x + z - \tau) \\
&= \int_{x=0}^{\infty} \int_{\tau=x}^{\infty} \int_{u=x}^{\infty} \lambda\, dx\, d_\tau G(x, \tau) e^{-\theta(u+\tau-x)}\, dB(u) \\
&= \int_{u=0}^{\infty} \lambda\, dB(u) \int_{x=0}^{u} e^{-\theta(u-x)-x\eta(\theta)}\, dx \qquad \text{from } (2.158) \\
&= \frac{\psi(\theta) - \psi(\eta)}{1 - \psi(\eta)}.
\end{aligned}
\tag{2.173}
$$

From (2.173) we find that $Pr\{Z < \infty\} = \lim_{\theta\to 0+} \phi(\theta) = \rho_2^{-1}$ if $\rho_2 > 1$, and $= 1$ if $\rho_2 \leqslant 1$; in the latter case we have

$$E(Z) = -\phi'(0) = \begin{cases} (\rho_2\eta_0)^{-1} & \text{if } \rho_2 < 1 \\ \infty & \text{if } \rho_2 = 1, \end{cases} \tag{2.174}$$

where η_0 is the largest positive root of the equation $x = \lambda - \lambda\psi(x)$.

We now consider the renewal process $\{\zeta_n\}$, where $\zeta_n = Z_1 + Z_2 + \cdots + Z_n$ $(n = 1, 2, \ldots)$, each Z_n having the d.f. (2.172). Let $N(t)$ be the number of renewals in this process, so that $N(t) = \max(n \mid \zeta_n \leqslant t)$; also let $U(t) = E[N(t)]$. From renewal theory we have

$$\begin{aligned} U^*(\theta) &= \int_0^\infty e^{-\theta t}\, dU(t) = [1 - \phi(\theta)]^{-1}\phi(\theta) \\ &= \frac{\psi(\theta) - \psi(\eta)}{1 - \psi(\theta)}. \end{aligned} \tag{2.175}$$

Inverting this transform, we find that

$$U(t) = \int_0^t dV(\tau)[B(t-\tau) - G(t-\tau)], \tag{2.176}$$

where

$$V(t) = \sum_{n=0}^{\infty} B_n(t), \qquad G(t) = \int_0^t dB(x)G(x, t), \tag{2.177}$$

Furthermore, from (2.175) we obtain

$$\lim_{t\to\infty} U(t) = \lim_{\theta\to 0+} U^*(\theta) = \begin{cases} \infty & \text{if } \rho_2 \leqslant 1 \\ (\rho_2 - 1)^{-1} & \text{if } \rho_2 > 1. \end{cases} \tag{2.178}$$

d. The Transition D.F. of $Y(t)$

In Section 2.10b, transitions of $Y(t)$ through nonzero values were investigated; we shall now consider transitions not necessarily avoiding zero. We assume that the process starts with a busy period at $t = 0$, and let

$$M(x, t) = Pr\{Y(t) \geqslant x\} \qquad (x \geqslant 0). \tag{2.179}$$

To obtain (2.179) we observe that if $Y(t) \geqslant x > 0$, a busy period is in progress, which is either the initial one itself or the $(n + 1)$st $(n = 1, 2, \ldots)$ commencing at time τ. Hence, using (2.169), we obtain

$$\begin{aligned} M(x, t) &= Pr\{Y(t) \geqslant x\} \\ &= Pr\{Y(t) \geqslant x;\, S(0) > t \mid Y(0) = 0\} + \sum_{n=1}^{\infty} \int_{0+}^{t} d_\tau Pr\{\zeta_n \leqslant \tau\} \\ &\qquad \times Pr\{Y(t-\tau) \geqslant x;\, S(0) > t - \tau \mid Y(0) = 0\} \\ &= F(x; 0, t) + \int_{0+}^{t-x} dU(\tau) F(x; 0, t-\tau). \end{aligned} \tag{2.180}$$

Since a d.f. is continuous to the right, we also obtain

$$\begin{aligned} Pr\{Y(t) = 0\} &= \lim_{x \to 0+} [1 - M(x, t)] \\ &= 1 - F(0; 0, t) - \int_{0+}^{t} dU(\tau)F(0; 0, t - \tau). \end{aligned} \tag{2.181}$$

The limiting distribution of $Y(t)$ as $t \to \infty$ can be obtained from the above results. We shall show that for $x \geqslant 0$,

$$\lim_{t \to \infty} M(x, t) = \begin{cases} 1 & \text{if} \quad \rho_2 \geqslant 1 \\ \rho_2 e^{-\eta_0 x} & \text{if} \quad \rho_2 < 1. \end{cases} \tag{2.182}$$

If $\rho_2 > 1$, we write

$$\int_0^{t-x} dU(\tau)F(x; 0, t - \tau) = \int_0^T + \int_T^{t-x} \qquad (0 < T < t), \tag{2.183}$$

and let first t, and then $T \to \infty$. Then in view of (2.178) and (2.162) we have

$$\begin{aligned} &\int_T^{t-x} \leqslant \int_T^{t-x} dU(\tau) \to 0 \\ &\int_0^T \to (1 - \rho_2^{-1}) \int_0^T dU(\tau) \to \rho_2^{-1}, \end{aligned} \tag{2.184}$$

so that $M(x, t) \to (1 - \rho_2^{-1}) + \rho_2^{-1} = 1$. If $\rho_2 < 1$, we have from (2.161),

$$\int_0^{\infty} F(x; 0, t)\, dt = \lim_{\theta \to 0+} F^*(x; 0, \theta) = e^{-\eta_0 x/\eta_0}, \tag{2.185}$$

from which

(2.186)

$$\int_0^t dU(\tau)F(x; 0, t - \tau) \to \frac{1}{E(Z)} \int_0^{\infty} F(x; 0, t)\, dt = (\rho_2 \eta_0) \cdot \frac{e^{-\eta_0 x}}{\eta_0} = \rho_2 e^{-\eta_0 x},$$

and $M(x, t) \to \rho_2 e^{-\eta_0 x}$. The case $\rho_2 = 1$ can be considered as the limiting case of (2.184) and (2.186), since $\eta_0 \to 0$ as $\rho_2 \to 1$. We have therefore proved (2.182) completely; thus if $\rho_2 \geqslant 1$, the waiting time $Y(t)$ increases indefinitely as $t \to \infty$, whereas if $\rho_2 < 1$, $Y(t)$ has the limiting d.f. $1 - \rho_2 e^{-\eta_0 x}$ $(x \geqslant 0)$.

2.11 THE IDLE AND BUSY PERIODS

The probability that an idle period $I(t)$ commences at time t and lasts at least until a time u is, apart from the factor $\lambda\, dt$, given by

$$\begin{aligned} Pr\{I(t) > u\} &= \int_{x=0+}^{t} -d_x Pr\{Y(t) \geqslant x\}[1 - B(x + u)] \\ &= \int_{x=0+}^{t} -d_x M(x, t)[1 - B(x + u)], \end{aligned} \tag{2.187}$$

since if a departure occurs at t and the next arrival occurs only after time $Y(t) + u$, then the idle period will extend at least up to time u. In particular, if the process starts with a busy period at $t = 0$, then proceeding as in (2.183) to (2.186) and using (2.182) we find from (2.187) that

$$\lim_{t\to\infty} Pr\{I(t) > u\} = \begin{cases} 0 & \text{if} \quad \rho_2 \geqslant 1 \\ \int_0^\infty \rho_2\eta_0 e^{-\eta_0 x}[1 - B(x + u)]\, dx & \text{if} \quad \rho_2 < 1. \end{cases} \tag{2.188}$$

Thus if $\rho_2 \geqslant 1$, idle periods are unlikely to occur (in fact, we have already seen in Section 2.10 that the server is always busy), whereas if $\rho_2 < 1$, they will occur according to the limiting distribution law

$$\lim_{t\to\infty} Pr\{u < I(t) < u + du\} = \rho_2\eta_0 \int_{v=u}^\infty e^{-\eta_0(v-u)}\, dB(v)\, du \qquad (u > 0), \tag{2.189}$$

Now, from (2.165) it is obvious that $S(y)$ is the busy period initiated by a waiting time $Y(0) = y \geqslant 0$; from (2.168) and (2.159) its d.f. is seen to be

$$Pr\{S(y) \leqslant t\} = \begin{cases} 1 - F(0; 0, t) & \text{if} \quad y = 0 \\ 1 - K(t + y, t) + \int_{\tau=0}^t F(0; 0, t - \tau)\, dK(\tau + y, \tau) & \text{if} \quad y > 0. \end{cases} \tag{2.190}$$

Furthermore, from (2.162) and (2.163) we find that

$$Pr\{S(y) < \infty\} = \begin{cases} 1 & (y \geqslant 0,\ \rho_2 \leqslant 1) \\ (1 - \rho_2^{-1}) \int_0^\infty dK(t + y, t) & (y > 0,\ \rho_2 > 1) \\ \rho_2^{-1} & (y = 0,\ \rho_2 > 1); \end{cases} \tag{2.191}$$

thus the busy period is of finite duration with probability one if and only if $\rho_2 \leqslant 1$.

Let us next consider the busy period $S(0)$ initiated by a waiting time $Y(0) = 0$, and denote by N the number of customers who complete their service during this busy period. To obtain the joint distribution of $S(0)$ and N, that is,

$$C_n(t) = Pr\{S(0) \leqslant t;\ N = n\}, \tag{2.192}$$

we consider the more general expression

$$C_n(x, t) = Pr\{Y(t) \geqslant x;\ S(0) > t;\ N = n \mid Y(0) = 0\}, \tag{2.193}$$

which is the probability that the busy period $S(0)$ extends at least up to t, and n customers complete their service during $(0, t]$, the value of $Y(t)$ being $\geqslant x$. To obtain $C_n(x, t)$ we observe that

$$d_x C_0(x, t) = e^{-\lambda t}\, d_x B_0(t - x), \tag{2.194}$$

since if the initial customer is still at the counter, then his service time is at least equal to t and $Y(t) = t$; moreover, for $n \geqslant 1$ we have the relation

$$d_x C_n(x, t) = \int_{\tau=0}^{x} \int_{u=0}^{t-x} d_x C_{n-1}(x - \tau + u, t - \tau)\lambda\, d\tau\, dB(u) e^{-\lambda\tau} \tag{2.195}$$

since if $(n - 1)$ customers complete their service in $(0, t - \tau]$ and the nth customer in $(t - \tau, t - \tau + d\tau]$, then $Y(t) = Y(t - \tau) - u + \tau$, where u is the interval between the arrival times of the $(n - 1)$st and the nth customer, and in this case a total of n customers would have completed their service in $(0, t]$. Using (2.194) and proceeding as in Section 2.2, we obtain

$$d_x C_n(x, t) = e^{-\lambda t} \frac{(\lambda t)^{n-1}}{n!} \lambda x\, d_x B_n(t - x) \qquad (n \geqslant 0). \tag{2.196}$$

It follows that $dC_n(t) = c_n(t)\, dt$, where

$$c_n(t) = \int_{x=0+}^{t} -d_x C_{n-1}(x, t)\lambda[1 - B(x)] \qquad (n \geqslant 1) \tag{2.197}$$

since the busy period ends in $(t, t + dt]$ with a total of n customers served if $(n - 1)$ customers complete their service in $(0, t]$ the nth customer in $(t, t + dt]$ and no customer had arrived during the time this last customer was present in the system. Substituting (2.196) in (2.197) we obtain

$$\begin{aligned} c_1(t) &= \lambda e^{-\lambda t}[1 - B(t)] \\ c_n(t) &= e^{-\lambda t} \frac{\lambda^n t^{n-2}}{(n-1)!} \int_{x=0+}^{t} x(-d_x)B_{n-1}(t - x) \\ &\quad \times [1 - B(x)] \qquad (n \geqslant 2). \end{aligned} \tag{2.198}$$

It follows that the distribution $\{f_n\}$ of the number of customers served during a busy period is given by

$$\begin{aligned} f_n &= \int_{t=0}^{\infty} c_n(t)\, dt \\ &= \int_{x=0+}^{\infty} \lambda\, dx[1 - B(x)] \\ &\quad \times \int_{t=x}^{\infty} e^{-\lambda t} \frac{(\lambda t)^{n-2}}{(n-1)!} \lambda x\, d_t B_{n-1}(t - x) \qquad (n \geqslant 1), \end{aligned} \tag{2.199}$$

whereas the d.f. of the length of the busy period $S(0)$ is given by

$$
\begin{aligned}
Pr\{S(0) \leqslant t\} &= \sum_{n=1}^{\infty} \int_0^t c_n(\tau)\, d\tau \\
&= \int_{x=0+}^{t} \lambda[1 - B(x)]\, dx \\
&\quad \times \int_{\tau=x}^{t} \sum_{n=1}^{\infty} e^{-\lambda\tau} \frac{(\lambda\tau)^{n-2}}{(n-1)!} \lambda x\, d_\tau B_{n-1}(\tau - x) \\
&= \int_{x=0+}^{t} \lambda G(x, t)[1 - B(x)]\, dx,
\end{aligned} \tag{2.200}
$$

an expression equivalent to the one obtained in Section 2.10b.

2.12 THE QUEUE-LENGTH AND THE WAITING TIME

Let $Q(t)$ be the queue-length (that is, the number of customers present in the system) at time t, and

$$P_j(t) = Pr\{Q(t) = j\}. \tag{2.201}$$

Clearly, $Q(t)$ is the number of customers who arrived during the time $Y(t)$, so that

$$Pr\{Q(t) = j \mid Y(t) = x\} = B_{j-1}(x) - B_j(x) = C_{j-1}(x) \qquad (j \geqslant 1) \tag{2.202}$$

$$Pr\{Q(t) = 0\} = Pr\{Y(t) = 0\}. \tag{2.203}$$

As before, let us assume that the process starts with a busy period at $t = 0$; we have then

$$
\begin{aligned}
P_j(t) &= \int_{x=0+}^{t} -d_x Pr\{Y(t) \geqslant x\} C_{j-1}(x) \\
&= \int_{0+}^{t} -d_x M(x; t) C_{j-1}(x) \qquad (j \geqslant 1),
\end{aligned} \tag{2.204}
$$

and

$$
\begin{aligned}
P_0(t) &= Pr\{Y(t) = 0\} \\
&= 1 - F(0; 0, t) - \int_{0+}^{t} dU(\tau) F(0; 0, t - \tau).
\end{aligned} \tag{2.205}
$$

The zero-avoiding transition probabilities of $Q(t)$ are given by

$$
\begin{aligned}
{}^0P_j(t) &= \int_{x=0+}^{t} -d_x Pr\{Y(t) \geqslant x; S(0) > t \mid Y(0) = 0\} C_{j-1}(x) \\
&= \int_{x=0+}^{t} -d_x F(x; 0, t) C_{j-1}(x)
\end{aligned} \tag{2.206}
$$

for $j \geqslant 1$. From (2.204), (2.180), and (2.206) it follows that

$$P_j(t) = {}^0P_j(t) + \int_{\tau=0+}^{t} dU(\tau)\,{}^0P_j(t-\tau) \qquad (j \geqslant 1), \tag{2.207}$$

a result which could have been derived by an argument similar to the one used in (2.180).

To obtain the limiting behavior of $Q(t)$ as $t \to \infty$, we write (2.204) as

$$P_j(t) = \int_{x=0+}^{t} M(x, t)\, dC_{j-1}(x) - e^{-\lambda t} C_{j-1}(t), \tag{2.208}$$

and proceed as in (2.183) to (2.186). We thus find that

$$\lim_{t\to\infty} P_j(t) = \begin{cases} 0 & \text{if } \rho_2 \geqslant 1 \\ \rho_2[\psi(\eta_0)]^{j-1}[1-\psi(\eta_0)] & \text{if } \rho_2 < 1 \end{cases} \tag{2.209}$$

and similarly from (2.205)

$$\lim_{t\to\infty} P_0(t) = \begin{cases} 0 & \rho_2 \geqslant 1 \\ 1-\rho_2 & \text{if } \rho_2 < 1. \end{cases} \tag{2.210}$$

Finally, the d.f. of the conventionally defined $W'(t)$ can now be obtained from the preceding results concerning $Q(t)$. Thus, when the process starts with a busy period at $t = 0$, so that $W'(0) = 0$, we have

$$Pr\{W'(t) = 0 \mid W'(0) = 0\} = P_0(t) \tag{2.211}$$

$$Pr\{W'(t) \leqslant x \mid W'(0) = 0\} = P_0(t) + \sum_{j=1}^{\infty} P_j(t) \int_0^x e^{-\lambda v} \frac{\lambda^j v^{j-1}}{(j-1)!}\, dv. \tag{2.212}$$

From (2.212) we obtain readily the result

$$\lim_{t\to\infty} Pr\{W'(t) \leqslant x \mid W'(0) = 0\} = 1 - \rho_2 e^{-\eta_0 x} \qquad (x \geqslant 0); \tag{2.213}$$

thus the limiting distribution of the (conventionally defined) waiting time is a negative exponential, whatever be the form of the inter-arrival time distribution. This is Smith's (1953) theorem.

COMPLEMENTS AND PROBLEMS

Section 2

1. The fundamental result of this section was obtained by the author in 1960a. This leads to explicit results concerning $T(x)$ and T_i, and has the advantage of being applicable to slightly modified arrival schemes (see Complements 6, 7, 8).

2. Show that $G(x, t)$ satisfies the following identities:

$$G(x, t) = \int_{y=0}^{t-x} d_y K(y, x) G(y, t-x), \tag{1}$$

$$G(x+y, t) = \int_{\tau=x}^{t-y} dG(x, \tau) G(y, t-\tau). \tag{2}$$

3. Show that

$$E[T(x)] = \begin{cases} x(1-\rho)^{-1} & \text{if } \rho < 1 \\ \infty & \text{if } \rho = 1. \end{cases} \tag{3}$$

4. The result (2.17) is due to Beneš (1957). The method used here is similar to the one used by Kendall (1957) for the problem of wet period in an infinite dam.

5. The results (2.27) and (2.31) were rigorously proved by Takács (1955). Earlier, they were derived heuristically by Kendall (1951) and Good [see the discussion in Kendall (1951)].

6. *Queues with balking* [*Takács* (1961a)]. Here customers arrive in a Poisson process and join the queue with probability one if the server is free, and with probability $p(<1)$ otherwise. Clearly, as long as the server is busy, the effective arrivals form a Poisson process with mean λpt, and therefore the expression for $G_n(x, t)$ is the same as (2.13) with λ replaced by λp.

7. *Batch arrivals* [*Gaver* (1959)]. Here customers arrive in a Poisson process of batches of random size having the distribution $(b_n, n = 1, 2, \ldots)$. The relation (2.9) now becomes

$$dG_n(x, t) = \int_{\tau=0}^{x} \int_{v=0}^{t-x} \lambda e^{-\lambda\tau} \sum_{k=0}^{n-1} dG_k(x-\tau+v, t-\tau)\, d\tau b_{n-k} dB_{n-k}(v), \tag{4}$$

which readily gives

$$G_n(x, t) = \sum_{k=0}^{n} \int_{\tau=x}^{t} e^{-\lambda\tau} \frac{(\lambda\tau)^{k-1}}{k!} b_n^{(k)} \lambda x\, dB_n(\tau - x), \tag{5}$$

where $[b_n^{(k)}]$ is the k-fold convolution of (b_n) with itself. Hence we find that

$$Pr\{T_i \leqslant t\} = \sum_{n=i}^{\infty} \sum_{k=1}^{n-i} \int_0^t e^{-\lambda\tau} \frac{(\lambda\tau)^k}{k!} b_{n-i}^{(k)} \frac{i}{n}\, dB_n(\tau). \tag{6}$$

For $i = 1$ this reduces to Gaver's equation (3.16*b*).

8. *Constant batch size.* As a special case of the system described in Complement 7, consider the system where the batches are of fixed size m. Here we have $b_n^{(k)} = 1$ if $n = km$, and $= 0$ otherwise; therefore

$$G_{nm}(x, t) = \int_{\tau=x}^{t} e^{-\lambda\tau} \frac{(\lambda\tau)^{n-1}}{n!} \lambda x\, dB_{nm}(\tau - x). \tag{7}$$

Hence we obtain

$$Pr\{t < T_1 < t + dt, N(T_1) = nm\}$$

(8)
$$= \int_{x=0}^{\infty} dB_m(x)\, dG_{nm-m}(x, t)$$

$$= e^{-\lambda t} \frac{(\lambda t)^{n-1}}{n!} dB_{nm}(t).$$

From this the distributions of T_1 and $N(T_1)$ can be deduced. The special case of the negative exponential service time has been considered by Takács (1962c).

9. *A moving single server problem* [*McMillan and Riordan* (*1957*)]. An assembly line moving with uniform speed has items for service spaced along it. The single server available moves with the line while serving and against it with infinite velocity while transferring service to the next item in line. The line has a barrier in which the server may be said to be "absorbed" in the sense that the service is disabled if the server moves into the barrier. The server with service time distributed according to the law $\lambda e^{-\lambda t}\, dt$ $(0 < t < \infty)$ starts service on the first time when it is x time units away from the barrier. Let the spacings between items be independent random variables with the d.f. $B(t)$. McMillan and Riordan postulated the integral equation

(9)
$$P(z, x) = \exp\left[-\lambda x + \lambda x z \int_0^{\infty} P(z, v)\, dB(v)\right]$$

for the p.g.f. $P(z, x)$ of the number of items completed before absorption, and derived $P(z, x)$ explicitly in the two special cases of uniform and random spacings.

This problem is analogous to the queue $M/G/1$, which can be seen as follows. Let $Z(t)$ be the distance from the barrier at time t, so that $Z(0) = x$, and $Z(t) = x + X(t) - t$, where $X(t)$ is the spacing between the first and the last item completed in $(0, t)$, and has the d.f. (2.4). The time until absorption is $T(x) = \inf\,[t \mid x + X(t) - t) \leqslant 0]$, which is the busy period $T(x)$ of the system $M/G/1$; moreover, the number of items completed before absorption is the number of "new" customers served during this busy period. By exploiting this analogy more fully, Karlin, Miller, and Prabhu (1959) proved the validity of (5) in the following manner. Clearly,

(10)
$$P(z, x) = E\{z^{N[T_{A(x)}]}\} = E[\xi^{A(x)}]$$
$$= e^{-\lambda x + \lambda x \xi}$$

where $\xi \equiv \xi(z)$ satisfies the functional equation (2.31). Hence we find that

(11)
$$P(z, x) = \exp\left[-\lambda x + \lambda x z \int_0^{\infty} e^{-(\lambda - \lambda \xi)v}\, dB(v)\right]$$
$$= \exp\left[-\lambda x + \lambda x z \int_0^{\infty} P(z, v)\, dB(v)\right]$$

which is (9).

10. *Idle time.* On account of the Markovian property of the negative exponential distribution, the idle period has the distribution $\lambda e^{-\lambda x}\, dx$ $(0 < x < \infty)$.

11. *Combinatorial methods.* For proofs of the results of this section using combinatorial arguments, see Takács (1961b, 1962b).

Section 2.3

12. The result (2.39) is new. An earlier proof [Prabhu (1960b)] of (2.40) consisted of verifying that the right-hand side of (2.40) is a solution of the integral equation

$$F(x; 0, t) = \int_{\tau=x}^{t} dG(x, \tau)F(0; 0, t - \tau). \tag{12}$$

The question of uniqueness of the solution was, however, left open.

13. The result (2.42) is due to Beneš (1957), who derived it by making use of the analytic property of $\Phi^*(x; \theta, s)$, as given below.

Section 2.4

14. The identity (2.48) is due to Beneš (1960). The present derivation is due to Kingman (1963). The result (2.55) was obtained by the author in (1960b).

15. The formula (2.56) can be written as

$$\Phi^*(x; \theta, s) = \frac{\theta^{-1}e^{-\theta x} - F^*(x; 0, s)}{s + \lambda - \lambda\psi(\theta) - \theta}. \tag{13}$$

Section 2.5

16. The explicit expressions for $P_{ij}(t)$ derived in this section are new. The transforms (2.75) and (2.76) were obtained by Gaver (1959) by direct arguments, but their inversion is by no means a pleasant task.

17. *Application of renewal theory.* Let I_j be the jth idle period, $T_1^{(j)}$ the jth busy period, $Z_j = I_j + T_1^{(j)}$ $(j = 1, 2, \ldots)$, and consider the renewal process $\{S_r\}$, where $S_r = Z_1 + Z_2 + Z_3 + \cdots + Z_r$ $(r \geqslant 1)$. Let $U(t)$ be the expected number of renewals in $(0, t]$; show that

$$P_{00}(t) = e^{-\lambda t} + \int_0^t \lambda e^{-\lambda(t-\tau)}\, dU(\tau). \tag{14}$$

18. *Use of supplementary variables.* As suggested by Kendall (1951), the non-Markovian process $Q(t)$ can be analysed by the inclusion of supplementary variables. Cox (1955) considered the joint distribution of $Q(t)$ and $Y(t)$, the time since the arrival of the customer at the counter, and obtained the Pollaczek-Khintchine formula (2.101) by proceeding to the limit as $t \to \infty$. Keilson and Kooharian (1960) studied the joint distribution of $Q(t)$ and the expended service time of the customer at the counter.

Section 2.6

19. The result (2.80) is due to Prabhu and Bhat (1963).

20. Show that

$$\sum_{j=1}^{\infty} \int_0^{\infty} {}^0P_{ij}(t)e^{-\theta t}\omega^j\, dt = \omega\, \frac{1 - \psi(\theta + \lambda - \lambda\omega)}{\omega - \psi(\theta + \lambda - \lambda\omega)} \cdot \frac{\omega^i - [\psi(\eta)]^i}{\theta + \lambda - \lambda\omega} \tag{15}$$

[Gaver (1959)].

21. Show that

$$P_{ij}(t) = {}^0P_{ij}(t) + \lambda \int_0^t P_{i0}(t - \tau)\,{}^0P_{1j}(\tau)\,d\tau \qquad (i \geqslant 1), \tag{16}$$

$$P_{0j}(t) = \lambda \int_0^t P_{00}(t - \tau)\,{}^0P_{1j}(\tau)\,d\tau \tag{17}$$

[Prabhu and Bhat (1963)].

Section 2.7

22. Note that the result (2.90) cannot be derived for any arbitrary initial waiting time $W(0) = x$ without first establishing the existence of $\lim_{t\to\infty} \Phi(x;\, \theta,\, t)$. The method used here is fairly straightforward. The Pollaczek-Khintchine formula (2.101) is usually proved by converting (2.44) to a result in characteristic functions and then letting $t \to \infty$.

23. The explicit result (2.106) for the limiting waiting time distribution was given by the author in (1960b); earlier, Beneš (1957) had obtained this in the form of a compound geometric distribution.

24. The result (2.103) can be proved directly [Prabhu (1960b)]. This can be written as

$$\sum_{n=0}^{\infty} \int_{t=x}^{\infty} e^{-\lambda t} \frac{(\lambda t)^n}{n!}\, dB_n(t - x) = (1 - \rho)^{-1} \qquad (\rho < 1,\, x > 0). \tag{18}$$

In the special case of constant service time ($= b$) this reduces to

$$\sum_{n=0}^{\infty} e^{-\lambda(x+nb)} \frac{\lambda^n}{n!} (x + nb)^n = (1 - \lambda b)^{-1} \qquad (\lambda b < 1,\, x > 0), \tag{19}$$

an identity due to Jensen, who proved it for complex values of λ, b such that $|e^{-(\lambda b-1)}\lambda b| < 1$.

25. The result (2.112) for the limiting distribution of $Q(t)$ is new.

Section 2.10

26. The definition of the process $Y(t)$ was proposed, and the results of Sections 2.10, 2.11, and 2.12 were derived by the author (1964).

Section 2.11

27. The distribution of $S(0)$ has been obtained by Takács (1962a) by combinatorial methods. From (2.42) we find that the L.S.T. of $S(0)$ is given by

$$E\{e^{-\theta S(0)}\} = \frac{\lambda[1 - \psi(\eta)]}{\eta(\theta)}, \tag{20}$$

a result due to Conolly (1959), who also obtained $Pr\{S(0) < \infty\}$.

28. The result (2.196) is due to U. N. Bhat (unpublished). Clearly,

$$Pr\{Y(t) \geqslant x;\ S(0) > t \mid Y(0) = 0\} = \sum_{n=0}^{\infty} C_n(x, t) = F(x; 0, t), \tag{21}$$

in agreement with (2.164).

29. Show that

$$\sum_{n=1}^{\infty} \int_0^{\infty} e^{-\theta t} c_n(t) z^n \, dt = \lambda z \frac{1 - \psi(\eta_1)}{\eta_1}, \tag{22}$$

where $\eta_1 \equiv \eta_1(\theta, z)$ is the root of the equation $\eta_1 = \theta + \lambda - \lambda z \psi(\eta_1)$ with $|\eta_1| < 1$ [Conolly (1959)].

Section 2.12

30. Show that

$$\int_0^{\infty} e^{-\theta t} P_{0j}(t) \, dt = \frac{[1 - \psi(\eta)]^2 [\psi(\eta)]^{j-1}}{[1 - \psi(\theta)]\eta(\theta)} \qquad (j \geqslant 1), \tag{23}$$

$$\int_0^{\infty} e^{-\theta t} P_{00}(t) \, dt = \frac{1}{\theta} \cdot \frac{[1 - \psi(\eta)]}{[1 - \psi(\theta)]\eta(\theta)}, \tag{24}$$

[Conolly (1958)]. These results actually follow from (2.204) and (2.205).

31. Show that

$$\int_0^{\infty} e^{-\theta t_0} P_{0j}(t) \, dt = \frac{[1 - \psi(\eta)][\psi(\eta)]^{j-1}}{\eta(\theta)} \qquad (j \geqslant 1). \tag{25}$$

REFERENCES

Beneš, V. E. (1957). On queues with Poisson arrivals. *Ann. Math. Statist.*, **28,** 670–677.

Beneš, V. E. (1960). Combinatory methods and stochastic Kolmogorov equations in the theory of queues with one server. *Trans. Amer. Math. Soc.*, **94,** 282–294.

Conolly, B. W. (1958). A difference equation technique applied to the simple queue with arbitrary arrival interval distribution. *J. Roy. Stat. Soc.*, **B21,** 168–175.

Conolly, B. W. (1959). The busy period in relation to the queueing process $GI/M/1$. *Biometrika*, **46,** 246–251.

Cox, D. R. (1955). The analysis of non-Markovian stochastic processes by the inclusion of supplementary variables. *Proc. Cam. Phil. Soc.*, **51,** 433–441.

Gaver, Donald P. (1959). Imbedded Markov chain analysis of a waiting line process in continuous time. *Ann. Math. Statist.*, **30,** 698–720.

Karlin, S., R. G. Miller, Jr., and N. U. Prabhu (1959). Note on a moving single server problem. *Ann. Math. Statist.*, **30,** 243–246.

Keilson, J. and A. Kooharian (1960). On time dependent queueing processes. *Ann. Math. Statist.*, **31,** 104–112.

Kendall, D. G. (1951). Some problems in the theory of queues. *J. Roy. Stat. Soc.*, **B13,** 151–185.

Kendall, D. G. (1957). Some problems in the theory of dams, *J. Roy. Stat. Soc.*, **B19,** 207–212.

Kingman, J. F. C. (1963). On continuous time models in the theory of dams. *J. Aust. Math. Soc.*, **3,** 480–487.

Luchak, G. (1956). The solution of the single channel queueing equations . . . holding times. *Opns. Res.*, **4,** 711–732.

McMillan, B., and J. Riordan (1957). A moving single server problem. *Ann. Math. Statist.*, **28,** 471–478.

Prabhu, N. U. (1960a). Some results for the queue with Poisson arrivals. *J. Roy. Stat. Soc.*, **22,** 104–107.

Prabhu, N. U. (1960b). Application of storage theory to queues with Poisson arrivals. *Ann. Math. Stat.*, **31,** 475–482.

Prabhu, N. U. (1964). A waiting time process in the queue $GI/M/1$. *Acta Math. Acad. Sci. Hung.*, **15,** 363–371.

Prabhu, N. U., and U. Narayan Bhat (1963). Further results for the queue with Poisson arrivals. *Opns. Res.*, **11,** 380–386.

Smith, W. L. (1953). On the distribution of queueing times. *Proc. Cam. Phil. Soc.*, **49,** 449–461.

Takács, Lajos (1955). Investigation of waiting time problems by reduction to Markov processes. *Acta Math.* (*Budapest*), **6,** 101–129.

Takács, Lajos (1961a). The transient behavior of a single server queueing process with Poisson input. *Proceedings of the fourth Berkely Symposium on Math. Stat. and Prob II*, 535–567, University of California Press.

Takács, Lajos (1961b). The probability law of the busy period for two types of queueing processes. *Opns. Res.* **9,** 402–407.

Takács, Lajos (1962a). A single server queue with recurrent input and exponentially distributed service times. *Opns. Res.*, **10,** 395–399.

Takács, Lajos (1962b). The time dependence of a single server queue with Poisson input and general service times. *Ann. Math. Statist.*, **33,** 1340–1348.

Takács, Lajos (1962c). A generalization of the ballot problem and its application to queues. *J. Amer. Stat. Assoc.*, **57,** 327–337.

Chapter 3

Some Imbedded Markov Chains

3.1 INTRODUCTION

Imbedded Markov chains were introduced in queueing theory by Kendall (1951) to deal with difficulties arising from the non-Markovian character of the basic stochastic processes. However, we have seen that at least in the two systems $M/G/1$ and $GI/M/1$ these processes present no real difficulties and that their properties can, in fact, be obtained in a fairly straightforward manner. Nevertheless the study of imbedded chains is interesting and throws further light on the behavior of queueing systems. In this chapter we study the systems $M/G/1$ and $GI/M/1$ with reference to their imbedded Markov chains; more general results will be discussed in the next chapter.

Considering first the queue-length, we shall find that in both systems, the basic process is the Markov chain $(Z_n, n = 0, 1, 2, \ldots)$, $Z_n = i + S_n - n$, where $S_0 \equiv 0$, and $S_n = X_0 + X_1 + \cdots + X_{n-1}$ $(n \geqslant 1)$ are the partial sums of the sequence $\{X_n, n = 0, 1, 2, \ldots\}$ of mutually independent and identically distributed random variables (r.v.), which assume nonnegative integral values. We define the r.v.

$$(3.1) \qquad T_i = \min(n \mid S_n - n \leqslant -i), \qquad U_j = \min(n \mid S_n - n \geqslant j)$$

$$(3.2) \qquad N = \min(n \mid S_n - n = 0),$$

where $i \geqslant 1, j \geqslant 0$; clearly T_i is the first passage time to a distance i to the left, and U_j the first passage time to a distance j to the right, whereas N is the recurrence time of the state 0 of the Markov chain $\{Z_n\}$. In Sections 3.2 to 3.4 we establish some results concerning these random variables. These results are then applied to the queue $GI/M/1$ in Section 3.5 and to $M/G/1$ in Section 3.6, and some particular cases are studied in Section 3.7.

Let

$$(3.3)\qquad Pr\{X_n = j\} = \begin{cases} k_j & (j = 0, 1, 2, \ldots) \\ 0 & \text{otherwise;} \end{cases}$$

$$(3.4)\qquad K(z) = \sum_0^\infty k_j z^j \quad (|z| < 1); \qquad 0 < \alpha = E(X_n) < \infty.$$

Furthermore, let

$$(3.5)\quad k_j^{(n)} = Pr\{S_n = j\} \quad (n \geqslant 1), \qquad k_j^{(1)} = k_j, \qquad k_j^{(0)} = \delta_{0j},$$

where $\delta_{ij} = 1$ if $i = j$, and $= 0$ if $i \neq j$. Finally, let

$$(3.6)\qquad K_j^{(n)} = Pr\{S_n \leqslant j\}, \qquad \alpha_j^{(n)} = Pr\{S_n > j\}, \qquad \alpha_j^{(1)} = \alpha_j.$$

The transition probabilities of the chain are then given by

$$(3.7)\qquad \begin{aligned} P_{ij}^{(n)} &= Pr\{Z_n = j \mid Z_0 = i\} = k_{n+j-i}^{(n)} \qquad (n \geqslant 1), \\ P_{ij}^{(0)} &= \delta_{ij} \qquad (i, j = \cdots, -1, 0, 1, 2, \ldots). \end{aligned}$$

3.2 DISTRIBUTION OF T_i

Since a first passage to a state $\leqslant 0$ can occur only through 0, we can write $T_i = \min(n \mid i + S_n - n = 0)$. Let us denote $g(i, n) = Pr\{T_i = n\}$ $(i \geqslant 1)$; we shall prove that

(3.8)

$$\begin{aligned} g(i, n) &= Pr\{i + S_r - r > 0 \quad (r = 1, 2, \ldots, n-1); \qquad i + S_n - n = 0\} \\ &= \begin{cases} 0 & \text{if } n < i \\ \dfrac{i}{n} k_{n-i}^{(n)} & \text{if } n \geqslant i. \end{cases} \end{aligned}$$

We have

$$(3.9)\qquad g(i, 1) = P_{i1} = k_{1-i} = \begin{cases} k_0 & \text{if } i = 1 \\ 0 & \text{if } i > 1, \end{cases}$$

and for $n \geqslant 1$,

$$(3.10)\qquad g(i, n+1) = \sum_{\nu > 0} P_{i\nu} g(\nu, n) = \sum_{\nu > 0} k_{\nu-i+1} g(\nu, n).$$

Using (3.9) in (3.10) with $n = 1$, we obtain

$$(3.11)\quad g(i, 2) = \sum_{\nu > 0} k_{\nu-i+1} k_{1-\nu} = k_{2-i} k_0 = \begin{cases} k_0 k_1 & \text{if } i = 1 \\ k_0^2 & \text{if } i = 2 \\ 0 & \text{if } i > 2. \end{cases}$$

We can write $g(i, 1) = ik_{1-i}$, $g(i, 2) = (i/2)k^{(2)}_{2-i}$, and these suggest the general result (3.8). To verify this we need the identity

$$\sum_{\nu=0}^{j} \nu k_\nu k^{(n)}_{j-\nu} = \frac{j}{n+1} k_j^{(n+1)} \qquad (j \geqslant 0), \tag{3.12}$$

which is a simple consequence of $(d/dz)[K(z)]^{n+1} = (n+1)[K(z)]^n K'(z)$. Now assume (3.8) to be true for some n; then substituting for $g(i, n)$ in (3.10) and applying (3.12), we obtain

$$\begin{aligned} g(i, n+1) &= \sum_{\nu=i-1}^{\infty} k_{\nu-i+1} \frac{\nu}{n} k^{(n)}_{n-\nu} = \sum_{\nu=0}^{\infty} \frac{\nu+i-1}{n} k_\nu k^{(n)}_{n-i+1-\nu} \\ &= \frac{1}{n}\left(\frac{n-i+1}{n+1} + i - 1\right) k^{(n+1)}_{n+1-i} \\ &= \frac{i}{n+1} k^{(n+1)}_{n+1-i} \end{aligned} \tag{3.13}$$

which proves (3.8) for $n + 1$. The result (3.8) then follows by induction.

To obtain the p.g.f. of T_i we note that a first passage from i to 0 can occur only through $i-1, i-2, \ldots, 1$; moreover, since P_{ij} depends only on the difference $j - i$, the first passage time from i to $i - 1$ is independent of i. It follows that T_i has the same distribution as the sum of i independent r.v., each having the same distribution as T_1. Hence

$$E(z^{T_i}) = \sum_{n=1}^{\infty} g(i, n) z^n = [\xi(z)]^i, \tag{3.14}$$

where $\xi(z) = E(z^{T_1})$. However, since

$$g(1, 1) = k_0, \qquad g(1, n+1) = \sum_{\nu=1}^{\infty} k_\nu g(\nu, n), \tag{3.15}$$

we find that

$$\begin{aligned} \xi &= \sum_{n=1}^{\infty} g(1, n) z^n = z k_0 + z \sum_{\nu=1}^{\infty} k_\nu \sum_{n=1}^{\infty} g(\nu, n) z^n \\ &= z k_0 + z \sum_{\nu=1}^{\infty} k_\nu \xi^\nu = zK(\xi), \end{aligned}$$

so that $\xi \equiv \xi(z)$ satisfies the functional equation

$$\xi = zK(\xi). \tag{3.16}$$

Proceeding as in Section 2.2 we see that the equation (3.16) has a unique root such that $0 < \xi(z) \leqslant 1$ for $0 < z \leqslant 1$, and moreover, as $z \to 1$, $\xi(z)$ tends to the smallest positive root of the equation $z = K(z)$. Thus

$$Pr\{T_i < \infty\} = \sum_{n=1}^{\infty} g(i, n) = \begin{cases} 1 & \text{if } \alpha \leqslant 1 \\ \zeta^i & \text{if } \alpha > 1, \end{cases} \tag{3.17}$$

where ζ is the smallest positive root of the equation

$$\zeta = K(\zeta). \tag{3.18}$$

From (3.14) we also find that in the case $\alpha \leqslant 1$,

$$E(T_i) = i\xi'(1) = \begin{cases} i(1-\alpha)^{-1} & \text{if } \alpha < 1 \\ \infty & \text{if } \alpha = 1. \end{cases} \tag{3.19}$$

From the obvious relations

$$P_{i0}^{(n)} = g(i, n) + \sum_{m=1}^{n-1} g(i, n-m)P_{00}^{(m)}$$

$$P_{ij}^{(n)} = \sum_{m=1}^{n-1} g(i, n-m)P_{0j}^{(m)} \qquad (j < 0)$$

we obtain the identities

$$g(i, n) = k_{n-i}^{(n)} - \sum_{m-1}^{n-1} g(i, n-m)k_m^{(m)} \tag{3.20}$$

$$k_{n+j-i}^{(n)} - \sum_{m=1}^{n-1} g(i, n-m)k_{m+j}^{(m)} = 0 \qquad (j < 0). \tag{3.21}$$

More generally we have for $i \geqslant 1$,

$$Pr\{i + S_r - r > 0 \ (r = 1, 2, \ldots, n-1); i + S_n - n = j\} \tag{3.22}$$
$$= k_{n+j-i}^{(n)} - \sum_{m=1}^{n-1} g(i, n-m)k_{m+j}^{(m)}.$$

For we have

$$\begin{aligned} k_{n+j-i}^{(n)} &= Pr\{i + S_n - n = j\} \\ &= Pr\{T_i \geqslant n, i + S_n - n = j\} \\ &\quad + Pr\{T_i < n; i + S_n - n = j\}. \end{aligned} \tag{3.23}$$

The first term in the last expression is the required probability, whereas the second term can be written as

$$\begin{aligned} &\sum_{m=1}^{n-1} Pr\{T_i = m\}Pr\{i + S_n - n = j \mid T_i = m\} \\ &= \sum_{m=1}^{n-1} g(i, m)Pr\{i + S_n - n = j \mid i + S_m - m = 0\} \\ &= \sum_{m=1}^{n-1} g(i, m)k_{n-m+j}^{(n-m)} \end{aligned} \tag{3.24}$$

which proves (3.22).

3.3 DISTRIBUTION OF U_j

We first prove the following results.

$$\begin{aligned} Pr\{U_0 = 1\} &= \alpha_0 \\ Pr\{U_0 = n+1\} &= \sum_{i=1}^{\infty} \alpha_i g(i, n) \qquad (n \geqslant 1); \end{aligned} \tag{3.25}$$

$$Pr\{U_0 < \infty\} = \begin{cases} 1 & \text{if } \alpha \geqslant 1 \\ \alpha & \text{if } \alpha < 1. \end{cases} \tag{3.26}$$

We have

$$Pr\{U_0 = 1\} = Pr\{X_0 - 1 \geqslant 0\} = \alpha_0, \tag{3.27}$$

and for $n \geqslant 1$,

(3.28)

$$\begin{aligned} Pr\{U_0 = n+1\} &= Pr\{S_r - r < 0\,(r = 1, 2, \ldots, n);\; S_{n+1} - (n+1) \geqslant 0\} \\ &= \sum_{i=1}^{\infty} Pr\{S_r - r < 0\,(r = 1, 2, \ldots, n-1);\; S_n - n = -i\} Pr\{S_{n+1} - (n+1) \geqslant 0 \mid S_n - n = -i\} \\ &= \sum_{i=1}^{\infty} Pr\{S_n - n - (S_r - r) > -i\,(r = 1, 2, \ldots, n-1);\; S_n - n = -i\} Pr\{S_{n+1} - (n+1) - (S_n - n + i) \geqslant 0\} \\ &= \sum_{i=1}^{\infty} Pr\{X_{n+1} > i\} Pr\{S_{n-r} - (n-r) > -i\; (r = 1, 2, \ldots, n-1);\; S_n - n = -i\} \\ &= \sum_{i=1}^{\infty} \alpha_i Pr\{i + S_r - r > 0\,(r = 1, 2, \ldots, n-1),\; i + S_n - n = 0\} \end{aligned}$$

and the result (3.25) now follows from (3.8). Furthermore, we have

$$\begin{aligned} Pr\{U_0 < \infty\} &= \sum_{1}^{\infty} Pr\{U_0 = n\} = \alpha_0 + \sum_{i=1}^{\infty} \alpha_i Pr\{T_i < \infty\} \\ &= \begin{cases} \sum_{0}^{\infty} \alpha_i = \alpha & \alpha < 1 \\ \sum_{0}^{\infty} \alpha_i \zeta^i = \dfrac{1 - K(\zeta)}{1 - \zeta} = 1 & \text{if } \alpha \geqslant 1, \end{cases} \end{aligned} \tag{3.29}$$

using (3.17).

For $j \geqslant 1$ we shall show that

$$\text{(3.30)}\qquad \begin{aligned} &Pr\{U_j = 1\} = \alpha_j \\ &Pr\{U_j = n+1\} = \sum_{i=1}^{\infty} \alpha_i \left\{ k_{n+j-i}^{(n)} - \sum_{m=1}^{n-1} g(i, n-m) k_{m+j}^{(m)} \right\} \quad (n \geqslant 1)\}; \end{aligned}$$

$$\text{(3.31)}\qquad Pr\{U_j < \infty\} = \begin{cases} 1 & \text{if } \alpha \geqslant 1 \\ (1-\alpha)\sum_{n=0}^{\infty} k_{n+j}^{(n)} & \text{if } \alpha < 1. \end{cases}$$

The proof of (3.30) is similar to that of (3.25), but we have now to apply (3.22). To prove (3.31) we note that

$$\text{(3.32)}\qquad \begin{aligned} Pr\{U_j < \infty\} &= \alpha_j + \sum_{n=1}^{\infty}\sum_{i=1}^{\infty} \alpha_i k_{n+j-i}^{(n)} - \sum_{n=1}^{\infty}\sum_{i=1}^{\infty}\sum_{m=1}^{n-1} \alpha_i k_{m+j}^{(m)} g(i, n-m) \\ &= \sum_{n=0}^{\infty}\sum_{i=0}^{\infty} \alpha_i k_{n+j-i}^{(n)} - \sum_{n=0}^{\infty} k_{n+j}^{(n)} Pr\{U_0 < \infty\}. \end{aligned}$$

This last expression is the coefficient of z^j in the formal expansion of

$$\text{(3.33)}\qquad \left[\sum_0^{\infty} \alpha_i z^i - 1 + Pr\{U_0 = \infty\}\right] \sum_0^{\infty} \left[\frac{K(z)}{z}\right]^n.$$

Now if $\alpha \geqslant 1$, take two real numbers α_1, α_2 such that $\zeta < \alpha_1 < 1$ and $K(\alpha_1) < K(\alpha_2) < \alpha_1$ [which is possible since $K(z)$ is continuous in z]; then in the annulus $\alpha_1 < |z| < \alpha_2$ we have $|K(z)| < K(|z|) < K(\alpha_2) < \alpha_1 < |z|$, so that $|K(z)/z| < 1$. If, however, $\alpha < 1$, let us assume that the p.g.f. $K(z)$ is capable of an analytic extension to the region $|z| \geqslant 1$. Then since $\alpha < 1$, an argument similar to the one used for (3.17) shows that the equation (3.18) has a root $\zeta > 1$. Taking $1 < \alpha_1 < \zeta$ and $K(\alpha_1) < K(\alpha_2) < \alpha_1$ we have as before, $|K(z)/z| < 1$ in the annulus $\alpha_1 < |z| < \alpha_2$. Therefore in both cases

$$\sum_0^{\infty} [K(z)/z]^n = [1 - K(z)/z]^{-1}, \qquad \text{and} \qquad \sum_0^{\infty} \alpha_i z^i = [1 - K(z)](1-z)^{-1}.$$

Thus the expression (3.33) reduces to

$$\text{(3.34)}\qquad \begin{aligned} &\frac{z}{z - K(z)}\left[\frac{z - K(z)}{1 - z} + Pr\{U_0 = \infty\}\right] \\ &= \begin{cases} \dfrac{z}{1-z} & (\alpha \geqslant 1, \zeta < \alpha_1 < |z| < \alpha_2 < 1) \\[2ex] \dfrac{z}{1-z} + (1-\alpha)\dfrac{z}{z - K(z)} & (\alpha < 1, 1 < \alpha_1 < |z| < \alpha_2 < \zeta). \end{cases} \end{aligned}$$

Expanding the functions in the regions of their validity we find from (3.34) that the coefficient of z^j is as given in (3.31).

We also have

(3.35)

$$\begin{aligned} Pr\{U_j > n+1\} &= \sum_{i=1}^{\infty} Pr\{S_1 - 1 = j - i;\ S_r - r < j \\ &\qquad\qquad (r = 2, 3, \ldots, n+1)\} \\ &= \sum_{i=1}^{\infty} Pr\{S_1 - 1 = j - i\} Pr\{S_r - r < j \\ &\qquad\qquad (r = 2, 3, \ldots, n+1) \mid S_1 - 1 = j - i\} \\ &= \sum_{i=1}^{\infty} k_{j+1-i} Pr\{S_{r-1} - (r-1) < i \\ &\qquad\qquad (r = 2, 3, \ldots, n+1)\} \\ &= \sum_{i=1}^{\infty} k_{j+1-i} Pr\{U_i > n\} \qquad (n \geqslant 1, j \geqslant 0). \end{aligned}$$

Letting $n \to \infty$ in (3.35) we obtain

$$Pr\{U_j = \infty\} = \sum_{i=1}^{\infty} k_{j+1-i} Pr\{U_i = \infty\} \qquad (j \geqslant 0) \tag{3.36}$$

from which we get the result

$$\sum_{0}^{\infty} z^j Pr\{U_j = \infty\} = \frac{K(z)}{K(z) - z} Pr\{U_0 = \infty\} \quad (|z| < 1). \tag{3.37}$$

3.4 THE DISTRIBUTION OF N; FURTHER RESULTS

Let $F_{00}^{(n)} = Pr\{N = n\}$; we have then

$$\begin{aligned} F_{00}^{(1)} &= k_1 \\ F_{00}^{(n+1)} &= \sum_{i=2}^{\infty} i k_i g(i-1, n) \qquad (n \geqslant 1). \end{aligned} \tag{3.38}$$

$$F_{00} = Pr\{N < \infty\} = \begin{cases} \alpha & \text{if } \alpha < 1 \\ K'(\zeta) < 1 & \text{if } \alpha \geqslant 1. \end{cases} \tag{3.39}$$

For, $F_{00}^{(1)} = Pr\{S_1 - 1 = 0\} = k_1$, and for $n \geqslant 1$ we have

(3.40)

$$\begin{aligned} F_{00}^{(n+1)} &= Pr\{S_r - r \neq 0\ (r = 1, 2, \ldots, n),\ S_{n+1} - (n+1) = 0\} \\ &= Pr\{S_r - r > 0\ (r = 1, 2, \ldots, n),\ S_{n+1} - (n+1) = 0\} \\ &\quad + Pr\{S_r - r < 0\ (r = 1, 2, \ldots, n),\ S_{n+1} - (n+1) = 0\} \\ &\quad + \sum_{m=1}^{n-1} Pr\{S_r - r < 0\ (r = 1, 2, \ldots, m), \\ &\qquad S_r - r > 0\ (r = m+1, \ldots, n),\ S_{n+1} - (n+1) = 0\}. \end{aligned}$$

Since† $S_r - r \sim S_{n+1} - (n+1) - S_{n+1-r} + (n+1-r)$, it is clear that the first term on the right-hand side of (3.40) is equal to the second; the latter, however, is

$$= \sum_{i=1}^{\infty} Pr\{S_r - r < 0\,(r = 1, 2, \ldots, n-1), S_n - n = -i, \\ S_{n+1} - (n+1) = 0\}$$

$$= \sum_{i=1}^{\infty} Pr\{i + S_{n-r} - (n-r) > 0\,(r = 1, 2, \ldots, n-1), \\ i + S_n - n = 0\}. \\ Pr\{S_{n+1} - (n+1) = 0 \mid S_n - n = -i\}$$

$$(3.41) \qquad = \sum_{i=1}^{\infty} k_{i+1} g(i, n).$$

The remaining term on the right-hand side of (3.40) is

$$= \sum_{m=1}^{n-1} \sum_{i=1}^{\infty} Pr\{S_r - r < 0\,(r = 1, 2, \ldots, m), S_{m+1} - (m+1) = i\}. \\ Pr\{S_r - r > 0\,(r = m+2, \ldots, n), \\ S_{n+1} - (n+1) = 0 \mid S_{m+1} - (m+1) = i\}$$

$$= \sum_{m=1}^{n-1} \sum_{i=1}^{\infty} g(i, n-m) \sum_{j=1}^{\infty} Pr\{S_r - r < 0\,(r = 1, 2, \ldots, m), \\ S_m - m = -j, S_{m+1} - (m+1) = i\}$$

$$(3.42) \qquad = \sum_{m=1}^{n-1} \sum_{i=1}^{\infty} g(i, n-m) \sum_{j=1}^{\infty} k_{j+i+1} g(j, m) = \sum_{i=1}^{\infty} \sum_{j=1}^{\infty} k_{j+i+1} g(j+i, n)$$

$$(3.43) \qquad = \sum_{\nu=2}^{\infty} (\nu - 2) k_\nu g(\nu - 1, n)$$

where in (3.42) we have used the property $T_i + T_j \sim T_{i+j}$ [see remarks preceding (3.14)]. From (3.41) and (3.43) we obtain (3.38) for $n \geqslant 1$. Furthermore, we have

$$(3.44) \qquad F_{00} = \sum_{1}^{\infty} F_{00}^{(n)} = k_1 + \sum_{2}^{\infty} i k_i Pr\{T_{i-1} < \infty\} \\ = \begin{cases} \alpha & \text{if } \alpha \leqslant 1 \\ \sum_{1}^{\infty} i k_i \zeta^{i-1} = K'(\zeta) < 1 & \text{if } \alpha > 1. \end{cases}$$

From (3.39) we see that the Markov chain $\{Z_n\}$ is transient except when $\alpha = 1$; moreover, the mean recurrence time of 0 is

$$E(N) = 1 + \sum_{2}^{\infty} i k_i E(T_{i-1}) = \infty$$

† For two random variables X, Y, we write $X \sim Y$ if they have the same distribution.

when $\alpha = 1$, so that in this case the states are persistent null. It follows from (3.7) that the series $\sum_{n=0}^{\infty} k_{n+j}^{(n)}$ converges except when $\alpha = 1$. More specifically we have the following.

$$(3.45)\qquad \sum_{n=i}^{\infty} k_{n-i}^{(n)} = \begin{cases} (1-\alpha)^{-1} & \text{if } \alpha < 1 \\ \zeta^i[1 - K'(\zeta)]^{-1} & \text{if } \alpha > 1 \end{cases} \qquad (i \geqslant 0),$$

$$(3.46)\qquad \sum_{n=0}^{\infty} k_{n+j}^{(n)} < \begin{cases} (1-\alpha)^{-1} & \text{if } \alpha < 1 \\ [1 - K'(\zeta)]^{-1} & \text{if } \alpha > 1 \end{cases} \qquad (j > 0).$$

From the familiar identity

$$(3.47)\qquad F_{ij} = \sum_1^{\infty} P_{ij}^{(n)} \Big/ \sum_0^{\infty} P_{jj}^{(n)} \qquad (\alpha \neq 1)$$

we obtain the following for special values of i, j:

1. Let $i = 0, j = 0$; then $\sum_0^{\infty} P_{00}^{(n)} = (1 - F_{00})^{-1}$

and using (3.39) we obtain (3.45) with $i = 0$.

2. Let $i > 0, j = 0$; then $\sum_1^{\infty} P_{i0}^{(n)} = F_{i0} \sum_0^{\infty} k_n^{(n)}$,

and, since $F_{i0} = Pr\{T_i < \infty\}$ we obtain (3.45) for $i > 0$.

3. Let $i = 0, j > 0$; then $\sum_1^{\infty} P_{0j}^{(n)} = F_{0j} \sum_0^{\infty} k_n^{(n)} < \sum_0^{\infty} k_n^{(n)}$

since $F_{0j} < 1$ for $\alpha \neq 1$; this gives (3.46).

3.5 THE QUEUE $GI/M/1$

We now apply the results of the preceding sections to the queue $GI/M/1$, in which the interarrival times have the distribution $dB(t)$ and the service time has the negative exponential distribution $\lambda e^{-\lambda t}\, dt$ $(0 < t < \infty)$. Let $\psi(\theta) = \int_0^{\infty} e^{-\theta t}\, dB(t)$ denote the Laplace-Stieltjes transform (L.S.T.) of $B(t)$ and let us assume that $0 < -\psi'(0) < \infty$. The relative traffic intensity of the system is then $\rho_2 = -[\lambda\psi'(0)]^{-1}$, $0 < \rho_2 < \infty$.

Let $t_0, t_1, t_2, \ldots$ be the epochs of arrival of the successive customers in the system, and Q_n denote the queue-length at $t = t_n - 0$. Also, let X_n be the number of departures during the interval $(t_n, t_{n+1} - 0)$ $(n = 0, 1, 2, \ldots)$; clearly $X_0, X_1, \ldots$ are mutually independent and identical random variables, with

$$(3.48)\qquad k_j = Pr\{X_n = j\} = \int_0^{\infty} e^{-\lambda t} \frac{(\lambda t)^j}{j!}\, dB(t) \qquad (j \geqslant 0).$$

We have

$$K(z) = \sum_0^\infty k_j z^j = \psi(\lambda - \lambda z), \qquad \alpha = E(X_n) = \rho_2^{-1}; \tag{3.49}$$

$$k_j^{(n)} = \int_0^\infty e^{-\lambda t} \frac{(\lambda t)^j}{j!}\, dB_n(t) \tag{3.50}$$

$$\alpha_j^{(n)} = \int_0^\infty e^{-\lambda t} \lambda^{j+1} \frac{t^j}{j!}\,[1 - B_n(t)]\, dt,\ K_j^{(n)} = \int_0^\infty e^{-\lambda t} \lambda^{j+1} \frac{t^j}{j!}\, B_n(t)\, dt, \tag{3.51}$$

where $B_n(t)$ is the n-fold convolution of $B(t)$ with itself, and $B_0(t) = 0$ if $t < 0$, and $= 1$ if $t \geqslant 0$.

For the Markov chain $\{Q_n\}$ we have the recurrence relations

$$Q_{n+1} = \begin{cases} Q_n + 1 - X_n & \text{if } Q_n + 1 - X_n > 0 \\ 0 & \text{if } Q_n + 1 - X_n \leqslant 0, \end{cases} \tag{3.52}$$

which can be written as $Q_{n+1} = \max(0, Q_n + 1 - X_n)$. If $Q_0 = i \geqslant 0$, we obtain from (3.52),

$$\begin{aligned} Q_n &= \max\,[r - S_n + S_{n-r}\ (r = 0, 1, \ldots, n-1);\ i + n - S_n] \\ &\sim \max\,\{r - S_r\ (r = 0, 1, 2, \ldots, n-1);\ i + n - S_n\}. \end{aligned} \tag{3.53}$$

The transition probabilities of $\{Q_n\}$ are therefore given by

$$\begin{aligned} Pr\{Q_n < j \mid Q_0 = i\} &= Pr\{r - S_r < j\ (r = 0, 1, \ldots, n-1); \\ &\qquad\qquad i + n - S_n < j\} \\ &= \sum_{v=i+1}^{\infty} Pr\{j + S_r - r > 0\ (r = 0, 1, \ldots, n-1); \\ &\qquad\qquad j + S_n - n = v\} \\ &= \sum_{i+1}^{\infty} \left\{ k_{n+v-j}^{(n)} - \sum_{m=1}^{n-1} g(j, n-m) k_{m+v}^{(m)} \right\} \text{ from (3.22)} \\ &= \alpha_{n-j+i}^{(n)} - \sum_{m=1}^{n-1} g(j, n-m) \alpha_{m+i}^{(m)} \qquad (i \geqslant 0), \end{aligned} \tag{3.54}$$

and

$$\begin{aligned} Pr\{Q_n < j \mid Q_0 = 0\} &= Pr\{r - S_r < j\ (r = 0, 1, \ldots, n)\} \\ &= Pr\{j + S_r - r > 0\ (r = 0, 1, \ldots, n)\} \\ &= Pr\{T_j > n\} = \sum_{m=n+1}^{\infty} g(j, m). \end{aligned} \tag{3.55}$$

We define the zero-avoiding transition probabilities ${}^0P_{ij}^{(n)}$ of $\{Q_n\}$ as follows:

(3.56) $${}^0P_{ij}^{(n)} = Pr\{Q_r > 0\ (r = 1, 2, \ldots, n-1); Q_n = j \mid Q_0 = i\}.$$

For $j > 0$ we have

$$\begin{aligned} {}^0P_{ij}^{(n)} &= Pr\{i + r - S_r > 0\ (r = 1, 2, \ldots, n-1); \\ &\qquad\qquad i + n - S_n = j\} \\ &= Pr\{(n-r) - S_{n-r} < j\ (r = 1, 2, \ldots, n-1); \\ &\qquad\qquad j + S_n - n = i\} \\ &= Pr\{j + S_r - r > 0\ (r = 1, 2, \ldots, n-1); \\ &\qquad\qquad j + S_n - n = i\} \\ &= \begin{cases} g(j, n) & \text{if} \quad i = 0 \\ k_{n+i-j}^{(n)} - \sum_{m=1}^{n-1} g(j, n-m) k_{m+i}^{(m)} & \text{if} \quad i > 0, \end{cases} \end{aligned} \tag{3.57}$$

whereas, for $j = 0$, we have

$$\begin{aligned} {}^0P_{i0}^{(n)} &= Pr\{i + r - S_r > 0\ (r = 1, 2, \ldots, n-1), \\ &\qquad\qquad i + n - S_n \leqslant 0\} \\ &= Pr\{S_r - r < i\ (r = 1, 2, \ldots, n-1), S_n - n \geqslant i\} \\ &= Pr\{U_i = n\} \qquad (i \geqslant 0). \end{aligned} \tag{3.58}$$

In particular, the distribution of N, the number of customers served during a busy period, is given by

$$\begin{aligned} f_n = Pr\{N = n\} = {}^0P_{00}^{(n)} &= Pr\{U_0 = n\} \\ &= \begin{cases} \alpha_0 & \text{if} \quad n = 1 \\ \sum_{i=1}^{\infty} \alpha_i g(i, n-1) & \text{if} \quad n \geqslant 2; \end{cases} \end{aligned} \tag{3.59}$$

furthermore, we have

$$Pr\{N < \infty\} = Pr\{U_0 < \infty\} = \begin{cases} 1 & \text{if} \quad \rho_2 \leqslant 1 \\ \rho_2^{-1} & \text{if} \quad \rho_2 > 1. \end{cases} \tag{3.60}$$

The limiting queue-length is given by

$$Q_\infty = \lim_{n\to\infty} Q_n \sim \max_{r\geqslant 0} (r - S_r), \tag{3.61}$$

where, possibly the last quantity is infinite; hence

$$\begin{aligned} Pr\{Q_\infty < j\} &= Pr\{\max_{r\geqslant 0} (r - S_r) < j\} = Pr\{j + S_r - r > 0, r \geqslant 0\} \\ &= Pr\{T_j = \infty\} = \begin{cases} 0 & \text{if} \quad \rho_2 \geqslant 1 \\ 1 - \zeta^j & \text{if} \quad \rho_2 < 1. \end{cases} \end{aligned} \tag{3.62}$$

This is a special case of Kendall's (1953) result for the system $GI/M/s$.

3.6 THE QUEUE $M/G/1$

In this system, the interarrival times have the distribution $\lambda e^{-\lambda t}\,dt$, whereas the service time has the distribution $dB(t)$ $(0 < t < \infty)$. Let $\psi(\theta)$ be the L.S.T. of the service time distribution, and assume that $0 < -\psi'(0) < \infty$. The relative traffic intensity of the system is $\rho = -\lambda\psi'(0)$, $0 < \rho < \infty$.

Here, let $t_0, t_1, t_2, \ldots$ denote the epochs of successive departures, and Q_n the queue-length at time $t = t_n + 0$. Furthermore, let X_n be the number of arrivals during $(t_n + 0, t_{n+1})$ $(n = 0, 1, \ldots)$; then $X_0, X_1, X_2, \ldots$ are mutually independent and identical random variables, with the distribution (3.48), and $\alpha = E(X_n) = \rho$. We have

$$Q_{n+1} = \begin{cases} Q_n - 1 + X_n & \text{if } Q_n > 0 \\ X_n & \text{if } Q_n = 0, \end{cases} \tag{3.63}$$

from which we obtain

$$Q_n = \max\,[X_{n-1} + X_{n-2} + \cdots + X_{n-r} - r + 1\ (1 \leqslant r \leqslant n-1),\ i + S_n - n],$$

where $Q_0 = i$. Since $X_{n-1} + X_{n-2} + \cdots + X_{n-r} = S_n - S_{n-r} \sim S_r$, we can write

$$Q_n \sim \max\,[S_r - r + 1\ (r = 1, 2, \ldots, n-1);\ i + S_n - n]. \tag{3.64}$$

For the limiting queue-length we have

$$Q_\infty \sim \max_{r \geqslant 1}\,(S_r - r + 1) \leqslant \infty, \tag{3.65}$$

and

$$\begin{aligned} Pr\{Q_\infty \leqslant j\} &= Pr\{\max_{r\geqslant 1}\,(S_r - r + 1) \leqslant j\} \\ &= Pr\{S_r - r < j,\ r \geqslant 1\} = Pr\{U_j = \infty\}. \end{aligned} \tag{3.66}$$

Hence we obtain

$$Pr\{Q_\infty = 0\} = \begin{cases} 0 & \text{if } \rho \geqslant 1 \\ 1 - \rho & \text{if } \rho < 1 \end{cases} \tag{3.67}$$

and

$$Pr\{Q_\infty \leqslant j\} = \begin{cases} 0 & \text{if } \rho \geqslant 1 \\ 1 - (1 - \rho)\sum_{0}^{\infty} k_{n+j}^{(n)} & \text{if } \rho < 1. \end{cases} \tag{3.68}$$

We also note that when $\rho < 1$, we have the Kendall's (1951) result

$$\sum_0^\infty z^j Pr\{Q_\infty \leqslant j\} = (1-\rho)\frac{K(z)}{K(z)-z} \quad (|z|<1), \tag{3.69}$$

as a consequence of (3.37); expanding (3.69) as a power series in z, we obtain

$$Pr\{Q_\infty \leqslant j\} = (1-\rho)\sum_{n=0}^{j} k_{j-n}^{(-n)}, \tag{3.70}$$

where $k_j^{-(n)}$ is the coefficient of z^j in the expansion of $K(z)^{-n}$; this alternative expression may be more useful in particular cases.

The transition probabilities of $\{Q_n\}$ are given by

$$\begin{aligned} Pr\{Q_n \leqslant j \mid Q_0 = i\} &= Pr\{S_r - r + 1 \leqslant j \ (r = 1, 2, \ldots, n-1); \\ &\qquad\qquad i + S_n - n \leqslant j\} \\ &= \sum_{\nu=i}^\infty Pr\{S_r - r < j \ (r = 1, 2, \ldots, n-1); \\ &\qquad\qquad S_n - n = j - \nu\} \\ &= \sum_{\nu=i}^\infty Pr\{S_{n-r} - (n-r) > -\nu \\ &\qquad\qquad (r = 1, 2, \ldots, n-1); S_n - n = j - \nu\} \\ &= \sum_{\nu=i}^\infty Pr\{\nu + S_r - r > 0 \ (r = 1, 2, \ldots, n-1); \\ &\qquad\qquad \nu + S_n - n = j\}. \end{aligned} \tag{3.71}$$

Hence, in particular, when $j = 0$ we obtain

$$P_{i0}^{(n)} = Pr\{Q_n = 0 \mid Q_0 = i\} = \sum_{\nu=i}^\infty g(\nu, n), \tag{3.72}$$

and for $j \geqslant 0$,

$$\begin{aligned} Pr\{Q_n \leqslant j \mid Q_0 = i\} &= \sum_{\nu=i}^\infty \left[k_{n+j-\nu}^{(n)} - \sum_{m=1}^{n-1} g(\nu, n-m)k_{m+j}^{(m)}\right] \\ &= K_{n+j-i}^{(n)} - \sum_{m=1}^{n-1} P_{i0}^{(n-m)} k_{m+j}^{(m)}, \end{aligned} \tag{3.73}$$

The zero-avoiding transition probabilities of $\{Q_n\}$ are given by

$$\begin{aligned} {}^0P_{ij}^{(n)} &= Pr\{Q_\nu > 0 \ (\nu = 1, 2, \ldots, n-1); Q_n = j \mid Q_0 = i\} \\ &= \begin{cases} Pr\{i + S_r - r > 0 \ (r = 1, 2, \ldots, n-1), \\ \qquad\qquad i + S_n - n = j\} & (i \geqslant 1) \\ Pr\{1 + S_r - r > 0 \ (r = 1, 2, \ldots, n-1), \\ \qquad\qquad 1 + S_n - n = j\} & (i = 0) \end{cases} \end{aligned} \tag{3.74}$$

and these are given by (3.22). In particular,

$$(3.75)\quad {}^0P_{i0}^{(n)} = g(i, n) = \frac{i}{n}\int_0^\infty e^{-\lambda t}\frac{(\lambda t)^{n-i}}{(n-i)!}\,dB_n(t) \qquad (n \geqslant i)$$

gives the distribution of the number of customers served during a busy period initiated by i customers.

3.7 SOME PARTICULAR CASES

The Queue $D/M/1$

Let $B(t) = 0$ if $t < a$, and $= 1$ if $t \geqslant a$. Then $K(z) = e^{-(1-z)/\rho_2}$, so that

$$(3.76)\quad \alpha_j^{(n)} = \sum_{r=j+1}^{\infty} e^{-n/\rho_2}\frac{(n/\rho_2)^r}{r!}, \qquad g(j, n) = \frac{j}{n}\,e^{-n/\rho_2}\frac{(n/\rho_2)^{n-j}}{(n-j)!}.$$

Hence

$$(3.77)\quad Pr\{Q_n < j \mid Q_0 = i\} = \sum_{s=n-j+i+1}^{\infty} e^{-n/\rho_2}\frac{\rho_2^{-s}}{s!}\{n^s - \beta_j^{(n)}(s)\},$$

where

$$(3.78)\quad \beta_j^{(n)}(s) = \begin{cases} 0 & \text{if } n < j \\ \displaystyle\sum_{m=0}^{m-j}\frac{j}{m+j}\binom{s}{m}(m+j)^m(n-j-m)^{s-m} & \text{if } n \geqslant j. \end{cases}$$

The Queue $E_k/M/1$

Let $dB(t) = (k\lambda^{-1})^k\, e^{-kt/\lambda}t^{k-1}\,dt/(k-1)!$ $(0 < t < \infty)$; then $K(z) = a^k(1-bz)^{-k}$, where $b = (1 + k\rho_2)^{-1}$ and $a = 1 - b$. Hence

$$(3.79)\quad \alpha_j^{(n)} = \sum_{r=j+1}^{\infty}\binom{-nk}{r}a^{nk}(-b)^r,\ g(j, n) = \frac{j}{n}\binom{-nk}{n-j}a^{nk}(-b)^{n-j},$$

and

$$(3.80)\quad Pr\{Q_n < j \mid Q_0 = i\} = a^{nk}\sum_{s=n-j+i+1}^{\infty}(-b)^s$$
$$\times\left[\binom{-nk}{s} - \sum_{m=0}^{s}\frac{j}{m+j}\binom{-jk-mk}{m}\binom{-nk+jk+mk}{s-m}\right].$$

The Queue $M/D/1$

Let the service time distribution be given by $B(t) = 0$ if $t < b$, and $= 1$ if $t \geqslant b$. Then $K(z) = e^{-\rho(1-z)}$, and hence

$$(3.81)\qquad P_{i0}^{(n)} = \sum_{i}^{\infty} \nu e^{-n\rho}(n\rho)^{n-\nu}n(n-\nu)!,$$

and

$$
\begin{aligned}
Pr\{Q_n \leqslant j \mid Q_0 = i\} &= \sum_{0}^{n+j-i} e^{-n\rho} \frac{(n\rho)^s}{s!} - \sum_{m=i}^{n} e^{-(n-m)\rho} \frac{(n\rho - m\rho)^{n-m+j}}{(n-m+j)!} \\
&\qquad \times \sum_{\nu=i}^{m} \frac{\nu e^{-m\rho}}{m(m-\nu)!} (m\rho)^{m-\nu} \\
&= \sum_{s=0}^{n+j-i} e^{-n\rho} \frac{\rho^s}{s!} [n^s - \beta_{n+j-s}^{(n)}(s)].
\end{aligned} \tag{3.82}
$$

The limiting distribution of the queue-length is given by

$$
Pr\{Q_\infty \leqslant j\} = (1 - \rho) \sum_{n=0}^{j} e^{n\rho} (-n\rho)^{j-n} (j-n)! \qquad (\rho < 1). \tag{3.83}
$$

The Queue $M/E_k/1$

Let the service time distribution be given by $dF(t) = (k\lambda^{-1})^k e^{-kt/\lambda} t^{k-1} \, dt/(k-1)!$ $(0 < t < \infty)$; then $K(z) = a^k(1 - bz)^{-k}$, where $a = k(k + \rho)^{-1}$ and $b = 1 - a$. Hence

$$
P_{i0}^{(n)} = \sum_{\nu=i}^{n} \frac{\nu}{n} \binom{-nk}{n-\nu} a^{nk} (-b)^{n-\nu}, \tag{3.84}
$$

and

$$
\begin{aligned}
Pr\{Q_n \leqslant j \mid Q_0 = i\} &= a^{nk} \sum_{s=0}^{n+j-i} \binom{-nk}{s} (-b)^s - a^{nk} \sum_{s=j}^{n+j-i} (-b)^s \\
&\times \sum_{m=0}^{s-j} \frac{n+j-s}{n+j-s+m} \binom{-nk - jk + sk - mk}{m} \binom{mk + jk - sk}{s-m}
\end{aligned} \tag{3.85}
$$

The limiting distribution of queue-length is given by

$$
Pr\{Q_\infty \leqslant j\} = (1 - \rho) \sum_{n=0}^{j} a^{-nk} \binom{nk}{j-n} (-b)^{j-n} \qquad (\rho < 1). \tag{3.86}
$$

3.8 THE RANDOM VARIABLE $T(u)$

Consider the queueing system $GI/G/1$, in which (1) the customers arrive at the instants $t_0, t_1, t_2, \ldots$, where the interarrival times $u_r = t_{r+1} - t_r$ $(r = 0, 1, \ldots)$ are mutually independent and identically distributed r.v. with the distribution $dA(t)$; (2) there is only one server, and the queue-discipline is "first come, first served"; and (3) the service times $v_0, v_1, v_2, \ldots$ of the successive customers are identically distributed r.v., mutually independent, and independent of u_r, and have the distribution $dB(t)$ $(0 \leqslant t < \infty)$. Let W_n be the waiting time of the nth customer $(n = 0, 1, 2, \ldots)$; then for the imbedded Markov chain $\{W_n\}$ we define the first passage time

$$
T(u) = \min (n \mid W_n = 0;\ W(0) = u). \tag{3.87}
$$

To obtain the distribution of $T(u)$, let $X_n = v_n - u_n$ $(n = 0, 1, 2, \ldots)$, $S_0 = 0$, $S_n = X_0 + X_1 + \cdots + X_{n-1}$ $(n \geqslant 1)$; furthermore, let

$$K(x) = Pr\{X_n \leqslant x\} \qquad (-\infty < x < \infty) \tag{3.88}$$

be the d.f. of X_n $(n = 0, 1, \ldots)$. From the recurrence relations

$$W_{n+1} = \begin{cases} W_n + X_n & \text{if} \quad W_n + X_n > 0 \\ 0 & \text{if} \quad W_n + X_n \leqslant 0 \end{cases} \tag{3.89}$$

we find that the transition d.f. of $\{W_n\}$ is given by

$$F(y; x) = Pr\{W_{n+1} \leqslant x \mid W_n = y\} = K(x - y). \tag{3.90}$$

Now, let $g_n(u) = Pr\{T(u) = n\}$ $(n \geqslant 1)$; we have

$$g_1(u) = Pr\{W_1 = 0 \mid W_0 = u\} = H(-u) \tag{3.91}$$

$$\begin{aligned} g_{n+1}(u) &= Pr\{W_r > 0\ (r = 1, 2, \ldots, n),\ W_{n+1} = 0 \mid W_0 = u\} \\ &= \int_{0+}^{\infty} d_x Pr\{W_1 \leqslant x \mid W_0 = u\} Pr\{W_r > 0\ (r = 2, \ldots, n), \\ &\qquad\qquad W_{n+1} = 0 \mid W_1 = x\} \\ &= \int_{0+}^{\infty} dK(x - u) g_n(x) \qquad (n \geqslant 1). \end{aligned} \tag{3.92}$$

We shall also denote

$$g(u) = Pr\{T(u) < \infty\} = \sum_{n=1}^{\infty} g_n(u). \tag{3.93}$$

It is clear that $T(u)$ is the number of customers served in the interval of time between the commencement of a busy period initiated by $W_0 = u$, and the next busy period; in particular $T(0)$ is the number served in a busy cycle. In the next section we shall obtain the distribution of $T(u)$ in the system $M/G/1$; the general case will be discussed in Chapter 4.

3.9 THE DISTRIBUTION OF $T(u)$ IN THE SYSTEM $M/G/1$

Let us consider the system $M/G/1$ described in Section 3.6. We have

$$K(x) = \begin{cases} \int_0^{\infty} e^{-\lambda(v-x)}\, dB(v) & (x \leqslant 0) \\ B(x) + \int_x^{\infty} e^{-\lambda(v-x)}\, dB(v) & (x \geqslant 0), \end{cases} \tag{3.94}$$

so that

$$dK(x) = dx \lambda \int_{\max(0,x)}^{\infty} e^{-\lambda(v-x)}\, dB(v) \qquad (-\infty < x < \infty). \tag{3.95}$$

We shall show that the distribution of $T(u)$ in this case is given by

$$g_n(u) = \int_u^\infty e^{-\lambda y} \frac{\lambda^{n-1}}{n!} y^{n-2}(y + \overline{n-1}u)\, dB_n(y-u) \qquad (n \geqslant 1), \tag{3.96}$$

$$g(u) = \begin{cases} 1 & \text{if } \rho \leqslant 1 \\ \psi(\eta_0)e^{-\eta_0 u} & \text{if } \rho > 1, \end{cases} \tag{3.97}$$

where η_0 is the largest positive root of the equation

$$x = \lambda - \lambda\psi(x). \tag{3.98}$$

To prove these results, we substitute (3.95) in (3.92) and obtain, after some simplification,

$$g_{n+1}(u) = \int_{v=u}^\infty e^{-\lambda v}\, dB(v-u) \int_{x=0}^v \lambda e^{\lambda x} g_n(x)\, dx \qquad (n \geqslant 1). \tag{3.99}$$

From (3.91) and (3.94) we find that

$$g_1(u) = \int_u^\infty e^{-\lambda y}\, dB(y-u). \tag{3.100}$$

Putting $n = 1$ in (3.99) we obtain

$$\begin{aligned} g_2(u) &= \int_{v=u}^\infty e^{-\lambda v}\, dB(v-u) \int_{x=0}^v \lambda e^{\lambda x}\, dx \int_{y=x}^\infty e^{-\lambda y}\, dB(y-x) \\ &= \int_{v=u}^\infty dB(v-u) \int_{x=0}^v \lambda\, dx \int_{t=v}^\infty e^{-\lambda t}\, dB(t-v) \\ &= \int_{t=u}^\infty e^{-\lambda t} \int_{v=u}^t \lambda v\, dB(v-u)\, dB(t-v) \\ &= \int_{t=u}^\infty e^{-\lambda t} \frac{\lambda}{2}(t+u)\, dB_2(t-u). \end{aligned} \tag{3.101}$$

Here we have used the identity (2.11) of Section 2.2, with $m = 1$:

$$\int_0^y v\, dB(v)\, dB_n(y-v) = \frac{y}{n+1}\, dB_{n+1}(y). \tag{3.102}$$

We have thus proved (3.96) for $n = 1,2$. Now assume that (3.96) is true for some n; then substituting for $g_n(x)$ in (3.99), and proceeding as in (3.101), we obtain

$$\begin{aligned} g_{n+1}(u) &= \int_{t=u}^\infty e^{-\lambda t} \int_{v=u}^\infty dB(v-u)\, dB_n(t-v) \\ &\quad \times \int_{x=0}^v \frac{\lambda^n}{n!}(t-v+x)^{n-2}(t-v+nx)\, dx \\ &= \int_{t=u}^\infty e^{-\lambda t} \frac{\lambda^n t^{n-1}}{n!} \int_{v=u}^t v\, dB(v-u)\, dB_n(t-v) \\ &= \int_{t=u}^\infty e^{-\lambda t} \frac{\lambda^n}{(n+1)!} t^{n-1}(t+nu)\, dB_{n+1}(t-u), \end{aligned} \tag{3.103}$$

where we have again used (3.102). This completes the proof of (3.96). To prove (3.97), let us put $g(u; z) = \sum_1^\infty g_n(u)z^{n-1}$; then adding (3.99) over $(n = 1, 2, \ldots)$, we obtain

$$(3.104) \quad g(u; z) = g_1(u) + z\int_{v=u}^{\infty} e^{-\lambda v}\, dB(v-u)\int_{x=0}^{v} \lambda e^{\lambda x} g(x; z)\, dx.$$

Results obtained in Chapter 2 concerning the busy period encourage us to try the solution $g(u, z) = ce^{-\theta u}$, where $c = g(0) > 0$. Substitution in (3.104) then gives

$$\begin{aligned} ce^{-\theta u} &= e^{-\lambda u}\psi(\lambda) + z\int_{v=u}^{\infty} e^{-\lambda v}\, dB(v-u)\int_{x=0}^{v} c\lambda e^{(\lambda-\theta)x}\, dx \\ &= e^{-\lambda u}\psi(\lambda) + cz\frac{\lambda}{\lambda-\theta}\int_{v=u}^{\infty}(e^{-\theta v} - e^{-\lambda v})\, dB(v-u) \\ &= e^{-\lambda u}\psi(\lambda) + cz\frac{\lambda}{\lambda-\theta}[e^{-\theta u}\psi(\theta) - e^{-\lambda u}\psi(\lambda)], \end{aligned}$$

which can be written as

$$(3.105) \quad ce^{-\theta u}[\theta - \lambda + \lambda z\psi(\theta)] + e^{-\lambda u}\,\psi(\lambda)(\lambda - \theta - c\lambda z) = 0.$$

For this to be valid for $u \geqslant 0$, we must have $c = (\lambda - \theta)/\lambda z$ and $\theta - \lambda + \lambda z\psi(\theta) = 0$. Thus $g(u; z) = \psi(\theta)e^{-\theta u}$, where $\theta \equiv \theta(z)$ satisfies the functional equation

$$(3.106) \qquad \theta = \lambda - \lambda z\psi(\theta).$$

Proceeding as in Section 2.2, we can prove that the equation (3.106) has a unique positive root such that $\theta(0) = \lambda$, and furthermore, that

$$(3.107) \qquad g(u) = \lim_{z\to 1} g(u; z) = \begin{cases} 1 & \text{if } \rho \leqslant 1 \\ \psi(\eta_0)e^{-\eta_0 u} & \text{if } \rho > 1, \end{cases}$$

where η_0 is the largest positive root of the equation (3.98). We have thus proved (3.97).

3.10 A DUALITY RELATION

Let Q_1 be a queueing system as described in Section 3.8. By interchanging the interarrival and service time distributions of Q_1 we obtain a second system Q_2, which may be called the dual of Q_1. We have then the following *duality relation*.

Let $F(x)$ be the distribution function of the limiting waiting time in a queueing system and $g(x) = Pr\{T(x) < \infty\}$ in its dual system. Then we have

$$(3.108) \qquad F(x) = 1 - g(x) \qquad (x \geqslant 0).$$

To prove (3.108) we note that the recurrence relations (3.89) give

$$W_n = \max(0, X_{n-1} + X_{n-2} + \cdots + X_{n-r}(r = 1, 2, \ldots, n-1), u + S_n),$$
$$\sim \max\{S_r\,(r = 0, 1, \ldots, n-1); u + S_n\},$$

where $W(0) = u$. Hence we find that the limiting waiting time is given by

$$W^* = \lim_{n\to\infty} W_n \sim \max_{r\geqslant 0}(S_r), \tag{3.109}$$

and its distribution function by

$$\begin{aligned} F(x) &= Pr\{W^* < x\} = Pr\{S_n < x\,(n \geqslant 0)\} \\ &= Pr\{x + S_n' > 0\,(n \geqslant 0)\} \end{aligned} \tag{3.110}$$

where $-S_n = S_n' = x_0' + x_1' + \cdots + x'_{n-1}$, and $x_r' = v_r' - u_r'$, v_r', and u_r' being respectively the service time and interarrival time in the dual system. Moreover, in view of (3.89) we can write

$$T(x) = \min(n \mid x + S_n' \leqslant 0), \tag{3.111}$$

so that

$$1 - g(x) = Pr\{T(x) = \infty\} = Pr\{x + S_n' > 0\,(n \geqslant 0)\}, \tag{3.112}$$

and the result (3.108) now follows from (3.110) and (3.111).

As an application of the above relation, consider the system $GI/M/1$ and its dual $M/G/1$. If the relative traffic intensities of these two systems are denoted respectively by ρ_2 and ρ, then it is clear that $\rho_2 = \rho^{-1}$. Using (3.97) we then find that the limiting waiting time distribution in the system $GI/M/1$ is given by

$$F(x) = \begin{cases} 0 & \text{if } \rho_2 \geqslant 1 \\ 1 - \psi(\eta_0)e^{-\eta_0 x}(x \geqslant 0) & \text{if } \rho_2 < 1, \end{cases} \tag{3.113}$$

where η_0 is as defined in (3.98), and $\psi(\theta)$ is the L.S.T. of the interarrival time distribution. We remark that since a d.f. is continuous to the right, $Pr\{W^* = 0\} = F(+0) = 1 - \psi(\eta_0)$. The result (3.113) is due to Smith (see equation (1.310)).

COMPLEMENTS AND PROBLEMS

Section 3.1

1. Most of the results of Sections 3.2 to 5.7 are due to the author and U. Narayan Bhat (1963). The combinatorial methods used here enable old results to be derived in an elegant manner, and several new results to be obtained.

Section 3.2

2. If we interpret X_n as the amount of water which flows into a dam during a unit time interval, and suppose that a unit amount of water is released from the dam at the end of each such interval, unless the dam is empty, then T_i is the duration of the "wet period," that is, the time taken by the dam with an initial content i to dry up. These results are thus a restatement of those derived by Kendall (1957) for the analogous problem in continuous time [see also Gani (1958) and Takács (1961)].

Section 3.3

3. Show that

$$Pr\{U_0 > n\} = \sum_{i=1}^{n} g(i, n) \tag{1}$$

$$Pr\{U_j > n\} = K_{n+j-1}^{(n)} - \sum_{m=1}^{n-1} k_{m+j}^{(m)} Pr\{U_0 > n - m\} \qquad (j \geqslant 1). \tag{2}$$

4. Show that the p.g.f. of U_0 is given by

$$\sum_{n=1}^{\infty} Pr\{U_0 = n\} z^n = \frac{z - \xi}{1 - \xi}, \tag{3}$$

where $\xi \equiv \xi(z)$ satisfies the functional equation (3.16).

Section 3.4

5. The results of this section are implicit in the more general results derived by Kemperman (1961) using complex variable methods, but in their explicit forms are a consequence of the results of Sections 3.2 and 3.3.

6. Show that the p.g.f. of N is given by

$$E(z^N) = \sum_{n=1}^{\infty} F_{00}^{(n)} z^n = zK'(\xi), \tag{4}$$

[Kemperman (1961)].

Section 3.5

7. Show that

$$\sum_{n=0}^{\infty} \sum_{i=0}^{\infty} P_{ij}^{(n)} s^i z^n \tag{5}$$

$$= \frac{(1 - s)(1 - z)s^{j+1} + z\xi^j(1 - \xi)[s - K(s)]}{(1 - s)(1 - z)[s - zK(s)]} \qquad (|z| < 1, |s| \leqslant 1),$$

[Takács (1960)].

8. The result (3.54) has also been proved by Takács (1962).

9. Show that

$$E(z^N) = \sum_{n=1}^{\infty} f_n z^n = \frac{z - \xi}{1 - \xi}, \tag{6}$$

and furthermore, that

$$E(N) = \begin{cases} (1 - \zeta)^{-1} & \text{if } \rho_2 < 1 \\ \infty & \text{if } \rho_2 = 1. \end{cases} \tag{7}$$

Deduce that the states of the chain $\{Q_n\}$ are persistent non-null if $\rho_2 < 1$, persistent null if $\rho_2 = 1$, and transient if $\rho_2 > 1$. [Takács (1960)].

10. Show that when $\rho_2 < 1$,

$$ {}^0P^*_{0j} = \sum_{n=1}^{\infty} {}^0P^{(n)}_{0j} = \zeta^j (j \geqslant 1), \qquad {}^0P^*_{00} = 1. \tag{8}$$

Since $\sum_{j=0}^{\infty} {}^0P^*_{0j} = (1 - \zeta)^{-1}$, a result of Derman (1954) can be used to show that $(1 - \zeta)\zeta^j (j \geqslant 0)$ is the limiting distribution of $\{Q_n\}$.

Section 3.6

11. The result (3.68) is essentially the same as the one proved by Finch (1960) by incomplete arguments.

12. The result (3.71) is a generalization of the one due to Finch (1960), who proved it for $i = 1$. Yeo (1961) has proved an equivalent result for the dam.

13. Let it not be assumed that $E(X_n) < \infty$. Let

$$A \equiv \sum_{n=1}^{\infty} \frac{1}{n} k^{(n)}_{n-1}, \qquad B \equiv \sum_{n=1}^{\infty} k^{(n)}_{n-1}. \tag{9}$$

Then show that the states of the chain $\{Q_n\}$ are

(*a*) transient if $A < 1$,
(*b*) persistent null if $A = 1$, $B = \infty$, and
(*c*) persistent non-null if $A = 1$, $B < \infty$.

Section 3.7

14. The usual expression for the limiting distribution in the case $M/E_k/1$ is a weighted sum of k geometric terms, the common ratios and the weights being obtained from a certain characteristic equation (see Section 1.6); however, the result (3.85) appears to be much simpler.

Putting $k = 1$ in (3.85) we obtain the transition probabilities of $\{Q_n\}$ for the queue $M/M/1$ as

$$\begin{aligned} Pr\{Q_n \leqslant j \mid Q_0 = i\} &= a^n \sum_{s=0}^{n+j-i} \binom{-n}{s} (-b)^s \\ &\quad - a^n \sum_{s=j}^{n+j-i} (-b)^s \sum_{m=0}^{s-j} \frac{n+j-s}{n+j-s+m} \binom{-n-j+s-m}{m} \binom{m+j-s}{s-m}, \end{aligned} \tag{10}$$

where $a = (1 + \rho)^{-1}$, and $b = 1 - a$ [cf. Finch (1960), equation (33)].

Section 3.8

15. The elementary methods developed in Sections 2.9 and 2.10 are due to the author (1962). For a systematic discussion of the distribution of $T(u)$, see Kemperman (1961).

Section 3.9

16. The results (3.96) and (3.97) are due to Kemperman (1961). The present proof is based on the recurrence relations (3.92). From (3.96) it follows, in particular, that

$$g_n(0) = \int_0^\infty e^{-\lambda t} \frac{(\lambda t)^{n-1}}{n!}\, dB_n(t) = g(1, n). \tag{11}$$

Interpret this result. More generally, $T(u)$ is one more than the number of (new) customers served during a busy period initiated by $W(+0) = W(-0) + v = u + v$, where v is the initial customer's service time. Therefore, using the results of Section 2.2, we find that

$$\begin{aligned} g_n(u) &= \int_{t=u}^\infty \int_{v=0}^\infty dB(v)\, dG_{n-1}(u + v, t) \\ &= \int_{t=u}^\infty e^{-\lambda t} \frac{(\lambda t)^{n-2}}{(n-1)!} \int_{v=0}^{t-u} \lambda(v + u)\, dB(v)\, dB_{n-1}(t - u - v) \\ &= \int_{t=u}^\infty e^{-\lambda t} \frac{\lambda^{n-1} t^{n-2}}{n!} [t + (n-1)u]\, dB_n(t - u), \end{aligned} \tag{12}$$

in agreement with (3.96). Furthermore, the p.g.f. of $T(u)$ is given by

$$\begin{aligned} g(u, z) &= E[z^{T(u)-1}] = E[z^{N_A(u+v)}] = E[e^{-\lambda(u+v)(1-\xi)}] \\ &= e^{-\lambda u(1-\xi)}\psi(\lambda - \lambda\xi), \end{aligned} \tag{13}$$

a result equivalent to the one obtained in Section 2.9.

Section 3.10

17. Duality relations similar to (3.108) have been previously noted by some authors, but do not seem to have been explicitly used. Note that in Chapter 2 we have systematically used such relations to obtain the properties of the system $GI/M/1$ from those of $M/G/1$.

REFERENCES

Derman, C. (1954). A solution to a set of fundamental equations in Markov chains. *Proc. Amer. Math. Soc.*, **5**, 332–334.

Finch, P. D. (1960). On the transient behavior of a simple queue. *J. Roy. Stat. Soc.*, **B22**, 277–284.

Gani, J. (1958). Elementary methods in occupancy problem of storage. *Math. Ann.*, **136**, 454–465.

Kemperman, J. H. B. (1961). *The First Passage Problem for a Stationary Markov Chain.* University of Chicago Press.

Kendall, D. G. (1951). Some problems in the theory of queues. *J. Roy. Stat. Soc.*, **B13**, 151–185.

Kendall, D. G. (1953). Stochastic processes occurring in the theory of queues and their analysis by the method of the imbedded Markov chain. *Ann. Math. Statist.*, **24**, 338–354.

Kendall, D. G. (1957). Some problems in the theory of dams. *J. Roy. Stat. Soc.*, **B19,** 207–212.

Prabhu, N. U. (1962). Elementary methods for some waiting time problems. *Opns. Res.*, **10,** 559–566.

Prabhu, N. U., and U. Narayan Bhat (1963). Some first passage problems and their application to queues. *Sankhya*, **25,** 281–292.

Takács, Lajos (1960). The transient behavior of a single server queueing process with recurrent input and exponentially distributed service time. *Opns. Res.*, **8,** 231–245.

Takács, Lajos (1961). The probability law of the busy period for two types of queueing processes. *Opns. Res.*, **9,** 402–407.

Takács, Lajos (1962). A single server queue with recurrent input and exponentially distributed service times. *Opns. Res.*, **10,** 395–399.

Yeo, G. (1961). The time dependent solution for an infinite dam with discrete additive inputs. *J. Roy. Stat. Soc.*, **B23,** 173–179.

Chapter 4

The Queueing System $GI/G/1$; Bulk Queues

4.1 INTRODUCTION

In Chapter 3 we saw that the basic processes in the study of Markov chains imbedded in the queueing systems $M/G/1$ and $GI/M/1$ were sequences of partial sums of mutually independent random variables. This is indeed true of the general case, which we shall investigate in this chapter. The pioneering work in the fluctuation theory of independent random variables was done by Sparre Andersen (1953a, 1953b, 1954) using ingenious combinatorial methods. His work was simplified and extended by Spitzer (1956, 1960). Further simplification was introduced by Feller (1959) using the theory of recurrent events. Mention must also be made of the results obtained by Baxter (1958), and Kemperman (1961) using analytical methods.

We consider a sequence $\{X_n, n = 1, 2, \ldots\}$ of mutually independent random variables with the d.f.

$$K(x) = Pr\{X_n \leqslant x\} \qquad (-\infty < x < \infty). \tag{4.1}$$

Let $S_0 = 0$, $S_n = X_1 + X_2 + \cdots + X_n$ $(n \geqslant 1)$ be the partial sums of X_n and

$$K_n(x) = Pr\{S_n \leqslant x\} \quad (n \geqslant 1), \qquad K_1(x) = K(x). \tag{4.2}$$

The fluctuation theory of $\{S_n\}$ is concerned with the first passage times, the maximal term among $(0, S_1, S_2, \ldots, S_n)$, the number of positive (or negative) terms among them, and several other quantities. Some basic results are derived in Section 4.2, using Feller's treatment of the subject. To indicate applications to queueing theory, consider the system

$GI/G/1$, where u_n is the interval between the arrival times of the $(n-1)$st and the nth customers, v_n is the service time of the $(n-1)$st customer $(n \geqslant 1)$, and

$$(4.3) \qquad Pr\{u_n \leqslant x\} = A(x), \quad Pr\{v_n \leqslant x\} = B(x) \qquad (x \geqslant 0).$$

Then for the imbedded Markov chain $\{W_n\}$ we have

$$(4.4) \quad W_n \sim \max(0, S_1, S_2, \ldots, S_{n-1}, u + S_n), \qquad W_0 = u \geqslant 0,$$

where $S_n = X_1 + X_2 + \cdots + X_n$, $X_n = v_n - u_n$, and

(4.5)

$$K(x) = Pr\{X_n \leqslant x\} = \int_{u=\max(0,-x)}^{\infty} B(x+u)\, dA(u) \quad (-\infty < x < \infty).$$

The distribution of W_n is therefore that of the maximal term among $(0, S_1, S_2, \ldots, S_{n-1}, u + S_n)$. We may also consider the first passage time $T(u) = \min(n \mid W_n = 0, W_0 = u)$, which can be written as

$$(4.6) \qquad T(u) = \min(n \mid u + S_n \leqslant 0).$$

The distribution of the busy period can also be obtained from the fluctuation theory of $\{S_n\}$. Finally, we remark that the results of Section 4.2 are also valid in the discrete case with obvious modifications and can be applied to the imbedded chain $\{Q_n\}$ in some particular systems.

4.2 SOME RESULTS OF FLUCTUATION THEORY

a. Ladder Indices

Given a sequence $\{S_n\}$ of partial sums of mutually independent and identically distributed random variables, we define a sequence $\{N_k, k \geqslant 0\}$ of random variables as follows:

$$(4.7) \qquad \begin{aligned} N_0 &\equiv 0 \\ N_1 &= \min(n \mid S_n > 0) \\ N_k &= \min(n > N_{k-1} \mid S_n - S_{N_{k-1}} > 0) \qquad (k \geqslant 2); \end{aligned}$$

these are called ladder indices of $\{S_n\}$. We have

$$(4.8) \quad \begin{aligned} f_n &= Pr\{N_1 = n\} \\ &= Pr\{S_1 \leqslant 0, S_2 \leqslant 0, \ldots, S_{n-1} \leqslant 0, S_n > 0\} \qquad (n \geqslant 1). \end{aligned}$$

Since

$$S_n - S_{N_{k-1}} = X_{N_{k-1}+1} + \cdots, + X_n,$$

it follows that $S_n - S_{N_{k-1}}$ is distributed as $S_{n-N_{k-1}}$, independently of $S_{N_{k-1}}$; therefore the random variables $N_1, N_2 - N_1, N_3 - N_2, \ldots$ are mutually independent and have the same distribution. Thus, if

$$f_n^{(r)} = Pr\{N_r = n\} \qquad (1 \leqslant r \leqslant n), \tag{4.9}$$

it follows that $[f_n^{(r)}, n \geqslant 1]$ is the r-fold convolution of (f_n) with itself. These statements are equivalent to the following. Let E_n be the event

$$E_n = (n \text{ is a ladder index}); \tag{4.10}$$

then the sequence $\{E_n, n \geqslant 1\}$ defines a recurrent event. In Feller's (1957) notation, let

$$\begin{aligned} u_n &= Pr\{E_n\} = Pr\{n \text{ is a ladder index}\} \\ &= Pr\{S_r < S_n \qquad (r = 0, 1, \ldots, n-1)\} \\ &= Pr\{S_1 > 0, S_2 > 0, \ldots, S_n > 0\} \qquad (n \geqslant 1). \end{aligned} \tag{4.11}$$

Also,

$$f_n = Pr\{n \text{ is the first ladder index}\}, \tag{4.12}$$

and more generally,

$$f_n^{(r)} = Pr\{n \text{ is the } r\text{th ladder index}\}, \tag{4.13}$$

where f_n and $f_n^{(r)}$ are defined by (4.8) and (4.9). Finally, we set

$$u_0 = 1, \qquad f_0 = 0. \tag{4.14}$$

Let us define the probability generating functions (p.g.f.)

$$F(z) = \sum_1^\infty f_n z^n, \qquad U(z) = \sum_0^\infty u_n z^n \qquad (|z| < 1); \tag{4.15}$$

we have then the result

$$U(z) = [1 - F(z)]^{-1} = \exp\left[\sum_1^\infty \frac{z^n}{n} Pr\{S_n > 0\}\right]. \tag{4.16}$$

The proof of (4.16) depends on Feller's (1959) fundamental lemma:

$$\sum_{r=1}^n \frac{1}{r} f_n^{(r)} = \frac{1}{n} Pr\{S_n > 0\}. \tag{4.17}$$

Using this we find that

(4.18)

$$\sum_1^\infty \frac{z^n}{n} Pr\{S_n > 0\} = \sum_{r=1}^\infty \frac{1}{r} \sum_{n=r}^\infty f_n^{(r)} z^n = \sum_1^\infty \frac{1}{r} [F(z)]^r = \log[1 - F(z)]^{-1}.$$

However, since it is known that $U(z) = [1 - F(z)]^{-1}$, the required result (4.16) follows.

Now, let

$$A = \sum_1^\infty \frac{1}{n} Pr\{S_n \leqslant 0\}, \qquad B = \sum_1^\infty \frac{1}{n} Pr\{S_n > 0\}. \tag{4.19}$$

From the theory of recurrent events we know that lim u_n as $n \to \infty$ exists; this limit is easily obtained from (4.16). Thus

$$\begin{aligned}\lim_{n\to\infty} u_n = \lim_{z\to 1-0} (1 - z)U(z) &= \exp\left[-\sum_1^\infty \frac{z^n}{n} Pr\{S_n \leqslant 0\}\right] \\ &= \begin{cases} e^{-A} & \text{if } A < \infty \\ 0 & \text{if } A = \infty. \end{cases}\end{aligned} \tag{4.20}$$

b. The Renewal Process $\{\zeta_k\}$

Let $N_1, N_2, \ldots$ be the successive ladder indices of a sequence $\{S_n\}$, and set

$$\zeta_k = S_{N_k} \qquad (k \geqslant 1). \tag{4.21}$$

From the definition of the N_k it is clear that $\zeta_1, \zeta_2 - \zeta_1, \zeta_3 - \zeta_2, \ldots$ are mutually independent and identically distributed random variables which assume only positive values. Let the joint distribution of N_1 and ζ_1 be denoted by

$$\begin{aligned} f_n(x) &= Pr\{N_1 = n, \zeta_1 \leqslant x\} \\ &= Pr\{n \text{ is the first ladder index, and } S_n \leqslant x\} \\ &= Pr\{S_1 \leqslant 0, S_2 \leqslant 0, \ldots, S_{n-1} \leqslant 0, 0 < S_n \leqslant x\} \\ &\qquad\qquad (n \geqslant 1, x > 0). \end{aligned} \tag{4.22}$$

As a generalization of (4.16) we have the result

$$\begin{aligned} f(\theta, z) &= \sum_1^\infty z^n \int_{0+}^\infty e^{\theta x}\, df_n(x) \\ &= 1 - \exp\left[-\sum_1^\infty \frac{z^n}{n} \int_{0+}^\infty e^{\theta x}\, dK_n(x)\right] \qquad [|z| < 1, \operatorname{Re}(\theta) < 0]. \end{aligned} \tag{4.23}$$

To prove this, let

$$\begin{aligned} f_n^{(r)}(x) &= Pr(N_r = n, \zeta_r \leqslant x) \\ &= Pr(n \text{ is the } r\text{th ladder index, and } S_n \leqslant x) \\ &\qquad\qquad (1 \leqslant r \leqslant n, x > 0), \end{aligned} \tag{4.24}$$

and

$$f^{(r)}(\theta, z) = \sum_1^\infty z^n \int_{0+}^\infty e^{\theta x}\, df_n^{(r)}(x) \qquad [|z| < 1, \operatorname{Re}(\theta) < 0]. \tag{4.25}$$

From the convolution properties of N_k and ζ_k it follows that $f^{(r)}(\theta, z) = [f^{(1)}(\theta, z)]^r = [f(\theta, z)]^r$ $(r \geqslant 1)$. Now from Feller's lemma (4.17) we obtain

$$\sum_{r=1}^{n} \frac{1}{r} f_n^{(r)}(x) = \frac{1}{n} Pr\{0 < S_n \leqslant x\}. \tag{4.26}$$

Therefore

$$\sum_{1}^{\infty} \frac{z^n}{n} \int_{0+}^{\infty} e^{\theta x}\, d_x Pr\{0 < S_n \leqslant x\} = \sum_{r=1}^{\infty} \frac{1}{r} \sum_{n=r}^{\infty} z^n \int_{0+}^{\infty} e^{\theta x}\, df_n^{(r)}(x) \tag{4.27}$$

$$= \sum_{1}^{\infty} \frac{1}{r} [f(\theta, z)]^r = \log\,[1 - f(\theta, z)]^{-1},$$

which leads to (4.23).

Letting $z \to 1 - 0$ in (4.23) we find that the transform of the distribution of ζ_1 is given by

$$E(e^{\theta \zeta_1}) = 1 - \exp\left[-\sum_{1}^{\infty} \frac{1}{n} \int_{0+}^{\infty} e^{\theta x}\, dK_n(x)\right] \qquad [\text{Re}\,(\theta) < 0]. \tag{4.28}$$

Therefore

$$Pr\{\zeta_1 < \infty\} = \lim_{\theta \to 0-} E(e^{\theta \zeta_1}) = \begin{cases} 1 & \text{if} \quad B = \infty \\ 1 - e^{-B} & \text{if} \quad B < \infty; \end{cases} \tag{4.29}$$

thus ζ_1 is a proper random variable if, and only if, $B = \infty$.

We can also express (4.23) in a slightly different form. Let

$$\begin{aligned} u_n(x) &= Pr\{n \text{ is a ladder index, and } S_n \leqslant x\} \\ &= Pr\{S_1 > 0, S_2 > 0, \ldots, S_{n-1} > 0, 0 < S_n \leqslant x\} \\ &\qquad\qquad\qquad\qquad (n \geqslant 1, x > 0), \end{aligned} \tag{4.30}$$

and

$$u(\theta, z) = 1 + \sum_{1}^{\infty} z^n \int_{0+}^{\infty} e^{\theta x}\, du_n(x) \qquad [|z| < 1, \text{Re}\,(\theta) < 0]. \tag{4.31}$$

Clearly,

$$u_n(x) = \sum_{r=1}^{n} f_n^{(r)}(x), \tag{4.32}$$

so that

$$\begin{aligned} u(\theta, z) &= 1 + \sum_{r=1}^{\infty} \sum_{n=r}^{\infty} z^n \int_{0+}^{\infty} e^{\theta x}\, df_n^{(r)}(x) \\ &= 1 + \sum_{1}^{\infty} f^{(r)}(\theta, z) = 1 + \sum_{1}^{\infty} [f(\theta, z)]^r \\ &= [1 - f(\theta, z)]^{-1}. \end{aligned} \tag{4.33}$$

Hence

$$(4.34)\quad u(\theta, z) = [1 - f(\theta, z)]^{-1} = \exp\left[\sum_1^\infty \frac{z^n}{n}\int_{0+}^\infty e^{\theta x}\, dK_n(x)\right]$$

$$[|z| < 1, \operatorname{Re}(\theta) < 0].$$

Finally, we shall prove that the series

$$(4.35)\qquad \sum_1^\infty u_n(x) < \infty \qquad \text{for all finite} \quad x > 0.$$

First, let $B = \infty$ and consider the renewal process $\{\zeta_k\}$. The renewal function of this process is given by

$$(4.36)\qquad \sum_{k=1}^\infty Pr\{\zeta_k \leqslant x\} = \sum_{k=1}^\infty \sum_{n=k}^\infty Pr\{N_k = n, \zeta_k \leqslant x\}$$

$$= \sum_{n=1}^\infty \sum_{k=1}^n f_n^{(k)}(x) = \sum_1^\infty u_n(x)$$

and since the renewal function is finite for all $x > 0$, (4.35) holds in this case. If $B < \infty$, we find from (4.16) that

$$(4.37)\qquad \sum_0^\infty u_n = \lim_{z\to 1-0} u(z) = e^B < \infty$$

and since $u_n(x) \leqslant u_n(\infty) = u_n$, (4.35) follows.

c. Some Further Results

If in the definition (4.7) the inequalities $<$ are replaced by $\leqslant$, we get weak ladder indices, for which results similar to the above can be derived. By applying these results to the random variables $-X_n$, we obtain what may be called their duals. In particular, let us consider the weak ladder indices of the partial sums $\{-S_n\}$, and let

$$(4.38)\qquad g_n^* = Pr\{n \text{ is the first weak ladder index of } (-S_n)\}$$

$$= Pr\{S_1 > 0, S_2 > 0, \ldots, S_{n-1} > 0, S_n \leqslant 0\},$$

$$(4.39)\qquad v_n^* = Pr\{n \text{ is a weak ladder index of } (-S_n)\}$$

$$= Pr\{S_r \geqslant S_n\ (r = 0, 1, \ldots, n-1)\}$$

$$= Pr\{S_1 \leqslant 0, S_2 \leqslant 0, \ldots, S_n \leqslant 0\}$$

for $n \geqslant 1$, and $g_0^* = 0$, $v_0^* = 1$. Then if

$$(4.40)\qquad G^*(z) = \sum_1^\infty g_n^* z^n, \qquad V^*(z) = \sum_0^\infty v_n^* z^n \qquad (|z| < 1),$$

we have the result

$$V^*(z) = [1 - G^*(z)]^{-1} = \exp\left[\sum_1^\infty \frac{z^n}{n} Pr\{S_n \leqslant 0\}\right]. \tag{4.41}$$

From (4.41) we find that

$$\lim_{n\to\infty} v_n^* = \begin{cases} e^{-B} & \text{if } B < \infty \\ 0 & \text{if } B = \infty. \end{cases} \tag{4.42}$$

Furthermore, let

$$g_n^*(x) = Pr\{S_1 > 0, S_2 > 0, \ldots, S_{n-1} > 0, x \leqslant S_n \leqslant 0\} \tag{4.43}$$

$$v_n^*(x) = Pr\{S_1 \leqslant 0, S_2 \leqslant 0, \ldots, S_{n-1} \leqslant 0, x \leqslant S_n \leqslant 0\} \quad (n \geqslant 1, x \leqslant 0) \tag{4.44}$$

and

$$g^*(\theta, z) = \sum_1^\infty z^n \int_{-\infty}^{0+} e^{\theta x}(-d_x) g_n^*(x) \tag{4.45}$$

$$v^*(\theta, z) = 1 + \sum_1^\infty z^n \int_{-\infty}^{0+} e^{\theta x}(-d_x) v_n^*(x). \tag{4.46}$$

Then we have

$$v^*(\theta, z) = [1 - g^*(\theta, z)]^{-1} = \exp\left[\sum_1^\infty \frac{z^n}{n} \int_{-\infty}^{0+} e^{\theta x}\, dK_n(x)\right] \quad [|z| < 1, \text{Re}(\theta) > 0], \tag{4.47}$$

and

$$\sum_1^\infty v_n^*(x) < \infty \quad \text{for all finite } x \leqslant 0. \tag{4.48}$$

4.3 THE BUSY PERIOD AND THE BUSY CYCLE

a. The Busy Period

It is clear that the random variable

$$N = \min(n \mid S_n \leqslant 0) \tag{4.49}$$

represents the number of customers served during a busy period. The length of the busy period is given by

$$T = v_1 + v_2 + \cdots + v_N. \tag{4.50}$$

To obtain the joint distribution of N and T, we let

$$V_n = v_1 + v_2 + \cdots + v_n, \qquad U_n = u_1 + u_2 + \cdots + u_n, \tag{4.51}$$

and

$$B_n(v) = Pr\{V_n \leqslant v\}, \qquad A_n(u) = Pr\{U_n \leqslant u\} \qquad (n \geqslant 1). \tag{4.52}$$

Furthermore, let $B_0(v) = 0$ if $v < 0$, and $= 1$ if $v \geqslant 0$, and let $A_0(u)$ be defined similarly. We have

$$(4.53)\quad \begin{aligned} G_n(t) &= Pr\{N = n,\ T \leqslant t\} \\ &= Pr\{S_1 > 0,\ S_2 > 0, \ldots, S_{n-1} > 0,\ S_n \leqslant 0,\ V_n \leqslant t\} \\ &= Pr[n \text{ is the first weak ladder index of } (-S_n), \text{ and } V_n \leqslant t] \\ &\qquad\qquad (n \geqslant 1,\ t \geqslant 0). \end{aligned}$$

Now Feller's fundamental lemma (4.17) gives

$$(4.54)\quad \sum_{r=1}^{n} \frac{1}{r} Pr\{n \text{ is the first weak ladder index of } (-S_n), \text{ and } V_n \leqslant t\} = \frac{1}{n} Pr\{S_n \leqslant 0;\ V_n \leqslant t\}.$$

However,

$$(4.55)\quad \begin{aligned} a_n(t) &= Pr\{S_n \leqslant 0;\ V_n \leqslant t\} \\ &= Pr\{U_n \geqslant V_n;\ V_n \leqslant t\} \\ &= \int_0^t [1 - A_n(v)]\, dB_n(v). \end{aligned}$$

Using (4.54) and (4.55) and proceeding as in Section 4.2a, we obtain

$$(4.56)\quad \begin{aligned} E(z^N e^{-\theta T}) &= \sum_1^\infty z^n \int_0^\infty e^{-\theta t}\, dG_n(t) \\ &= 1 - \exp\left\{-\sum_1^\infty \frac{z^n}{n} \int_0^\infty e^{-\theta t}[1 - A_n(t)]\, dB_n(t)\right\} \\ &\qquad [|z| < 1,\ \text{Re}\,(\theta) > 0]. \end{aligned}$$

for the transform of the joint distribution of N and T.

Letting $\theta \to 0+$ in (4.56) we find that the p.g.f. of the distribution of the number of customers served during a busy period is given by

$$(4.57)\quad E(z^N) = 1 - \exp\left[-\sum_1^\infty \frac{z^n}{n} Pr\{S_n \leqslant 0\}\right] \qquad (|z| < 1)$$

since $a_n(\infty) = Pr\{S_n \leqslant 0\}$. Furthermore, letting $z \to 1 - 0$ in (4.56) we obtain the L.S.T. of the busy period distribution as

$$(4.58)\quad E(e^{-\theta T}) = 1 - \exp\left[-\sum_1^\infty \frac{1}{n} \int_0^\infty e^{-\theta t}[1 - A_n(t)]\, dB_n(t)\right] \qquad [\text{Re}\,(\theta) > 0].$$

From (4.57) and (4.58) we find that

$$Pr\{N < \infty\} = Pr\{T < \infty\} = \begin{cases} 1 & \text{if } A = \infty \\ 1 - e^{-A} & \text{if } A < \infty. \end{cases} \tag{4.59}$$

b. The Busy Cycle

The interval of time between the commencement of two consecutive busy periods is called a busy cycle. Let Z be the duration of the busy cycle; we have

$$Z = u_1 + u_2 + \cdots + u_N = U_N, \tag{4.60}$$

where N is the number of customers served during such a cycle and is equal to the number served during the busy period. The joint distribution of N and Z is given by

$$\begin{aligned} &Pr\{N = n, Z \leqslant z\} \\ &\quad = Pr\{S_1 > 0, S_2 > 0, \ldots, S_{n-1} > 0, S_n \leqslant 0, U_n \leqslant z\}. \end{aligned} \tag{4.61}$$

Proceeding as in Section 4.3a we find that we have now to evaluate the probability

$$\begin{aligned} b_n(t) &= Pr\{S_n \leqslant 0; U_n \leqslant t\} \\ &= Pr\{V_n \leqslant U_n \leqslant t\} \\ &= \int_0^t B_n(u)\, dA_n(u). \end{aligned} \tag{4.62}$$

The transform of the joint distribution of N and Z is then given by

$$E(z^N e^{-\theta Z}) = 1 - \exp\left[-\sum_1^\infty \frac{z^n}{n} \int_0^\infty e^{-\theta t} B_n(t)\, dA_n(t)\right] \tag{4.63}$$

$$[|z| < 1, \text{Re}(\theta) > 0].$$

c. The First Passage Time $T(u)$

For $u \geqslant 0$, the random variable

$$T(u) = \min(n \mid u + S_n \leqslant 0) \tag{4.64}$$

represents the number of customers served during a busy period initiated by a waiting time $W_0 = u$. We have

$$Pr\{T(u) > n\} = u_n + \sum_{m=1}^n v_m^*(-u) u_{n-m} \qquad (n \geqslant 1). \tag{4.65}$$

In order to prove this, let m_n be the index at which

$$\min(u + S_r, r = 0, 1, \ldots, n)$$

is last attained and consider the more general probability

$$(4.66)\quad Pr\{T(u) > n, u + S_n \leqslant x\} = Pr\{u + S_1 > 0, u + S_2 > 0, \ldots, u + S_{n-1} > 0, 0 < u + S_n \leqslant x\}.$$

We have

$$\begin{aligned}(4.67)\quad & Pr\{T(u) > n, u + S_n \leqslant x\} \\ &= \sum_{m=0}^{n} Pr\{T(u) > n, u + S_n \leqslant x, m_n = m\} \\ &= \sum_{m=1}^{n-1} \int_{0+}^{u} (-d_y) Pr\{u + S_r \geqslant u + S_m \, (r = 0, 1, \ldots, m-1), \\ &\qquad 0 < y \leqslant u + S_m \leqslant u, \\ &\qquad u + S_r > u + S_m \, (r = m+1, \ldots, n-1), \\ &\qquad 0 < u + S_n \leqslant x\} \\ &\quad + Pr\{u + S_1 > u, u + S_2 > u, \ldots, u + S_{n-1} > u, \\ &\qquad u < u + S_n \leqslant x\} \\ &\quad + Pr\{u + S_r \geqslant u + S_n \, (r = 0, 1, \ldots, n-1), \\ &\qquad 0 < u + S_n \leqslant x\} \\ &= \sum_{m=1}^{n-1} \int_{0+}^{u} (-d_y) Pr\{S_1 \leqslant 0, S_2 \leqslant 0, \ldots, S_{m-1} \leqslant 0, \\ &\qquad y - u \leqslant S_m \leqslant 0\}. \\ &\qquad Pr\{S_1 > 0, S_2 > 0, \ldots, S_{n-m-1} > 0, 0 < S_{n-m} \leqslant x - y\} \\ &\quad + Pr\{S_1 > 0, S_2 > 0, \ldots, S_{n-1} > 0, 0 < S_n \leqslant x - u\} \\ &\quad + Pr\{S_1 \leqslant 0, S_2 \leqslant 0, \ldots, S_{n-1} \leqslant 0, -u < S_n \leqslant x - u\} \\ &= \sum_{m=1}^{n-1} \int_{-u+0}^{\min(0, x-u]+0} (-d_y) v_m{}^*(y) u_{n-m}(x - u - y) + u_n(x - u) \\ &\quad + \int_{-u+0}^{\min(0, x-u]+0} (-d_y) v_n{}^*(y).\end{aligned}$$

Letting $x \to \infty$ in (4.67) we obtain (4.65) since $u_n(\infty) = u_n$. Now since $\Sigma\, v_n{}^*(-u) < \infty$ $(u > 0)$, whereas $u_n \to e^{-A}$ or 0 depending on whether $A < \infty$ or $A = \infty$, we find from (4.67) that for $u > 0$

$$(4.68)\quad Pr\{T(u) = \infty\} = \begin{cases} 0 & \text{if } A = \infty \\ e^{-A}\left[1 + \sum_{1}^{\infty} v_n{}^*(-u)\right] & \text{if } A < \infty. \end{cases}$$

For $u = 0$ the same arguments lead to (4.59).

From (4.67) we also obtain the result

$$\sum_0^\infty z^n \int_{0+}^\infty e^{\theta x}\, d_x Pr\{T(u) > n,\, u + S_n \leqslant x\} = e^{\theta u} u(\theta, z)\left[1 + \int_{-u+0}^{0+} e^{\theta y}(-d_x)V^*(x, z)\right] \quad [|z| < 1,\ \text{Re}\,(\theta) < 0], \tag{4.69}$$

where

$$V^*(x, z) = \sum_1^\infty z^n v_n^*(x) \qquad (|z| < 1,\ x \leqslant 0). \tag{4.70}$$

4.4 THE IDLE PERIOD

The length of the idle period following a busy period is given by

$$I = u_N - (W_{N-1} + v_N) = -(S_{N-1} + v_N - u_N) = -S_N \geqslant 0, \tag{4.71}$$

where N is the number of customers served during the busy period. We can also obtain (4.71) from the identity $Z = T + I$, which gives

$$I = Z - T = U_N - V_N = -S_N \tag{4.72}$$

on account of (4.50) and (4.60). The d.f. of I is given by

$$\begin{aligned} Pr\{I \leqslant x\} &= \sum_{n=1}^\infty Pr\{N = n,\, I \leqslant x\} \\ &= \sum_{n=1}^\infty Pr\{S_1 > 0,\, S_2 > 0, \ldots, S_{n-1} > 0,\, 0 \leqslant -S_n \leqslant x\} \\ &= \sum_{n=1}^\infty g_n^*(-x), \end{aligned} \tag{4.73}$$

so that the L.S.T. of I is given by

$$\int_0^\infty e^{-\theta x}\, d_x Pr\{I \leqslant x\} = g^*(\theta, 1) = 1 - \exp\left[-\sum_1^\infty \frac{1}{n}\int_{-\infty}^{0+} e^{\theta x}\, dK_n(x)\right] \quad [\text{Re}\,(\theta) > 0]. \tag{4.74}$$

4.5 THE WAITING TIME

a. The Distribution of W_n

Let

$$F_n(u; x) = Pr\{W_n \leqslant x \mid W_0 = u\} \tag{4.75}$$

be the transition d.f. of the Markov chain $\{W_n\}$. From (4.4) we find that

$$F_n(u; x) = Pr\{S_r \leqslant x \quad (r = 0, 1, \ldots, n-1);\ u + S_n \leqslant x\}. \tag{4.76}$$

To obtain (4.76) let M_n be the index at which max $(0, S_1, S_2, \ldots, S_{n-1}, u + S_n)$ is first attained; we can then write

$$\begin{aligned} F_n(u; x) &= \sum_{m=0}^{n} Pr\{W_n \leqslant x; M_n = m \mid W_0 = u\} \\ &= \sum_{m=1}^{n-1} Pr\{S_r < S_m \leqslant x\,(r = 0, 1, \ldots, m-1), \\ &\qquad S_r \leqslant S_m\,(r = m+1, \ldots, n-1), u + S_n \leqslant S_m\} \\ &\qquad + Pr\{S_1 \leqslant 0, S_2 \leqslant 0, \ldots, S_{n-1} \leqslant 0, u + S_n \leqslant 0\} \\ &\qquad + Pr\{S_r < u + S_n\,(r = 0, 1, \ldots, n-1), u + S_n \leqslant x\} \\ &= \sum_{m=1}^{n-1} Pr\{S_1 > 0, S_2 > 0, \ldots, S_{m-1} > 0, 0 < S_m \leqslant x\}. \\ &\qquad Pr\{S_1 \leqslant 0, S_2 \leqslant 0, \ldots, S_{n-m-1} \leqslant 0, S_{n-m} \leqslant -u\} \\ &\qquad + Pr\{S_1 \leqslant 0, S_2 \leqslant 0, \ldots, S_{n-1} \leqslant 0, S_n \leqslant -u\} \\ &\qquad + Pr\{u + S_1 > 0, u + S_2 > 0, \ldots, u + S_{n-1} > 0, \\ &\qquad\qquad 0 < u + S_n \leqslant x\} \\ &= \sum_{m=1}^{n-1} u_m(x) \int_{-\infty}^{-u} (-d_y) v_{n-m}^*(y) \\ &\qquad + \int_{-\infty}^{-u} (-d_y) v_n^*(y) + Pr\{T(u) > n, u + S_n \leqslant x\}. \end{aligned} \tag{4.77}$$

Hence, using (4.69) we obtain the result

$$\begin{aligned} &\sum_0^\infty z^n \int_{0-}^{\infty} e^{\theta x}\, d_x F_n(u; x) \\ &= u(\theta, z)\left\{\int_{-\infty}^{-u} (-d_y) V^*(y, z) + e^{\theta u} + e^{\theta u} \int_{-u+0}^{0+} e^{\theta y} (-d_y) V^*(y, z)\right\} \\ &\hspace{20em} (|z| < 1,\ \mathrm{Re}\,(\theta) < 0], \end{aligned} \tag{4.78}$$

where $V^*(x, z)$ is defined by (4.70) and we note that $F_0(u; x) = 0$ if $x < u$, and $= 1$ if $x \geqslant u$. When $u = 0$, the right-hand side member of (4.78) reduces to

$$u(\theta, z)\left\{\int_{-\infty}^{0} (-d_y)V^*(y, z) + 1\right\} = u(\theta, z)v^*(0, z);$$

using (4.34) and (4.47) we obtain the elegant result

$$(4.79)\quad \sum_0^\infty z^n \int_{0-}^\infty e^{\theta x}\, dF_n(x) = \exp\left[\sum_1^\infty \frac{z^n}{n} Pr\{S_n \leqslant 0\} + \sum_1^\infty \frac{z^n}{n}\int_{0+}^\infty e^{\theta x}\, dK_n(x)\right]$$
$$[|z| < 1, \operatorname{Re}(\theta) < 0],$$

where we have written $F_n(x) = F_n(0; x)$ for convenience.

b. The Limiting Distribution

Since $v_n^*(-\infty) = v_n^*$ we can write (4.77) as

$$(4.80)\quad F_n(u; x) = \left[v_n^* + \sum_1^{n-1} u_m(x)v_{n-m}^*\right] - \left[v_n^*(-u) - \sum_1^{n-1} u_m(x)v_{n-m}^*(-u)\right] + Pr\{T(u) > n, u + S_n \leq x\}$$

Now since $\Sigma\, u_n(x) < \infty$ $(x \geqslant 0)$ and $\Sigma\, v_n^*(-u) < \infty$ $(u \geqslant 0)$, the product of these two series also converges and therefore its general term

$$(4.81)\quad v_n^*(-u) + \sum_1^{n-1} u_m(x)v_{n-m}^*(-u) \to 0$$

as $n \to \infty$. From (4.68) we find similarly that

$$(4.82)\quad Pr\{T(u) > n, u + S_n \leqslant x\} \to 0 \quad \text{as} \quad n \to \infty.$$

Finally, we note that $v_n^* \to e^{-B}$ or 0 depending on whether $B < \infty$ or $B = \infty$, and therefore

$$(4.83)\quad v_n^* + \sum_1^{n-1} u_m(x)v_{n-m}^* \to e^{-B}\left[1 + \sum_1^\infty u_n(x)\right] \quad \text{if} \quad B < \infty.$$

From (4.80) to (4.83) we obtain the result

$$(4.84)\quad \lim_{n\to\infty} F_n(u; x) = \begin{cases} 0 & \text{if} \quad B = \infty \\ e^{-B}\left[1 + \sum_1^\infty u_n(x)\right] & \text{if} \quad B < \infty. \end{cases}$$

We have thus proved that the limiting d.f.

$$F^*(x) = \lim_{n\to\infty} F_n(u; x) \qquad (x \geqslant 0) \tag{4.85}$$

exists independently of the initial waiting time $W_0 = u$; $F^*(x) \equiv 0$ if $B = \infty$, whereas

$$F^*(x) = e^{-B}\left[1 + \sum_1^\infty u_n(x)\right] \qquad \text{if} \quad B < \infty. \tag{4.86}$$

The transform of this limiting d.f. is given by

$$\begin{aligned}\int_{0-}^{\infty} e^{\theta x}\, dF^*(x) &= e^{-B} u(\theta, 1)\\ &= \exp\left[-\sum_1^\infty \frac{1}{n}\int_{0+}^{\infty} (1 - e^{\theta x})\, dK_n(x)\right] \qquad [\text{Re}(\theta) < 0].\end{aligned}$$

In particular,

$$F^*(0) = e^{-B}. \tag{4.87}$$

4.6 TWO SPECIAL CASES

a. The Expressions $u(\theta, z)$ and $v^*(\theta, z)$

In the application of the results of the preceding sections to special cases, we shall have to evaluate the expressions

$$u(\theta, z) = \exp\left[\sum_1^\infty \frac{z^n}{n}\int_{0+}^{\infty} e^{\theta x}\, dK_n(x)\right] \qquad [|z| < 1, \text{Re}(\theta) \leqslant 0], \tag{4.88}$$

and

$$v^*(\theta, z) = \exp\left[\sum_1^\infty \frac{z^n}{n}\int_{-\infty}^{0+} e^{\theta x}\, dK_n(x)\right] \qquad [|z| < 1, \text{Re}(\theta) \geqslant 0]. \tag{4.89}$$

It is easily verified that

$$u(\theta, z)v^*(\theta, z) = [1 - z\phi(\theta)]^{-1} \qquad \text{if} \quad \text{Re}(\theta) = 0, \tag{4.90}$$

where $\phi(\theta) = E(e^{\theta} X_n)$ is the moment generating function of X_n, and we assume that $\phi(\sigma) < \infty$, where $\sigma = \text{Re}(\theta)$.

In the case where the basic random variables are discrete, we set

$$u(\theta, z) = \exp\left[\sum_{n=1}^\infty \frac{z^n}{n}\sum_{j=1}^\infty \theta^j Pr(S_n = j)\right] \qquad (|z| < 1, |\theta| \leqslant 1), \tag{4.91}$$

and

$$v^*(\theta, z) = \exp\left[\sum_{n=1}^\infty \frac{z^n}{n}\sum_{j=-\infty}^{0} \theta^j Pr(S_n = j)\right] \qquad (|z| <, |\theta| \geqslant 1), \tag{4.92}$$

in analogy with (4.88) and (4.89).

b. Case (1)

We shall first consider the special case where the random variables X_n have the distribution given by

$$dK(x) = Pr\{x < X_n < x + dx\} \tag{4.93}$$

$$= dx \int_{v=\max(0,x)}^{\infty} e^{-\lambda(v-x)} \frac{\lambda^s(v-x)^{s-1}}{(s-1)!} dB(v) \qquad (-\infty < x < \infty),$$

where $B(x)$ is a d.f. with the L.S.T. $\psi(\theta)$. Let us assume that

$$0 < -\psi'(0) < \infty.$$

We have

$$\phi(\theta) = \int_{-\infty}^{\infty} e^{\theta x}\, dK(x)$$

$$= \int_{v=0}^{\infty} dB(v) \int_{x=-\infty}^{v} e^{\theta x - \lambda(v-x)} \frac{\lambda^s(v-x)^{s-1}}{(s-1)!} dx \tag{4.94}$$

$$= \int_0^{\infty} dB(v) e^{\theta v} \left(\frac{\lambda}{\theta+\lambda}\right)^s = \frac{\lambda^s \psi(-\theta)}{(\theta+\lambda)^s}.$$

From (4.93) and (4.94) we find that the distribution of S_n is given by

$$dK_n(x) = Pr\{x < S_n < x + dx\} \tag{4.95}$$

$$= dx \int_{v=\max(0,x)}^{\infty} e^{-\lambda(v-x)} \frac{\lambda^{ns}(v-x)^{ns-1}}{(ns-1)!} dB_n(v) \qquad (-\infty < x < \infty).$$

The expressions (4.88) and (4.89) involve the roots of the functional equation $1 - z\phi(\theta) = 0$, which in this case reduces to

$$(\theta + \lambda)^s = z\lambda^s\psi(-\theta) \qquad (|z| < 1). \tag{4.96}$$

Substituting $\xi = (\theta + \lambda) \mid \lambda$ we can write (4.96) as

$$\xi^s = z\psi(\lambda - \lambda\xi) \qquad (|z| < 1). \tag{4.97}$$

Let us, however, consider the more general equation

$$\gamma^s = z\psi(\theta + \lambda - \lambda\gamma) \qquad [\text{Re}\,(\theta) \geqslant 0,\ |z| < 1]. \tag{4.98}$$

For Re $(\theta) \geqslant 0$, $|z| < 1$, and $|\gamma| = 1 - \epsilon$, where ϵ is arbitrarily small, we have

$$\left|\frac{\psi(\theta + \lambda - \lambda\gamma)}{\gamma^s}\right| \leqslant \frac{\psi(\lambda - \lambda\,|\gamma|)}{|\gamma|^s} < |z|^{-1},$$

so that by Rouche's theorem the equation (4.98) has exactly s roots $\gamma_r \equiv \gamma_r(\theta, z)$ within the unit circle. We have

$$\gamma_r = \omega_r z^{1/s}[\psi(\theta + \lambda - \lambda\gamma_r)]^{1/s} \qquad (r = 1, 2, \ldots, s) \tag{4.99}$$

where $\omega_1, \omega_2, \ldots, \omega_s$ are the sth roots of unity. It is easily seen that for $z \neq 0$, these roots are distinct, and γ_r is uniquely determined by (4.99). We now obtain the Lagrange expansion of $\log(1 - \gamma\gamma_r)$ as

$$\log(1 - \gamma\gamma_r) = \sum_{j=1}^{\infty} \frac{(\omega_r z^{1/s})^j}{j!} \left(\frac{\partial}{\partial x}\right)^{j-1} \left[\psi(\theta + \lambda - \lambda x)^{j/s} \frac{-\gamma}{1 - x\gamma}\right]_{x=0} \tag{4.100}$$

in the region $|\gamma| \leqslant 1$. Adding (4.100) over $r = 1, 2, \ldots, s$, we obtain

$$\sum_{r=1}^{s} \log(1 - \gamma\gamma_r) = \sum_{j=1}^{\infty} \frac{z^{j/s}}{j!} \left(\frac{\partial}{\partial x}\right)^{j-1} \times \left[\psi(\theta + \lambda - \lambda x)^{j/s} \frac{-\gamma}{1 - x\gamma}\right]_{x=0} \sum_{r=1}^{s} \omega_r^{\,j}; \tag{4.101}$$

since $\omega_1^{\,j} + \omega_2^{\,j} + \cdots + \omega_s^{\,j} = s$ if j is a multiple of s, and $= 0$ otherwise, we find that

$$\sum_{r=1}^{s} \log(1 - \gamma\gamma_r) = \sum_{n=1}^{\infty} \frac{sz^n}{(ns)!} \left(\frac{\partial}{\partial x}\right)^{ns-1} \times \left[\psi(\theta + \lambda - \lambda x)^n \frac{-\gamma}{1 - x\gamma}\right]_{x=0} \qquad (|\gamma| \leqslant 1). \tag{4.102}$$

To evaluate the derivatives in (4.102) we note that

$$\psi(\theta + \lambda - \lambda x)^n \left(\frac{\gamma}{1 - x\gamma}\right) = \int_0^{\infty} e^{-(\theta+\lambda-\lambda x)v}\, dB_n(v) \gamma(1 - x\gamma)^{-1} = \int_0^{\infty} e^{-(\theta+\lambda)v}\, dB_n(v) \sum_{p=0}^{\infty} \frac{(\lambda x v)^p}{p!} \sum_{q=0}^{\infty} x^q \gamma^{q+1} \tag{4.103}$$

$$= \int_0^{\infty} e^{-(\theta+\lambda)v}\, dB_n(v) \sum_{q=0}^{\infty} x^q \sum_{p=0}^{q} \frac{(\lambda v)^p \gamma^{q-p+1}}{p!}, \tag{4.104}$$

and therefore

$$\sum_{r=1}^{s} \log(1 - \gamma\gamma_r) = -\sum_{n=1}^{\infty} \frac{sz^n}{(ns)!} \int_0^{\infty} e^{-(\theta+\lambda)v}\, dB_n(v), \quad (ns - 1)! \sum_{p=0}^{ns-1} \frac{(\lambda v)^p \gamma^{ns-p}}{p!}$$
$$= -\sum_{n=1}^{\infty} \frac{z^n}{n} \sum_{p=1}^{ns} \gamma^p \int_0^{\infty} e^{-(\theta+\lambda)v} \frac{(\lambda v)^{ns-p}}{(ns - p)!}\, dB_n(v). \tag{4.105}$$

Now it is clear that $\gamma_r(\theta, z)$ are continuous functions of θ and z in the region $\text{Re}(\theta) \geqslant 0$, $|z| < 1$, and as $\theta \to 0$, $\gamma_r(\theta, z) \to \gamma_r(0, z) = \xi_r(z)$ (say), where $\xi_r \equiv \xi_r(z)$ $(r = 1, 2, \ldots, s)$ are the roots of the functional equation (4.97). We have $|\xi_r| < 1$ $(r = 1, 2, \ldots, s)$, and

$$(4.106) \quad \sum_{r=1}^{s} \log(1 - \gamma\xi_r) = -\sum_{n=1}^{\infty} \frac{z^n}{n} \sum_{p=1}^{ns} \gamma^p \int_0^\infty e^{-\lambda v} \frac{(\lambda v)^{ns-p}}{(ns-p)!} dB_n(v) \qquad (|\gamma| \leqslant 1).$$

Furthermore, it is seen that the equation (4.96) has s roots $\theta_r \equiv \theta_r(z)$ $(r = 1, 2, \ldots, s)$ with $\text{Re}(\theta_r) < 0$; we can therefore write the left-hand side of (4.106) as

$$(4.107) \qquad \sum_{r=1}^{s} \log\left(1 - \gamma \frac{\lambda + \theta_r}{\lambda}\right).$$

Let us now consider the expression in the exponent in (4.89). We have

$$\begin{aligned}
&\sum_1^\infty \frac{z^n}{n} \int_{-\infty}^{0+} e^{\theta x}\, dK_n(x) \\
&= \sum_1^\infty \frac{z^n}{n} \int_{-\infty}^{0} e^{\theta x}\, dx \int_{v=0}^{\infty} e^{-\lambda(v-x)} \frac{\lambda^{ns}(v-x)^{ns-1}}{(ns-1)!} dB_n(v) \\
&= \sum_1^\infty \frac{z^n}{n} \int_{v=0}^{\infty} dB_n(v) e^{-\lambda v} \int_0^\infty e^{-(\theta+\lambda)x} \frac{\lambda^{ns}(v+x)^{ns-1}}{(ns-1)!} dx \\
(4.108) \quad &= \sum_1^\infty \frac{z^n}{n} \int_{v=0}^{\infty} dB_n(v) e^{-\lambda v} \lambda^{ns} \sum_{p=0}^{ns-1} \frac{v^{ns-1-p}}{(ns-1-p)!} \int_0^\infty e^{-(\theta+\lambda)x} \frac{x^p}{p!} dx \\
&= \sum_1^\infty \frac{z^n}{n} \sum_{p=1}^{ns} \left(\frac{\lambda}{\theta+\lambda}\right)^p \int_0^\infty e^{-\lambda v} \frac{(\lambda v)^{ns-p}}{(ns-p)!} dB_n(v) \\
&= -\sum_{r=1}^{s} \log\left(1 - \frac{\lambda}{\theta+\lambda} \frac{\lambda+\theta_r}{\lambda}\right) = \sum_{r=1}^{s} \log\left(\frac{\theta+\lambda}{\theta-\theta_r}\right) \\
&\qquad [\text{Re}(\theta) \geqslant 0],
\end{aligned}$$

using (4.106) and (4.108) and since $|\lambda(\theta + \lambda)^{-1}| \leqslant 1$ for $\text{Re}(\theta) \geqslant 0$. Thus

$$(4.109) \quad v^*(\theta, z) = \prod_{r=1}^{s} \left(\frac{\theta+\lambda}{\theta-\theta_r}\right) \qquad [\text{Re}(\theta) \geqslant 0, |z| < 1],$$

and

$$(4.110) \quad u(\theta, z) = \frac{1}{1 - z\phi(\theta)} \prod_{r=1}^{s} \left(\frac{\theta-\theta_r}{\theta+\lambda}\right) \qquad [\text{Re}(\theta) \leqslant 0, |z| < 1].$$

In (4.110) we have used (4.90) and the fact that $u(\theta, z)$ is uniquely determined by its properties of analyticity and boundedness for Re $(\theta) \leqslant 0$ [see Kemperman (1961), page 72].

c. Case (2)

Our second special case is the sequence $\{X_n - s\}$, where

(4.111) $$Pr\{X_n = j\} = \begin{cases} k_j & (j = 0, 1, 2, \ldots), \\ 0 & \text{otherwise}, \end{cases}$$

and

(4.112) $$K(\theta) = E(\theta^{X_n}) = \sum_{j=0}^{\infty} k_j \theta^j \qquad (|\theta| < 1).$$

The partial sums of this sequence are $S_n = X_1 + X_2 + \cdots + X_n - ns$ $(n \geqslant 1)$, and therefore

(4.113) $$Pr\{S_n = j\} = \begin{cases} k_{j+ns}^{(n)} & (j \geqslant -ns) \\ 0 & (j < -ns), \end{cases}$$

where

(4.114) $$\sum_{j=0}^{\infty} k_j^{(n)} \theta^j = [K(\theta)]^n \qquad (n \geqslant 1).$$

The moment generating function $\phi(\xi)$ in this case is given by $\phi(\xi) = E(\xi^{X_n - s}) = K(\xi)\xi^{-s}$; the equation $1 - z\phi(\xi) = 0$ therefore reduces to

(4.115) $$\xi^s = zK(\xi).$$

It is seen that (4.97) is a special case of the functional equation (4.115). Proceeding as in the last section we find that for $|z| < 1$, (4.115) has s roots $\xi_r = \xi_r(z)$ $(r = 1, 2, \ldots, s)$ with $|\xi_r| < 1$, and that

$$\sum_{r=1}^{s} \log (1 - \xi_r \theta^{-1}) = - \sum_{1}^{\infty} \frac{z^n}{n} \sum_{j=-ns}^{-1} \theta^j k_{j+ns}^{(n)}$$

$$|\theta| > \max (|\xi_1|, |\xi_2|, \ldots, |\xi_s|).$$

Hence we obtain

(4.117) $$v^*(\theta, z) = \exp \left[\sum_{1}^{\infty} \frac{z^n}{n} \sum_{j=-ns}^{-1} \theta^j k_{j+ns}^{(n)} + \sum_{1}^{\infty} \frac{z^n}{n} k_{ns}^{(n)} \right]$$

$$= \frac{\exp \left[\sum_{1}^{\infty} \frac{z^n}{n} k_{ns}^{(n)} \right]}{\prod_{r=1}^{s} (1 - \xi_r \theta^{-1})} \qquad (|z| < 1, |\theta| \geqslant 1),$$

and

$$u(\theta, z) = \{[1 - z\phi(\theta)]v^*(\theta, z)\}^{-1}$$

$$= \frac{\exp\left[-\sum_1^\infty \frac{z^n}{n} k_{ns}^{(n)}\right]}{1 - z\phi(\theta)} \prod_{r=1}^{s} (1 - \xi_r\theta^{-1})$$

$$= \frac{\exp\left[-\sum_1^\infty \frac{z^n}{n} k_{ns}^{(n)}\right]}{\theta^s - zK(\theta)} \prod_{r=1}^{s} (\theta - \xi_r) \qquad (|z| < 1, |\theta| \leqslant 1).$$

4.7 THE QUEUE $E_s/G/1$

a. The Waiting Time

Let us consider the queueing system in which the interarrival time u_n has the distribution

$$(4.119) \qquad dA(x) = Pr(x < u_n < x + dx) = e^{-\lambda x} \frac{\lambda^s x^{s-1}}{(s-1)!} dx,$$

whereas the service time v_n has the distribution $dB(x)$ $(0 < x < \infty)$. Let $\psi(\theta)$ be the L.S.T. of $B(x)$, and assume that $0 < -\psi'(0) < \infty$. The relative traffic intensity is then given by $\rho = -\lambda\psi'(0)/s < \infty$. If $X_n = v_n - u_n$, then the distribution of X_n is given by (4.93). The expressions $u(\theta, z)$ and $v^*(\theta, z)$ in this case are therefore given by (4.110) and (4.109) respectively. It follows that the generating function of the waiting time W_n is given by

$$(4.120) \quad \sum_0^\infty z^n \int_{0-}^\infty e^{\theta x}\, dF_n(x) = u(\theta, z)v^*(0, z)$$

$$= \frac{\lambda^s}{(\theta + \lambda)^s - z\lambda^s\psi(-\theta)} \prod_{r=1}^{s} \left(1 - \frac{\theta}{\theta_r}\right)$$

$$[|z| < 1, \text{Re}(\theta) \leqslant 0]$$

To obtain the limiting distribution $F^*(x)$ from (4.120) we observe that as $z \to 1 - 0$, $\xi_r(z) \to \zeta_r$ $(r = 1, 2, \ldots, s)$, where the ζ_r are the roots of the equation

$$(4.121) \qquad \zeta^s = \psi(\lambda - \lambda\zeta)$$

within the unit circle. Moreover, if $\rho \leqslant 1$, then $|\zeta_r| < 1$ $(r = 1, 2, \ldots, s - 1)$ and $\zeta_s = 1$, whereas if $\rho > 1$, then $|\zeta_r| < 1$ $(r = 1, 2, \ldots, s)$. Accordingly, as $z \to 1$, $\theta_r(z) \to \theta_r^0$, where θ_r^0 $(r = 1, 2, \ldots, s)$ are the roots of the equation

$$(4.122) \qquad (\theta + \lambda)^s = \lambda^s\psi(-\theta)$$

with $\text{Re}(\theta) \leqslant 0$. We have $\text{Re}(\theta_r^0) < 0$ ($r = 1, 2, \ldots, s-1$), whereas $\text{Re}(\theta_s^0) < 0$ or $\theta_s^0 = 0$ depending on whether $\rho > 1$ or $\rho \leqslant 1$. Hence if $\rho < 1$,

$$(4.123) \quad \int_{0-}^{\infty} e^{\theta x}\, dF^*(x) = \lim_{z\to 1-0} (1-z) \sum_0^{\infty} z^n \int_{0-}^{\infty} e^{\theta x}\, dF_n(x)$$
$$= \frac{(1-\rho)s\lambda^{s-1}\theta}{(\theta+\lambda)^s - \lambda^s \psi(-\theta)} \prod_{r=1}^{s-1}\left(1 - \frac{\theta}{\theta_r^0}\right) \quad (\text{Re}(\theta) \leqslant 0),$$

because $\theta_s'(1) = \lambda(s - s\rho)^{-1}$; if $\rho \geqslant 1$, $F^*(x) \equiv 0$.

b. The Busy Period

To obtain the transform of the joint distribution of the length of the busy period and the number of customers served during this period, we have to evaluate the expression

$$\sum_1^{\infty} \frac{z^n}{n} \int_0^{\infty} e^{-\theta t}[1 - A_n(t)]\, dB_n(t) \qquad [\text{Re}(\theta) > 0, |z| < 1].$$

We find that this expression

$$(4.124) \quad = \sum_1^{\infty} \frac{z^n}{n} \int_0^{\infty} e^{-\theta t}\, dB_n(t) \int_t^{\infty} e^{-\lambda u} \frac{\lambda^{ns} u^{ns-1}}{(ns-1)!}\, du$$
$$= \sum_1^{\infty} \frac{z^n}{n} \int_0^{\infty} e^{-\theta t}\, dB_n(t) \sum_{p=1}^{ns} e^{-\lambda t} \frac{(\lambda t)^{ns-p}}{(ns-p)!}$$
$$= -\sum_{r=1}^{s} \frac{z^n}{n} \sum_{p=1}^{ns} \int_0^{\infty} e^{-(\theta+\lambda)t} \frac{(\lambda t)^{ns-p}}{(ns-p)!}\, dB_n(t)$$
$$= -\sum_{r=1}^{s} \log(1 - \gamma_r)$$

using the identity (4.105). Hence using (4.56) we find that

$$(4.125) \quad \sum_1^{\infty} z^n \int_0^{\infty} e^{-\theta t}\, dG_n(t) = 1 - \prod_{r=1}^{s} (1 - \gamma_r) \qquad [\text{Re}(\theta) > 0, |z| < 1].$$

c. The Queue-Length

In this system the customers can be assumed to pass through s different stages, the durations of the stages being mutually independent random variables with the distribution $\lambda e^{-\lambda t}\, dt$ ($0 < t < \infty$). Let $Q(t)$ be the number of stages completed by the customers at time t; then except in the special case $E_s/M1$, the process $Q(t)$ is non-Markovian. However, let the instants of departure of the successive customers be denoted by $t_0, t_1, t_2, \ldots$, and put $Q_n = Q(t_n + 0)$ ($n = 0, 1, \ldots$); then $\{Q_n\}$ is a Markov chain imbedded in the process $Q(t)$. Now, let X_n denote the number of stages which are completed during $(t_{n-1}+0, t_n)$ $(n = 1, 2, \ldots)$; then $X_1, X_2, X_3, \ldots$ are mutually independent and identically distributed random variables. We have

$$k_j = Pr\{X_n = j\} = \int_0^\infty e^{-\lambda t}\frac{(\lambda t)^j}{j!}\,dB(t) \qquad (j \geqslant 0), \tag{4.126}$$

$$K(\theta) = E(\theta^{X_n}) = \sum_0^\infty k_j\theta^j = \psi(\lambda - \lambda\theta), \tag{4.127}$$

and

$$E(X_n) = K'(1) = -\lambda\psi'(0) = s\rho < \infty. \tag{4.128}$$

We have the recurrence relations

$$Q_{n+1} = \begin{cases} Q_n + X_{n+1} - s & \text{if } \; Q_n > s \\ X_{n+1} & \text{if } \; Q_n \leqslant s, \end{cases}$$

which can be written as

$$Q_{n+1} = \max\,(X_{n+1}, Q_n + X_{n+1} - s) \qquad (n = 0, 1, \ldots). \tag{4.129}$$

If $Q_0 = 0$, we obtain from (4.129) the result

$$Q_n = X_n + \max\,[S_{n-1} - S_{n-r-1}\,(0 \leqslant r \leqslant n-1)], \tag{4.130}$$

where $S_n = X_1 + X_2 + \cdots + X_n - ns$ $(n \geqslant 1)$. Since $S_{n-1} - S_{n-r-1}$ has the same distribution as S_r, we find that

$$Q_n \sim X_n + w_{n-1} \qquad (n \geqslant 1), \tag{4.131}$$

where

$$w_n = \max\,(0, S_1, S_2, \ldots, S_n). \tag{4.132}$$

The basic random variables here are of the form $X_n - s$, where the distribution of X_n is given by (4.126). Using (4.117) and (4.118) we find that the transform of the distribution of w_n is given by

$$\begin{aligned} \sum_1^\infty z^n E(\theta^{w_n}) &= u(\theta, z)v^*(1, z) \\ &= \frac{1}{\theta^s - zK(\theta)}\prod_{r=1}^{s}\left(\frac{\theta - \xi_r}{1 - \xi_r}\right) \qquad (|z| < 1, |\theta| \leqslant 1). \end{aligned} \tag{4.133}$$

For the probability generating function of the random variable $w_\infty = \lim_{n\to\infty} w_n$, we have

$$\begin{aligned} E(\theta^{w_\infty}) &= \lim_{z\to 1}\,(1 - z)\sum_0^\infty z^n E(\theta^{w_n}) \\ &= \frac{(s-\alpha)(1-\theta)}{K(\theta) - \theta^s}\prod_{r=1}^{s-1}\left(\frac{\theta - \zeta_r}{1 - \zeta_r}\right) \end{aligned} \tag{4.134}$$

if $K'(1) < s$, whereas $w_\infty = \infty$ with probability one if $K'(1) \geqslant s$.

From (4.131) and (4.133) we obtain the result

$$\sum_0^\infty z^n E(\theta^{Q_n}) = 1 + \sum_{n=0}^\infty z^{n+1} E(\theta^{X_{n+1}+w_n}) = 1 + \frac{zK(\theta)}{\theta^s - zK(\theta)} \prod_{r=1}^s \left(\frac{\theta - \xi_r}{1 - \xi_r}\right). \tag{4.135}$$

The distribution of the limiting queue length Q_∞ is given by

$$E(\theta^{Q_\infty}) = D(\theta^{X_n + w_\infty}) = K(\theta)E(\theta^{w_\infty}) = \frac{s(1-\rho)(1-\theta)}{1 - \theta^s/K(\theta)} \prod_{r=1}^{s-1} \left(\frac{\theta - \zeta_r}{1 - \zeta_r}\right) \tag{4.136}$$

if $\rho < 1$, whereas $Q_\infty = \infty$ with probability one if $\rho \geqslant 1$.

4.8 THE QUEUE $GI/E_s/1$

a. The Waiting Time

The queue $GI/E_s/1$ is obtained from $E_s/G/1$ by interchanging the inter-arrival and service times and is thus the dual of $E_s/G/1$. Here the inter-arrival time u_n' has the distribution $dB(x)$ and the L.S.T. $\psi(\theta)$, whereas the service time v_n' has the gamma distribution (4.119). The relative traffic intensity is in this case given by $\rho_2 = s[-\lambda\psi'(0)]^{-1} = \rho^{-1} < \infty$. Furthermore,

$$K_n'(x) = Pr\{v_n' - u_n' \leqslant x\} = Pr\{v_n - u_n \geqslant -x\} = 1 - K_n(-x) \quad (-\infty < x < \infty), \tag{4.137}$$

where $K_n(x)$ is defined by (4.95). Hence

$$u(\theta, z) = \exp\left[\sum_1^\infty \frac{z^n}{n} \int_{0+}^\infty e^{\theta x}\, dK_n'(x)\right] = \exp\left[\sum_1^\infty \frac{z^n}{n} \int_{-\infty}^{0-} e^{-\theta x}\, dK_n(x)\right] = \prod_{r=1}^s \left(\frac{\theta - \lambda}{\theta + \theta_r}\right) \quad [|z| < 1, \operatorname{Re}(\theta) \leqslant 0], \tag{4.138}$$

$$v^*(\theta, z) = \exp\left[\sum_1^\infty \frac{z^n}{n} \int_{-\infty}^{0+} e^{\theta x}\, dK_n'(x)\right] = \exp\left[\sum_1^\infty \frac{z^n}{n} \int_{0-}^\infty e^{-\theta x}\, dK_n(x)\right] = \frac{1}{1 - z\phi(-\theta)} \prod_{r=1}^s \frac{\theta + \theta_r}{\theta - \lambda} \quad [|z| < 1, \operatorname{Re}(\theta) \geqslant 0]. \tag{4.139}$$

It follows that

$$\sum_{n=0}^{\infty} z^n \int_{0-}^{\infty} e^{\theta x}\, dF_n(x) = \frac{1}{1-z} \prod_{r=1}^{s} \left(\frac{1-\theta/\lambda}{1+\theta/\theta_r}\right) \tag{4.140}$$

$$[|z| < 1, \text{Re}(\theta \leqslant 0)].$$

As in (4.123), it is found that the limiting distribution $F^*(x) \equiv 0$ if $\rho_2 \geqslant 1$, whereas if $\rho_2 < 1$, $F^*(x)$ has the transform

$$\int_{0-}^{\infty} e^{\theta x}\, dF^*(x) = \prod_{r=1}^{s} \left(\frac{1-\theta/\lambda}{1+\theta/\theta_r^0}\right) \qquad (\text{Re}(\theta) \leqslant 0), \tag{4.141}$$

where $\text{Re}(\theta_r^0) < 0$ $(r = 1, 2, \ldots, s)$.

b. The Busy Period

Proceeding as in Section 4.7b we find that

$$\begin{aligned}
&\sum_1^{\infty} \frac{z^n}{n} \int_0^{\infty} e^{-\theta t}[1 - B_n(t)]\, dA_n(t) \\
&= \sum_1^{\infty} \frac{z^n}{n} \int_0^{\infty} e^{-(\theta+\lambda)t} \frac{\lambda^{ns} t^{ns-1}}{(ns-1)!}\, dt \int_t^{\infty} dB_n(v) \\
&= \sum_1^{\infty} \frac{z^n}{n} \left(\frac{\lambda}{\theta+\lambda}\right)^{ns} \int_0^{\infty} dB_n(v) \int_0^{(\theta+\lambda)v} e^{-\tau} \frac{\lambda^{ns}\tau^{ns-1}}{(ns-1)!}\, d\tau \\
&= \sum_1^{\infty} \frac{z^n}{n} \left(\frac{\lambda}{\theta+\lambda}\right)^{ns} \int_0^{\infty} dB_n(v) \left\{1 - \sum_{p=1}^{ns} e^{-(\theta+\lambda)v} \frac{[(\theta+\lambda)v]^{ns-p}}{(ns-p)!}\right\} \\
&= \sum_1^{\infty} \frac{z^n}{n} \left(\frac{\lambda}{\theta+\lambda}\right)^{ns} - \sum_1^{\infty} \frac{z^n}{n} \sum_1^{\infty} \left(\frac{\lambda}{\theta+\lambda}\right)^{p} \\
&\quad \times \int_0^{\infty} e^{-(\theta+\lambda)v} \frac{(\lambda v)^{ns-p}}{(ns-p)!}\, dB_n(v) \\
&= \log\left[1 - \frac{z\lambda^s}{(\theta+\lambda)^s}\right]^{-1} + \sum_{r=1}^{s} \log\left(1 - \frac{\lambda}{\theta+\lambda}\gamma_r\right) \\
&= \log\left\{[(\theta+\lambda)^s - z\lambda^s]^{-1} \prod_{r=1}^{s} (\theta + \lambda - \lambda\gamma_r)\right\}
\end{aligned} \tag{4.142}$$

$$[\text{Re}(\theta) > 0, |z| < 1].$$

Therefore, using (4.56) we obtain the result

$$\sum_1^{\infty} z^n \int_0^{\infty} e^{-\theta t}\, dG_n(t) = 1 - \frac{(\theta+\lambda)^s - z\lambda^s}{\prod_{r=1}^{s} (\theta + \lambda - \lambda\gamma_r)} \tag{4.143}$$

$$[\text{Re}(\theta) > 0, |z| < 1].$$

c. The Queue-Length

We can suppose that customers are served in s consecutive phases, the time required for each phase having the distribution $\lambda e^{-\lambda t}\,dt$ $(0 < t < \infty)$ independently of the others. Let $Q(t)$ be the number of phases present in the system; again, $Q(t)$ is a non-Markovian process except in the special case $M/E_s/1$. Here we consider the imbedded Markov chain $\{Q_n\}$, where $Q_n = Q(t_n - 0)$, $t_0, t_1, t_2, \ldots$ being the instants of successive arrivals. Let X_n be the number of phases of service completed during $(t_{n-1}, t_n - 0)$ $(n = 1, 2, \ldots)$; then $X_1, X_2, X_3, \ldots$ are mutually independent random variables with the distribution given by (4.126). The p.g.f. of X_n is given by (4.127), and

$$E(X_n) = -\lambda\psi'(0) = \frac{s}{\rho_2} < \infty.$$

We have the recurrence relations

$$Q_{n+1} = \max(0, Q_n + s - X_{n+1}) \qquad (n = 0, 1, \ldots) \tag{4.144}$$

which give, if $Q_0 = 0$,

$$\begin{aligned} Q_n &= \max[-S_n + S_{n-r}\ (0 \leqslant r \leqslant n)] \\ &\sim \max(0, -S_1, -S_2, \ldots, -S_n) \qquad (n \geqslant 1). \end{aligned} \tag{4.145}$$

Now, considering the sequence $\{s - X_n\}$ we obtain

$$\begin{aligned} \sum_1^\infty \frac{z^n}{n} \sum_{j=1}^\infty \theta^j Pr\{-S_n = j\} &= \sum_1^\infty \frac{z^n}{n} \sum_{j=1}^{ns} \theta^j k_{ns-j}^{(n)} \\ &= \sum_1^\infty \frac{z^n}{n} \sum_{j=-ns}^{-1} \theta^j k_{j+ns}^{(n)} \end{aligned} \tag{4.146}$$

$$\begin{aligned} \sum_1^\infty \frac{z^n}{n} \sum_{j=-\infty}^{0} \theta^j Pr\{-S_n = j\} &= \sum_1^\infty \frac{z^n}{n} \sum_{j=-\infty}^{0} \theta^j k_{ns-j}^{(n)} \\ &= \sum_1^\infty \frac{z^n}{n} \sum_0^\infty \theta^j k_{j+ns}^{(n)}. \end{aligned} \tag{4.147}$$

Hence for the expressions defined by (4.91) and (4.92) we have

$$u(\theta, z) = \prod_{r=1}^{s} \left(\frac{1}{1 - \theta\xi_r}\right) \qquad (|z| < 1, |\theta| \leqslant 1) \tag{4.148}$$

$$v^*(\theta, z) = \frac{1}{1 - z\phi\left(\dfrac{1}{\theta}\right)} \prod_{r=1}^{s} (1 - \theta\xi_r) \qquad (|z| < 1, |\theta| \geqslant 1). \tag{4.149}$$

It follows that

$$(4.150)\quad \sum_{0}^{\infty} z^n E(\theta^{Q_n}) = u(\theta, z)v^*(1, z)$$
$$= \frac{1}{1-z}\prod_{r=1}^{s}\left(\frac{1-\xi_r}{1-\theta\xi_r}\right) \qquad (|z| < 1, |\theta| \leqslant 1).$$

The distribution of the limiting queue length Q_∞ is given by

$$(4.151)\qquad E(\theta^{Q_\infty}) = \prod_{r=1}^{s}\left(\frac{1-\zeta_r}{1-\theta\zeta_r}\right) \qquad (|\theta| \leqslant 1)$$

if $\rho_2 < 1$, whereas no such distribution exists if $\rho_2 \geqslant 1$.

4.9 BULK QUEUES

a. Some Particular Cases of Bulk Queues

Consider a queueing system in which customers arrive in groups of random size and are served by a single server in batches of random size. Such a system is called a bulk queue. It would have been noted from the discussion of the systems $E_s/G/1$ and $GI/E_s/1$, where the main interest was in the number of stages or phases, we were in effect dealing with bulk queues. As more specific examples we have the following.

Bulk service. Bailey (1954) considers a system in which customers arrive in a Poisson process with mean λt and are served in batches of not more than s. The intervals of time between successive occasions of service are mutually independent random variables with the distribution $dB(v)$ $(0 < v < \infty)$ and the L.S.T. $\psi(\theta)$. Let $t_0 = 0$ and t_n the instant of commencement of the nth service $(n \geqslant 1)$. Then, if Q_n is the queue length at $t_n - 0$ $(n = 0, 1, \ldots)$, it is seen that Q_n satisfies the recurrence relations (4.129), where the distribution of X_n is given by (4.126). It follows that the results (4.135) and (4.136) hold in the present case.

Group arrivals. Consider the system in which customers arrive in groups of fixed size s, the interarrival times being mutually independent random variables with the distribution $dB(u)$ $(0 < u < \infty)$. Customers are served individually by a single server, the service time having the distribution $\lambda e^{-\lambda v}\,dv$ $(0 < v < \infty)$. The groups are served in the order of arrival, and the customers within a group are served in some predetermined order. Let t_n be the instant of arrival of the nth group, and Q_n the queue-length at time $t_n - 0$ $(n = 0, 1, 2, \ldots)$. Then Q_n satisfies the recurrence relations (4.144) and therefore the results (4.150) and (4.151) hold.

The general bulk queueing system may be denoted as $GI^{(X)}/M^{(Y)}/1$, where the exponents X and Y represent the sizes of the arriving groups and service batches (assumed to be random variables). It is clear that such a system can be analyzed by the methods developed in the preceding sections. To illustrate this we consider the system $M^{(X)}/G^{(Y)}/1$ in the next section.

b. The Queue $M^{(X)}/G^{(Y)}/1$

This system is described as follows.

1. Customers arrive in a Poisson process with parameter λt in groups of size C_n having the distribution

$$Pr\{C_n = j\} = c_j \qquad (j = 1, 2, \ldots). \tag{4.152}$$

2. The customers are served in batches of variable size. The maximum size of a service batch is called the "capacity" for that service, and it is assumed that this capacity is independent of the queue-length at that time. Let $t_1, t_2, \ldots$ be the instants of departure of the successive batches, and Y_n the capacity for service ending at t_{n+1} $(n = 0, 1, \ldots)$. We assume that the random variables $Y_1, Y_2, \ldots$ are identically distributed, are mutually independent, and also independent of the arrival process. Let

$$Pr\{Y_n = j\} = b_j \qquad (j = 0, 1, \ldots). \tag{4.153}$$

If at some instant t_n, the queue-length is less than the service capacity, then the server has a variety of alternatives; thus, for instance, he may wait till his maximum capacity is reached, or he may take the available customers into service. However, the imbedded Markov chains considered below are the same in all such cases, even though the basic processes are different.

3. Let v_n be the service time of the batch departing at t_n $(n \geqslant 1)$. We assume that the random variables $v_1, v_2, \ldots$ are mutually independent, independent of the arrival process, and, moreover, are identically distributed with the d.f. $B(v)$ $(0 \leqslant v < \infty)$.

Let

$$c(\theta) = E(\theta^{C_n}) = \sum_1^\infty c_j\theta^j, \quad b(\theta) = E(\theta^{Y_n}) = \sum_0^\infty b_j\theta^j \qquad (|\theta| \leqslant 1) \tag{4.154}$$

be the p.g.f's of group size and service capacity respectively, and

$$\psi(\theta) = \int_0^\infty e^{-\theta v}\, dB(v) \qquad [\text{Re}(\theta) > 0] \tag{4.155}$$

the L.S.T. of the service time distribution. We assume that

$$0 < c'(1) < \infty, \qquad 0 < b'(1) < \infty, \qquad 0 < -\psi'(0) < \infty. \tag{4.156}$$

Now let X_n be the number of customers arrived during the period $(t_{n-1} + 0, t_n)$; the distribution of X_n is given by

$$(4.157) \qquad Pr\{X_n = j\} = \int_0^\infty \sum_{n=0}^{j} e^{-\lambda t} \frac{(\lambda t)^n}{n!} c_j^{(n)} \, dB(t),$$

where $[c_j^{(n)}]$ is the n-fold convolution of (c_j) with itself ($n \geqslant 1$), and $c_j^{(0)} = 1$ if $j = 0$, and $= 0$ if $j \neq 0$. The p.g.f. of X_n is given by

$$(4.158) \qquad K(\theta) = E(\theta^{X_n}) = \psi[\lambda - \lambda c(\theta)] \qquad (|\theta| \leqslant 1).$$

We define the relative traffic intensity of the system as

$$(4.159) \qquad \rho = \frac{E(X_n)}{E(Y_n)} = \frac{-\lambda\psi'(0)c'(1)}{b'(1)}$$

and from (4.156) we find that $0 < \rho < \infty$.

Let Q_n be the queue-length (number of customers present, including those being served) at time $t_n + 0$ ($n \geqslant 0$). For the imbedded Markov chain $\{Q_n\}$ we have then the recurrence relations

$$(4.160) \qquad Q_{n+1} = \max(X_{n+1}, X_{n+1} + Q_n - Y_n) \qquad (n = 0, 1, \ldots).$$

If we assume that the process started at time $t_0 + 0$ with all available persons taken into service, so that $Q_0 = Y_0$, we find from (4.160) that

$$(4.161) \qquad Q_n = \max[(X_n, X_n + S_{n-1} - S_{n-1-r}, 1 \leqslant r \leqslant n-1)]$$
$$\sim X_n + w_{n-1} \qquad (n \geqslant 1),$$

where $S_0 = 0$, $S_n = Z_1 + Z_2 + \cdots + Z_n$, $Z_n = X_n - Y_n$ ($n \geqslant 1$), and $w_n = \max(0, S_1, S_2, \ldots, S_n)$. The p.g.f. of Z_n is given by

$$(4.162) \qquad \phi(\theta) = E(\theta^{Z_n}) = E(\theta^{X_n - Y_n}) = b(\theta^{-1})K(\theta).$$

Let the distribution of S_n be denoted by

$$(4.163) \qquad Pr\{S_n = j\} = k_j^{(n)} \qquad (j = \cdots -1, 0, 1, \ldots).$$

The expressions (4.91) and (4.92) can now be written as

$$(4.164) \qquad u(\theta, z) = \exp\left[\sum_{n=1}^{\infty} \frac{z^n}{n} \sum_{j=1}^{\infty} k_j^{(n)} \theta^j\right] \qquad (|z| < 1, |\theta| \leqslant 1)$$

$$(4.165) \qquad v^*(\theta, z) = \exp\left[\sum_{n=1}^{\infty} \frac{z^n}{n} \sum_{j=-\infty}^{0} k_j^{(n)} \theta^j\right] \qquad (|z| < 1, |\theta| \geqslant 1).$$

From (4.161) we find that the transform of the distribution of Q_n is given by

$$(4.166) \qquad \sum_1^\infty z^n E(\theta^{Q_n}) = zK(\theta)u(\theta, z)v^*(1, z) \qquad (|z| < 1, |\theta| \leqslant 1).$$

The distribution of the limiting queue-length Q_∞ is given by

$$(4.167)\quad E(\theta^{Q_\infty}) = \lim_{z\to 1-0} (1 - z)zk(\theta)u(\theta, z)v^*(1, z)$$
$$= K(\theta) \exp\left[-\sum_{n=1}^{\infty} \frac{1}{n} \sum_{j=1}^{\infty} (1 - \theta^j)k_j^{(n)}\right] \qquad (|\theta| \leqslant 1)$$

if $\rho < 1$, whereas $Q_\infty = \infty$ with probability one if $\rho \geqslant 1$.

c. The Capacity Busy Period in a Bulk Queue

The concept of a busy period in a bulk queue is one which has to be carefully examined. Since it is possible that the service may proceed even with no customers (as in Bailey's bulk service queue described in Section 4.9a), the server may be said to be always busy. However, if we consider the service capacity and find that at a given instant this capacity is not being fully utilized because of lack of customers in the system, we may say that the server is slack at that time. Accordingly, in the system $M^{(X)}/G^{(Y)}/1$ we let $Q_0 = Y_0$ and define the random variable

$$(4.168)\qquad T = \min\,(n \mid Q_n < Y_n);$$

T is the "capacity busy" period (more accurately, T is the number of batches served before the server becomes slack). Using (4.160) we can write (4.168) as

$$(4.169)\qquad T = \min\,(n \mid S_n < 0),$$

and therefore

$$(4.170)\quad Pr\{T = n\} = Pr\{S_1 \geqslant 0, S_2 \geqslant 0, \ldots, S_{n-1} \geqslant 0, S_n < 0\}.$$

The p.g.f. of T is given by

$$(4.171)\quad E(z^T) = 1 - \exp\left[-\sum_1^{\infty} \frac{z^n}{n} Pr\{S_n < 0\}\right]$$
$$= 1 - [v^*(1, z)]^{-1} \exp\left[\sum_1^{\infty} \frac{z^n}{n} k_0^{(n)}\right] \qquad (|z| < 1),$$

where $v^*(\theta, z)$ is defined by (4.92).

The Capacity Busy Period in a Bulk Service Queue. For the bulk service queue described in Section 4.9a, we obtain the result

$$(4.172)\qquad E(z^T) = 1 - \prod_{r=1}^{s} (1 - \xi_r) \qquad (|z| < 1);$$

using (4.117); the number of customers served during a capacity busy period is sT.

COMPLEMENTS AND PROBLEMS

Section 4.2

1. *Proof of Feller's lemma* (4.17). We first prove that if $S_n > 0$, then there exist $r > 1$ cyclic permutations of $(X_1, X_2, \ldots, X_n)$ such that n is a ladder index for the corresponding sequence of partial sums; for each such cyclic permutation the sequence contains exactly r ladder indices.

Let us consider the cyclic permutation $(X_{a+1}, X_{a+2}, \ldots, X_a)$, and denote by $S_j^{(a)}$ its partial sums. We have

$$S_0^{(a)} = 0$$

$$(1) \quad S_j^{(a)} = \begin{cases} X_{a+1} + X_{a+2} + \cdots + X_{a+j} = S_{a+j} - S_a & (j = 1, 2, \ldots, n-a) \\ X_{a+1} + \cdots + X_n + X_1 + \cdots + X_{j-n+a} = S_n - S_a + S_{j-n+a} & (j = n-a, n-a+1, \ldots, n). \end{cases}$$

Let S_a be the first maximal term among $(S_0, S_1, \ldots, S_n)$, that is, $S_j < S_a$ $(j = 1, 2, \ldots, a-1)$ and $S_j \leqslant S_a$ $(j = a, a+1, \ldots, n)$. Then from (1) we obtain

$$(2) \quad \begin{aligned} S_j^{(a)} &\leqslant 0 < S_n \qquad (j = 0, 1, \ldots, n-a) \\ S_j^{(a)} &< S_n \qquad (j = n-a+1, \ldots, n); \end{aligned}$$

thus $S_j^{(a)} < S_n = S_n^{(a)}$ for all j, and hence n is a ladder index for

$$(S_0^{(a)}, S_1^{(a)}, \ldots, S_n^{(a)}).$$

Accordingly, there is at least one cyclic permutation for which the sequence of partial sums has n as a ladder index, and without loss of generality we take this to be the initial one itself, that is, $S_j < S_n$ $(j = 0, 1, \ldots, n-1)$. It follows from (1) that $S_j^{(a)} < S_n^{(a)}$ if, and only if, $S_j < S_a$ $(j = 0, 1, \ldots, a-1)$, that is, if a is a ladder index for $(S_0, S_1, \ldots, S_n)$. In other words, n is a ladder index for $(S_0^{(a)}, S_1^{(a)}, \ldots, S_n^{(a)})$ if, and only if, a is a ladder index for $(S_0, S_1, \ldots, S_n)$. This proves our assertion.

To prove the lemma (4.17), let us call two permutations which differ only by a cyclic permutation as equivalent. There are $n!\, f_n^{(r)}$ permutations which have n as the rth ladder index; the equivalence class of each contains n permutations and exactly r among them have the same property. The number of equivalence classes is therefore

$$(3) \qquad (n-1)! = \sum_{r=1}^{n} \frac{n!\, f_n^{(r)}}{r},$$

which is the desired result.

2. The result (4.16) is due to Sparre Andersen (1954), and the more general result (4.23) is due to Baxter (1958).

Section 4.3

3. The results of Sections a and b are due to Finch (1961). Kingman (1962) has carried out a detailed investigation of the busy period and also considered some particular cases. See also Rice (1962).

4. The result (4.70) is due to Kemperman (1961). See also Complement 14.

Section 4.5

5. The result (4.78) is due to Kemperman (1961), and the special case (4.79) due to Spitzer (1956).

6. Show that

$$E(W_n) = \sum_{r=1}^{n} \frac{1}{r} \int_0^{\infty} x \, dK_r(x) \tag{4}$$

[see Spitzer (1956)].

7. Prove that

(*a*) If $B < \infty$, then

$$W_n \to \sup_{k \geqslant 0} S_k < \infty \tag{5}$$

with probability one;

$$\limsup_{n \to \infty} S_n = -\infty \tag{6}$$

with probability one except in the trivial case when $Pr\{X_n = 0\} = 1$.

(*b*) If $B = \infty$, then

$$W_n \to \sup_{k \geqslant 0} S_k = \limsup_{n \to \infty} S_n = \infty \tag{7}$$

with probability one [Spitzer (1956)].

8. *Zero-avoiding transitions.* Let

$$\begin{aligned} &{}^0F_n(x) = Pr\{W_r \neq 0 \ (r = 1, 2, \ldots, n-1), W_n \leqslant x\} \qquad (n \geqslant 1, x \geqslant 0) \\ &{}^0F_0(x) = 0 \quad \text{if} \quad x < 0, \quad \text{and} \quad = 1 \quad \text{if} \quad x \geqslant 0. \end{aligned} \tag{8}$$

We have

$$\begin{aligned} {}^0F_n(x) &= Pr\{S_1 > 0, S_2 > 0, \ldots, S_{n-1} > 0, S_n \leqslant x\} \\ &= Pr\{S_1 > 0, S_2 > 0, \ldots, S_{n-1} > 0, S_n \leqslant 0\} \\ &\quad + Pr\{S_1 > 0, S_2 > 0, \ldots, S_{n-1} > 0, 0 < S_n \leqslant x\} \\ &= g_n^*(-\infty) + u_n(x), \end{aligned} \tag{9}$$

from which we find that

$$\begin{aligned} \sum_0^{\infty} z^n \int_{0-}^{\infty} e^{-\theta x} \, d\,{}^0F_n(x) &= -\exp\left[-\sum_1^{\infty} \frac{z^n}{n} Pr\{S_n \leqslant 0\}\right] \\ &\quad + \exp\left[\sum_1^{\infty} \frac{z^n}{n} \int_{0+}^{\infty} e^{-\theta x} \, dK_n(x)\right]. \end{aligned} \tag{10}$$

9. *The case of the finite mean.* Throughout this chapter we have not mentioned the mean of the random variables X_n. Let us now assume that $E\,|X_n| < \infty$ and ignore the trivial case where $Pr\{X_n = 0\} = 1$. Show that $B = \sum \frac{1}{n} Pr\{S_n > 0\} = \infty$ if $E(X_n) \geqslant 0$, and $B < \infty$ if $E(X_n) < 0$ [Spitzer (1956)]. Deduce that $A = \sum \frac{1}{n} Pr\{S_n \leqslant 0\} < \infty$ if $E(X_n) > 0$, and $A = \infty$ if $E(X_n) \leqslant 0$. In particular, when $E(X_n) = 0$, we have $A = \infty$, $B = \infty$.

10. *Lindley's integral equation.* The limiting distribution $F^*(x)$ satisfies Lindley's (1952) integral equation

$$F(x) = \int_{0-}^{\infty} K(x - y)\, dF(y) \qquad (x \geqslant 0). \tag{11}$$

A "regular" solution $F(x)$ of (11) is such that $F(x)$ is nondecreasing and continuous to the right, $F(x) = 0$ for $x < 0$ and $F(x) \to 1$ as $x \to \infty$. Assuming that $E|X_n| < \infty$, Lindley proved that (11) has either a unique regular solution or no regular solution at all, depending on whether $E(X_n) < 0$ or $\geqslant 0$. Let us now relax the last condition that $F(x)$ be bounded as $x \to \infty$. Show that a solution in this sense exists uniquely if $A = \infty$, or if the X_n have a finite mean $E(X_n) \leqslant 0$. Furthermore, if $E(X_n) = 0$ and $0 < \sigma^2(X_n) = \sigma^2$, then show that such a solution is given by

$$G(x) = c \sum_{n=1}^{\infty} {}^0F_n(x) < \infty, \tag{12}$$

where

$$0 < c = \exp\left\{ \sum_1^{\infty} \frac{1}{n} [\tfrac{1}{2} - Pr\{S_n > 0\}] \right\} < \infty \tag{13}$$

[Spitzer (1960)].

Section 4.6

11. Modifying Kemperman's (1961) notations slightly, let

$$M^+(\theta, z) = \exp\left[\sum_1^{\infty} \frac{z^n}{n} \int_{0+}^{\infty} e^{\theta x}\, dK_n(x) \right] = u(\theta, z) \tag{14}$$

$$M^-(\theta, z) = \exp\left[-\sum_1^{\infty} \frac{z^n}{n} \int_{-\infty}^{0+} e^{\theta x}\, dK_n(x) \right] = [v^*(\theta, z)]^{-1}. \tag{15}$$

We can then write (4.90) as

$$\frac{1}{1 - z\phi(\theta)} = \frac{M^+(\theta, z)}{M^-(\theta, z)} \qquad \text{if} \quad \mathrm{Re}\,(\theta) = 0. \tag{16}$$

The result (16) is a Wiener-Hopf decomposition.

In the particular case where $dK_n(x)$ is a weighted sum of expressions similar to the right-hand side member of (4.93), Kemperman obtains simplified expressions for $M^+(\theta, z)$ and $M^-(\theta, z)$ similar to (4.109) and (4.110) respectively. The discrete versions (4.117) and (4.118) are also due to Kemperman. He, however, uses deep complex variable methods.

Section 4.7

12. The results (4.120) and (4.123) for the waiting time and (4.135) and (4.136) for the queue-length are due to Takács (1961a). The queue-length just before the commencement of the nth service is given by $Q_n' = [Q_n/s]$.

13. The result (4.125) for the busy period is due to Conolly (1963).

14. Show that

$$E[z^{T(u)} e^{\theta S_{T(u)}}] = M^-(\theta, z) \int_{-\infty}^{-u} e^{\theta y} (-d_y) V(y, z), \tag{17}$$

and hence that, for the system $E_s/G/1$,

$$E[z^{T(u)}e^{\theta S_{T(u)}}] = \sum_{r=1}^{s} e^{-(\theta-\theta_r)u}\left(\frac{\theta_r+\lambda}{\theta+\lambda}\right)^s \prod_{p\neq r}^{s}\left(\frac{\theta-\theta_p}{\theta_r-\theta_p}\right). \tag{18}$$

From (18) it follows that

$$Pr\{T(u) < \infty\} = \sum_{r=1}^{s} e^{\theta_r^0 u}\frac{(1+\theta_r^0/\lambda)^s}{\prod_{p\neq r}^{s}(1-\theta_r^0/\theta_p^0)}. \tag{19}$$

In particular, for the system $M/G/1$,

$$E[z^{T(u)}] = \left(1-\frac{\eta}{\lambda}\right)e^{-\eta u}, \tag{20}$$

where η is the unique positive root of the functional equation $\eta = \lambda - \lambda z\psi(\eta)$, and

$$Pr\{T(u) < \infty\} = \psi(\eta_0)e^{-\eta_0 u} \tag{21}$$

where η_0 is the largest positive root of the equation $x = \lambda - \lambda\psi(x)$ [Kemperman (1961)].

Section 4.8

15. *The queue $GI/E_s/1$.* From (4.141) we obtain

$$\int_{0-}^{\infty} e^{-\theta x}\,dF^*(x) = \prod_{r=1}^{s}\left(\frac{1+\theta/\lambda}{1+\theta/\theta_r^0}\right) \qquad [\text{Re}\,(\theta) \geqslant 0], \tag{22}$$

where $\theta_1^0, \theta_2^0, \ldots, \theta_s^0$ are the roots of the equation $(\lambda-\theta)^s = \lambda^s\psi(\theta)$, Re $(\theta_r^0) > 0$ $(r = 1, 2, \ldots, s)$. It is easily seen that

$$\prod_{r=1}^{s}\left(\frac{1+\theta/\lambda}{1+\theta/\theta_r^0}\right) = A + \sum_{r=1}^{s}\frac{A_r}{1+\theta/\theta_r^0}, \tag{23}$$

where

$$A_r = (1+\theta_r/\lambda)^s\prod_{p\neq r}^{s}\left(\frac{1}{1-\theta_r^0/\theta_p^0}\right) \qquad (r = 1, 2, \ldots, s) \tag{24}$$

$$A = \theta_1^0\theta_2^0\cdots\theta_s^0/\lambda_s.$$

Therefore

$$\int_{0-}^{\infty} e^{-\theta x}\,dF^*(x) = A + \sum_{r=1}^{s} A_r\theta_r^0\int_{0}^{\infty} e^{-(\theta+\theta_r^0)x}\,dx$$

so that

$$F^*(x) = 1 - \sum_{1}^{s} A_r e^{-\theta_r^0 x} \qquad (x \geqslant 0) \tag{25}$$

for the limiting distribution of the waiting time. For the system $D/E_s/1$, Lindley (1952) postulates a solution of the type $F^*(x) = \Sigma\, c_i e^{-\lambda_i x}$ and determines the constants c_i, λ_i.

16. The result (4.143) for the busy period is due to Conolly (1960).

17. *The queue-length in the system $GI/E_s/1$.* The result (4.151) is due to Takács (1961b). The queue-length just before the arrival of the nth customer is given by $Q_n' = [Q_n + s - 1/s]$.

Proceeding as in Complement 15, show that

$$Pr\{Q_\infty = j\} = \sum_{r=1}^{s} a_r \zeta_r^{\,j} \qquad (j \geqslant 0), \tag{26}$$

where

$$a_r = \prod_{1}^{s} (1 - \zeta_r) \prod_{p \neq r}^{s} \left(1 - \frac{\zeta_p}{\zeta_r}\right)^{-1} \qquad (r = 1, 2, \ldots, s) \tag{27}$$

[Wishart (1956)].

Section 4.9

18. *Bulk service.* Bailey (1954) obtains

$$E(\theta^{Q_\infty}) = \frac{\sum_{0}^{s-1} u_i(\theta^s - \theta^i)}{\theta^s \mid K(\theta) - 1}, \tag{28}$$

where $u_i = Pr\{Q_\infty = i\}$ $(i \geqslant 0)$. Show that

$$\sum_{0}^{s-1} u_i(\theta^s - \theta^i) = s(1 - \rho)(\theta - 1) \prod_{r=1}^{s} \left(\frac{\theta - \zeta_r}{1 - \zeta_r}\right), \tag{29}$$

and hence that (28) is identical with (4.136).

19. *Group arrivals.* The number N, of groups served during a busy period in a queue with group arrivals is given by

$$N = \min (n \mid S_n \geqslant 0). \tag{30}$$

Show that the p.g.f. of N is given by

$$E(z^N) = 1 - \frac{1 - z}{\prod_{1}^{s} (1 - \xi_r)} \qquad (|z| < 1). \tag{31}$$

20. The results of Section 4.5b are due to Bhat (1964), who also considers the queue $GI^{(x)}/M^{(y)}/1$.

21. *The queue $M/D/s$.* Consider the system $M/D/s$ in which (a) customers arrive in a Poisson process with mean λt, (b) the service time is a constant ($= b$ say), and (c) there are s servers ($1 \leqslant s < \infty$) and the queue-discipline is "first come, first served." It has already been noted (Section 1.7) that the queue-length process $Q(t)$ in the system is non-Markovian; the limiting distribution of $Q(t)$ was, however, obtained. Now let us consider the instants of time nb ($n = 0, 1, \ldots$), and let X_n be the number of arrivals during $(nb - b, nb - 0)$ $(n \geqslant 1)$; $X_1, X_2, X_3, \ldots$ are mutually independent random variables with the distribution given by

$$k_j = Pr\{X_n = j\} = e^{\lambda b} \frac{(\lambda b)^j}{j!} \qquad (j = 0, 1, \ldots). \tag{32}$$

The p.g.f. of X_n is given by

$$K(\theta) = E(\theta^{X_n}) = e^{-\lambda b(1-\theta)}. \tag{33}$$

Let us consider the imbedded Markov chain $\{Q_n\}$, where $Q_n = Q(nb - 0)$; it is seen that Q_n satisfies the recurrence relations (4.129). Therefore the results (4.135) and (4.136) hold in this case and can be written as

$$\sum_{0}^{\infty} z^n E(\theta^{Q_n}) = 1 + \frac{z}{\theta^s e^{\lambda b(1-\theta)} - z} \prod_{r=1}^{s\cdot} \left(\frac{\theta - \xi_r}{1 - \xi_r}\right) \tag{34}$$

$$E(\theta^{Q_\infty}) = \frac{s(1-\rho)(1-\theta)}{1 - \theta^s e^{\lambda b(1-\theta)}} \prod_{r=1}^{s-1} \left(\frac{\theta - \zeta_r}{1 - \zeta_r}\right), \tag{35}$$

the second result being valid if and only if $\rho < 1$, where $\rho = \lambda b/s$ is the traffic intensity of the system. The result (35) may be compared with Crommelin's (1932) result [equation (1.253)].

From (4.87) we find that the probability that the system is empty is given by

$$Pr\{Q_\infty = 0\} = \exp\left[-\sum_{1}^{\infty} \frac{1}{n} Pr\{X_1 + X_2 + \cdots + X_n > ns\}\right];$$

since $X_1 + X_2 + \cdots + X_n$ has a Poisson distribution with mean nb, we find that

$$Pr\{Q_\infty = 0\} = \exp\left[-\sum_{1}^{\infty} \frac{1}{n} \sum_{ns+1}^{\infty} e^{-\lambda nb} \frac{(\lambda nb)^j}{j!}\right]. \tag{36}$$

REFERENCES

Andersen, Sparre E. (1953a). On sums of symmetrically dependent random variables. *Skan. Aktuar.*, **36,** 123–138.

Andersen, Sparre E. (1953b). On the fluctuations of sums of random variables I. *Math. Scand.* **1,** 263–285.

Andersen, Sparre E. (1954). On the fluctuations of sums of random variables II. *Math. Scand.*, **2,** 195–223.

Bailey, Norman T. J. (1954). On queueing processes with bulk service. *J. Roy. Stat. Sov.*, **B16,** 80–87.

Bhat, U. Narayan (1963). Imbedded Markov chain analysis of bulk queues. *J. Aust. Math. Soc.*, **4,** 244–263.

Baxter, Glen (1958). An operator identity. *Pacific J. Math*, **8,** 649–663.

Conolly, B. W. (1960). The busy period in relation to the single server queueing system with general independent arrivals and Erlangian service times. *J. Roy. Stat. Soc.*, **22,** 89–96.

Conolly, B. W. (1963). The busy period in relation to the queueing process $E_k/G/1$. (To appear.)

Feller, W. (1957). *An Introduction to Probability Theory and Its Applications*, 2nd edition. John Wiley, New York.

Feller, W. (1959). *On Combinatorial Methods in Fluctuation Theory*. The Harald Cramer Volume, 75–91, John Wiley, New York.

Finch, P. D. (1961). On the busy period in the queueing system $GI/G/1$. *J. Aust. Math. Soc.*, **2,** 217–227.

Kemperman, J. H. B. (1961). *The First Passage Problem for a Stationary Markov Chain*. University of Chicago Press.

Kingman, J. F. C. (1962). The use of Spitzer's identity in the investigation of the busy period and other quantities in the queue $GI/G/1$. *Aust., J. Math.* **2,** 345–356.

Lindley, D. V. (1952). Theory of queues with a single server. *Proc. Cam. Phil. Soc.*, **48,** 277–289.

Rice, S. O. (1962). Single server systems—II. Busy periods. *Bell System Tech. J.*, **41,** 279–310.

Spitzer, Frank (1956). A combinatorial lemma and its application to probability theory. *Trans. Amer. Math. Soc.*, **82,** 323–339.

Spitzer, Frank (1960). A Tauberian theorem and its probability interpretation. *Trans. Amer. Math. Soc.*, **94,** 150–160.

Takács, Lajos (1961a). Transient behavior of single server queueing processes with Erlang input. *Trans. Amer. Math. Soc.*, **100,** 1–28.

Takács, Lajos (1961b). The transient behavior of a single server queueing process with recurrent input and gamma service time. *Ann. Math. Stat.*, **32,** 1286–1298.

Wishart, D. M. G. (1956). A queueing system with χ^2 service time distribution. *Ann. Math. Stat.*, **27,** 768–779.

Chapter 5

Some Inventory Models

5.1 INTRODUCTION

Inventory problems occurring in economics and in business administration have received considerable attention during the last few years. Although these problems are formulated in different terms in different contexts, their mathematical models have a certain degree of similarity; a systematic study of these models has been made by Arrow, Karlin, and Scarf (1958). A valuable review was given earlier by Gani (1957).

An inventory is an amount of material stored for the purpose of future sale or production. The inventory function Z_n is defined for discrete time $n = 0, 1, 2, \ldots$ by the recurrence relation

$$Z_{n+1} = Z_n + X_n - Y_n, \tag{5.1}$$

where X_n is the amount ordered (the "input") at time n in accordance with a specified ordering (or replacement) policy, and Y_n is the amount sold (the "output") during $(n, n + 1)$. Furthermore, let ξ_n be the demand for the material during $(n, n + 1)$; it is assumed that X_n, Y_n, and ξ_n are all random variables. We shall have $Z_n \gtrless 0$ in general, a negative value denoting a demand which was not fulfilled. For continuous time (5.1) is to be replaced by

$$\frac{dZ}{dt} = X(t) - Y(t), \tag{5.2}$$

which is a stochastic differential equation.

As particular cases of (5.1) we have the following important inventory models.

1. Here the demand ξ_n is assumed to be a random variable with a known distribution, and X_n is the amount ordered at time n in accordance with a certain ordering policy. The amount sold is then a function of the demand and the amount available; thus $Y_n = f(\xi_n, Z_n + X_n)$, where the function $f(\ldots)$ is specified by the ordering policy.

2. In the above model it is assumed that the supply of material is under control in the sense that the amount sold satisfies a relation of the type (5.1). However, there are situations in which this supply (for instance, the yield of grain) is a random variable, whereas the demand is assumed to be known and is met according to a specified storage policy.

The main problems arising in the analysis of an inventory model are as follows.

(*a*) *The optimization problem.* Let us consider a model of type (1), where the commonly adopted policy is to meet the demand if "physically possible," that is,

$$Y_n = \begin{cases} \xi_n & \text{if} \quad \xi_n \leqslant Z_n + X_n \\ Z_n + X_n & \text{if} \quad \xi_n > Z_n + X_n. \end{cases} \tag{5.3}$$

Clearly, such a policy leads to a deficit that is equal to $\xi_n - Z_n - X_n$ if $\xi_n > Z_n + X_n$, but is zero otherwise; this deficit will result in a penalty (which may be, for instance, in the form of loss of customer goodwill). It is then possible to write down the profit (revenue minus costs) function associated with it: the revenue is from the material sold and the costs are the storage and ordering costs, penalty costs, and so on. An important problem in inventory theory is to find an optimum ordering policy such that the profit function is a maximum, or equivalently, the cost function is a minimum.

(*b*) *The study of the underlying stochastic processes.* It is clear that the storage function Z_n associated with an inventory model is a stochastic process; this process depends on the given policy and the nature of supply and demand, but does not involve the cost structure of the model. An investigation of this process is essential for the detailed analysis of the model. In particular, the stationary distribution of Z_n is of fundamental importance in the theory of such models: we may minimize the "long run" cost function, that is, the cost function for the process when it has settled down to a statistical equilibrium. On the other hand, if we are interested in the cost structure for more than one period, we have to know the transient behavior of the process.

In this chapter we describe a few inventory models. Although we shall solve the optimization problem for a few of these, our main topic of study is the related stochastic processes.

5.2 AN INVENTORY MODEL OF THE (s, S) TYPE

a. The Model

As an example of the inventory model of type (1) we consider a policy of the (s, S) type, which is formulated as follows. Two real numbers s, S

are specified, where $0 \leqslant s < S$. Whenever the stock level Z_n falls below s, then positive ordering is done to bring up the level to S, but when this level exceeds s, no ordering is done. It is assumed that delivery of goods ordered is immediate. Thus we have

$$Z_{n+1} = \begin{cases} Z_n - \xi_n & \text{if } s < Z_n \leqslant S \\ S - \xi_n & \text{if } Z_n \leqslant s, \end{cases} \tag{5.4}$$

where the demand ξ_n is assumed to be a random variable with a known distribution function (d.f.) $G(\xi)$ $(0 \leqslant \xi < \infty)$. Here $n = 0, 1, 2, \ldots$ represent epochs of time at which decisions are made whether to order the material or not.

b. The Related Stochastic Process

If we start with an initial stock level S, the stock will get steadily depleted until it falls below s and then an ordering will be made to bring up the stock level to S. The period of time between successive orders is called a cycle, and this is of special importance in the analysis of the (s, S) model. The length of this cycle in terms of the number of epochs described in Section 5.2a is given by

$$N = \min (n \mid S - \eta_n \leqslant s) = \min (n \mid \eta_n \geqslant \Delta) \tag{5.5}$$

where $\eta_n = \xi_1 + \xi_2 + \cdots + \xi_n$, and $\Delta = S - s > 0$. From renewal theory we know that the random variable N is finite with probability one and that its mean is given by $\mu = E(N) = 1 + U(\Delta) < \infty$, where $U(x) = \sum_1^\infty G_n(x)$, $G_n(x)$ being the n-fold convolution of $G(x)$ with itself. It is clear that N is the "waiting time" of a recurrent event E [see Feller (1957)] and that

$$u_n = Pr\{E \text{ occurs at } n\} = Pr\{Z_n \leqslant s\} \quad (n \geqslant 1),\ u_0 = 1. \tag{5.6}$$

We have therefore

$$\begin{aligned} Pr\{S - x \leqslant Z_n \leqslant S\} &= \sum_{m=0}^{n-1} Pr\{\text{the last ordering is made at } m;\ S - x \leqslant Z_n \leqslant S\} \\ &= \sum_{m=0}^{n-1} u_m Pr\{S - x \leqslant S - \eta_{n-m} \leqslant S\} \\ &= \sum_0^{n-1} u_m Pr\{0 \leqslant \eta_{n-m} \leqslant x\} = \sum_0^{n-1} u_m G_{n-m}(x) \end{aligned} \tag{5.7}$$

for $0 \leqslant x < \Delta$, whereas for $x \leqslant s$,

$$(5.8)\quad \begin{aligned} Pr\{Z_n \leqslant x\} &= Pr\{Z_n \leqslant s\}Pr\{Z_n \leqslant x \mid Z_n \leqslant s\} \\ &= u_n Pr\{S - \eta_{n'} \leqslant x \mid S - \eta_{n'} \leqslant s \text{ for some } n' < n\} \\ &= u_n Pr\{\eta_{n'} \geqslant \Delta + s - x \mid \eta_{n'} \geqslant \Delta\} \\ &= u_n Pr\{Y(\Delta) \geqslant s - x\}, \end{aligned}$$

where Y is the "residual lifetime" of a renewal process and is independent of n. From renewal theory we again know that

$$(5.9)\quad Pr\{Y(\Delta) \geqslant s - x\} = \int_0^\Delta dU(\tau)[1 - G(\Delta + s - x - \tau)] + 1 - G(\Delta + s - x).$$

We have thus obtained the distribution of Z_n for the whole range $-\infty < x \leqslant S$. To obtain its limiting distribution as $n \to \infty$, we note from the theory of recurrent events that

$$(5.10)\quad u_n \to \frac{1}{\mu} = \frac{1}{1 + U(\Delta)} \quad \text{as} \quad n \to \infty.$$

Therefore (5.8) gives

$$(5.11)\quad \lim_{n\to\infty} Pr\{Z_n \leqslant x\} = \frac{Pr\{Y(\Delta) \geqslant s - x\}}{1 + U(\Delta)} \qquad (x \leqslant s).$$

Now let $n' < n$; then we can write

$$(5.12)\quad \begin{aligned} \sum_0^{n-1} u_m G_{n-m}(x) &= \sum_{m=1}^{n} u_{n-m} G_m(x) \\ &= \sum_{m=1}^{n'} u_{n-m} G_m(x) + \sum_{n'+1}^{n} u_{n-m} G_m(x). \end{aligned}$$

In this let $n \to \infty$ first and then $n' \to \infty$; then

$$(5.13)\quad \sum_1^{n'} u_{n-m} G_m(x) \to \frac{1}{\mu} \sum_1^{n'} G_m(x) \to \frac{U(x)}{1 + U(\Delta)},$$

and

$$(5.14)\quad \sum_{n'+1}^{n} u_{n-m} G_m(x) < \sum_{n'+1}^{n} G_m(x) \to 0$$

since the series $\sum_1^{\infty} G_m(x) = U(x) < \infty$. We thus find that

$$(5.15)\quad \lim_{n\to\infty} Pr\{S - x \leqslant Z_n \leqslant S\} = \frac{U(x)}{1 + U(\Delta)} \qquad (0 \leqslant x \leqslant \Delta).$$

c. The Optimum Policy

Let us now denote

$$\text{Ordering cost} = cx + K(x) = \begin{cases} cx + K & \text{if } x > 0 \\ 0 & \text{if } x = 0, \end{cases}$$

(5.16) $$\text{Penalty cost per unit shortage} = p$$

$$\text{Storage cost per unit} = h$$

Then the cost function associated with the (s, S) policy for the stock level Z_n is

$$(5.17)\quad L(Z_n) = \begin{cases} K + c(S - Z_n) + p\int_S^\infty (\xi - S)\,dG(\xi) \\ \qquad\qquad + h\int_0^S (S - \xi)\,dG(\xi) & (Z_n \leqslant s) \\ p\int_{Z_n}^\infty (\xi - Z_n)\,dG(\xi) + h\int_0^{Z_n} (Z_n - \xi)\,dG(\xi) \\ & (s < Z_n \leqslant S). \end{cases}$$

The expected cost when the process has settled down to an equilibrium is

$$(5.18)\qquad \mathscr{L}(s, S) = \int_{-\infty}^{S} L(x) \lim_{n\to\infty} d_x Pr\{Z_n \leqslant x\}.$$

The optimum policy is the one with $(s = s_0, S = S_0)$ where (s_0, S_0) are the values of (s, S) which make $\mathscr{L}(s, S)$ a minimum.

d. A Particular Case

As an example, let us consider the case where the demand ξ has the negative exponential distribution

$$(5.19)\qquad dG(x) = \mu e^{-\mu x}\,dx \qquad (0 < x < \infty).$$

We have in this case $U(x) = \mu x$ and $Pr\{Y(\Delta) \geqslant s - x\} = e^{-\mu(s-x)}$, on account of the well-known properties of the distribution (5.19). Therefore the limiting distribution of Z_n has the frequency function

$$(5.20)\qquad f(x) = \begin{cases} \dfrac{e^{-\mu(s-x)}\mu}{1 + \mu\Delta} & (x \leqslant s) \\ \dfrac{\mu}{1 + \mu\Delta} & (s < x \leqslant S). \end{cases}$$

Furthermore,

$$
(5.21)\quad L(Z_n) = \begin{cases} K + c(S - Z_n) + \dfrac{p}{\mu} e^{-\mu S} + h\left(S - \dfrac{1}{\mu} + \dfrac{1}{\mu} e^{-\mu S}\right) & (Z_n \leqslant s) \\ \dfrac{p}{\mu} e^{-\mu Z_n} + h\left(Z_n - \dfrac{1}{\mu} + \dfrac{1}{\mu} e^{-\mu Z_n}\right) & (s < Z_n \leqslant S), \end{cases}
$$

and

$$
(5.22)\quad \mathscr{L}(s, S) = \int_{-\infty}^{S} L(x) f(x)\, dx
$$

$$
= \frac{K}{1 + \mu\Delta} + \frac{c}{\mu^2} + h \frac{s - \dfrac{1}{\mu} + \dfrac{S^2 - s^2}{2}\mu}{1 + \mu\Delta} + \frac{(h + p)e^{-\mu s}}{1 + \mu\Delta}.
$$

Considering this as a function of s and Δ, we find that the optimum values of s and Δ are given by

$$
(5.23)\qquad \Delta_0 = \sqrt{\frac{2K}{\mu h}}, \qquad e^{-\mu s_0} = \frac{h + \sqrt{2Kh\mu}}{h + p}
$$

if $\sqrt{2Kh\mu} \leqslant p$; if $\sqrt{2Kh\mu} > p$, Δ_0 is as in (5.23), but $s_0 = 0$.

5.3 A GRAIN STORAGE PROBLEM

In the grain storage problem considered by Rosenblatt (1954) the model is of type (2). Here X_n is the yield of grain during the year $(n, n + 1)$, and it is assumed that $X_0, X_1, X_2, \ldots$ are mutually independent and identically distributed random variables. It is decided to store a proportion α $(0 < \alpha < 1)$ of the amount of grain available during any year for future use. If then Z_n is the amount stored during the nth year, we have the recurrence relation

$$
(5.24)\qquad Z_{n+1} = \alpha(Z_n + X_n) \qquad (n = 1, 2, \ldots),
$$

which is a stochastic difference equation of the first order. Let $Z_0 = 0$; then solving (5.24) successively for $Z_1, Z_2, \ldots,$ we obtain

$$
Z_n = \alpha X_{n-1} + \alpha^2 X_{n-2} + \alpha^3 X_{n-3} + \cdots + \alpha^n X_0,
$$

or since the X_n are identically distributed,

$$
(5.25)\qquad Z_n \sim \sum_{r=1}^{n} \alpha^r X_r \qquad (n \geqslant 1),
$$

a formula which determines the distribution of Z_n in terms of the X_n.

To study the behavior of Z_n as $n \to \infty$, let us assume that

$$
(5.26)\qquad E(X_n) = m, \qquad \operatorname{Var}(X_n) = \sigma^2,
$$

where both m and σ^2 are finite. Then since $0 < \alpha < 1$,

$$\text{Var}\left(\sum_1^\infty \alpha^r X_r\right) = \sigma^2 \sum_1^\infty \alpha^{2r} < \infty, \tag{5.27}$$

so the series $\sum_1^\infty \alpha^r X_r$ converges with probability one, and

$$Z^* = \lim_{n\to\infty} Z_n \sim \sum_1^\infty \alpha^r X_r. \tag{5.28}$$

It follows from (5.28) that

$$E(Z^*) = \frac{\alpha}{1-\alpha} m, \qquad E(Z^*)^2 = \frac{\alpha}{1-\alpha^2}\left(\sigma^2 + \frac{1+\alpha}{1-\alpha} m\right). \tag{5.29}$$

Now consider the cost function

$$L(Z_n) = cZ_n + K_1 + K_2(Y_n - M)^2, \tag{5.30}$$

where c = cost of storage per unit, K_1 and K_2 are constants, and $Y_n = (1-\alpha)(Z_n + X_n)$ is the amount released for sale during the year $(n, n+1)$ and M is a "desirable level" or release. The optimization problem here consists of finding α so as to minimize the expected cost when the process is in equilibrium. We can write (5.30) as

$$L(Z_n) = cZ_n + K_1 + K_2\left(\frac{1-\alpha}{\alpha} Z_{n+1} - M\right)^2, \tag{5.31}$$

so that the expected cost in equilibrium state is

$$\begin{aligned} \mathscr{L}(\alpha) &= E[L(Z^*)] \\ &= \frac{cm}{1-\alpha} + 2K_2 \frac{\sigma^2}{1+\alpha}. \end{aligned} \tag{5.32}$$

It is easily found that the optimum value of α is given by α_0, where

$$\alpha_0 = \begin{cases} \dfrac{\sqrt{2K_2\sigma^2/cm} - 1}{\sqrt{2K_2\sigma^2/cm} + 1} & \text{if } 2K_2\sigma^2 > cm \\ 0 & \text{if } 2K_2\sigma^2 \leqslant cm. \end{cases} \tag{5.33}$$

5.4 A CONTINUOUS TIME MODEL WITH TIME LAG

We now consider an inventory model in continuous time due to Pitt (1946). Here we have a store of finite capacity K, the stored material being measured in discrete units. The demand $\xi(t)$ which arises during a time interval $(0, t]$ has a Poisson distribution with mean at, so that

$$Pr\{\xi(t) = n\} = \frac{e^{-at}(at)^n}{n!} \qquad (n = 0, 1, \ldots). \tag{5.34}$$

This demand is met if physically possible, so that the stock function $Z(t) \geqslant 0$. Orders for M items are placed at times t at which $\xi(t) = M$, $2M, 3M, \ldots$, but the delivery is made after a time lag T. Thus we have

$$Z(t) = K + M\left[\frac{\xi(t-T)}{M}\right] - \xi(t) \tag{5.35}$$

where $[x]$ is the largest integer contained in x. To find the distribution of $Z(t)$, let us rewrite (5.35) as

(5.36)

$$Z(t) = K + M\left[\frac{\xi(t-T)}{M}\right] - \xi(t-T) - [\xi(t) - \xi(t-T)],$$

where $\xi(t) - \xi(t-T)$ is independent of $\xi(t-T)$ and has the same distribution as $\xi(T)$ on account of the additive property of the Poisson process. Therefore

$$\begin{aligned} Pr\{Z(t) = n\} &= \sum_{j=0}^{M-1} \sum_{\nu=0}^{\infty} Pr\{\xi(t-T) = \nu M + j\} \\ &\quad \times Pr\{\xi(t) - \xi(t-T) = K - j - n\} \\ &= \sum_{j=0}^{M-1} e^{-aT} \frac{(aT)^{k-j-n}}{(K-j-n)!} \sum_{\nu=0}^{\infty} e^{-a(t-T)} \\ &\quad \times \frac{[a(t-T)]^{\nu M+j}}{(\nu M + j)!}, \qquad (n = 0, 1, \ldots). \end{aligned} \tag{5.37}$$

To evaluate the second sum on the right-hand side of (5.37), we note that if ω_r $(r = 0, 1, \ldots, M-1)$ are the Mth roots of unity, then

$$\begin{aligned} \frac{1}{M}\sum_{r=0}^{M-1} \omega_r^{-j} e^{-\lambda(1-\omega_r)} &= \frac{1}{M}\sum_{r=0}^{M-1} \omega_r^{-j} e^{-\lambda} \sum_{n=0}^{\infty} \frac{(\lambda\omega_r)^n}{n!} \\ &= \sum_{n=0}^{\infty} e^{-\lambda} \frac{\lambda^n}{n!} \frac{1}{M} \sum_{r=0}^{M-1} \omega_r^{n-j}. \end{aligned} \tag{5.38}$$

However, since $\omega_0^p + \omega_1^p + \cdots + \omega_{M-1}^p = M$ if p is a multiple of M and $= 0$ otherwise, it follows that

$$\frac{1}{M}\sum_{r=0}^{M-1} \omega_r^{-j} e^{-\lambda(1-\omega_r)} = \sum_{\nu=0}^{\infty} e^{-\lambda} \frac{\lambda^{\nu M+j}}{(\nu M + j)!}. \tag{5.39}$$

Therefore

$$Pr\{Z(t) = n\} = \frac{1}{M}\sum_{j=0}^{M-1} e^{-aT} \frac{(aT)^{K-j-n}}{(K-j-n)!} \sum_{r=0}^{M-1} \omega_r^{-j} e^{-a(t-T)(1-\omega_r)}. \tag{5.40}$$

From (5.40) it follows readily that the limiting distribution of $Z(t)$ as $t \to \infty$ is given by

$$\lim_{t\to\infty} Pr\{Z(t) = n\} = \frac{1}{M} \sum_{j=0}^{M-1} e^{-aT} \frac{(aT)^{K-j-n}}{(K-j-n)!}. \tag{5.41}$$

5.5 THE RUIN PROBLEM OF COLLECTIVE RISK THEORY

a. Introduction

The theory of collective risk, as developed by the Swedish actuary, Filip Lundberg, deals with the business of an insurance company. Following a series of papers published by him during the years 1909 to 1934, a considerable amount of work has been done by Cramér, Segerdahl, Täcklind, Saxén, Arfwedson, and many others; a survey of the theory from the point of view of stochastic processes was given by Cramér [(1954, 1955)] and an excellent review has been given by Arfwedson [(1954, 1955)]. Briefly, the mathematical model used in this theory can be described as follows.

1. The claims occur entirely "at random," that is, during the infinitesimal interval of time $(t, t + dt]$, the probability of a claim occurring is dt and the probability of more than one claim occurring is of a smaller order than dt, these probabilities being independent of the claims which have occurred during $(0, t]$.
2. If a claim does occur, the amount claimed is a random variable with the probability distribution $dP(x)$ $(-\infty < x < \infty)$, negative claims occurring in the case of ordinary whole-life annuities.

Under the assumptions (1) and (2), it is easily seen that the total amount $X(t)$ of all claims which occur during $(0, t]$ has the compound Poisson distribution given by

$$K(x, t) = Pr\{X(t) \leqslant x\} = \sum_{n=0}^{\infty} e^{-t} \frac{t^n}{n!} P_n(x), \tag{5.42}$$

where $P_n(x)$ is the n-fold convolution of $P(x)$ with itself, and $P_0(x) = 0$ if $x < 0$ and $= 1$ if $x \geqslant 0$. The expected claim during $(0, t]$ is given by $t\alpha$, where

$$\alpha = \int_{-\infty}^{\infty} x \, dP(x); \tag{5.43}$$

$t\alpha$ is called the net risk premium.

3. During an interval of length t, the company receives an amount λt from the totality of its policyholders; λt is called the gross risk premium. The difference, $\lambda - \alpha$, is called the "safety loading," which is in practice

positive. However, we shall not assume this, but only that λ and α are of the same sign. The ratio $\rho = \lambda\alpha^{-1}$ (> 0) is called Lundberg's security factor and is of great importance in the theory of collective risk.

The function $Z(t) = u + \lambda t - X(t)$ is called the risk reserve, with the initial value $Z(0) = u$. Clearly, $Z(t)$ is a time homogeneous Markov process with the transition distribution function

$$P(u; z, t) = Pr\{Z(t) \leqslant z \mid Z(0) = u\} = 1 - K(\lambda t + u - z, t). \tag{5.44}$$

Starting with the initial value u, let $T \equiv T(u)$ be the first subsequent time at which the risk reserve becomes negative, that is, the company is "ruined." Thus

$$T(u) = \inf [t \mid u + \lambda t - X(t) < 0]. \tag{5.45}$$

We shall call T the "period of prosperity." The ruin problem of collective risk theory is concerned with the distribution of the random variable T. Let us denote by

$$G(t; u) = Pr\{T(u) \leqslant t\} \qquad (0 \leqslant t < \infty) \tag{5.46}$$

the distribution function of T. The expression

$$\psi(u) = G(\infty; u) = Pr\{T(u) < \infty\} \tag{5.47}$$

gives the probability that a company with the initial capital u will eventually be ruined.

b. The Case of a Positive Process

Let us first consider the case where all claims are positive (a "positive process"); thus $P(u) = 0$ for $u \leqslant 0$. Here $\alpha > 0$, and since λ and α are of the same sign, $\lambda > 0$; without loss of generality we can take $\lambda = 1$, so that the risk reserve in this case is given by $Z(t) = u + t - X(t)$. We first evaluate the expression

$$F(t; u, x) = Pr\{T(u) > t;\ Z(t) \geqslant x\}, \tag{5.48}$$

which is the probability that the company is not ruined during the interval $(0, t]$, its risk reserve at t exceeding a value x. We have

$$\begin{aligned} F(t; u, x) &= Pr\left\{\inf_{0\leqslant\tau\leqslant t} [u + \tau - X(\tau)] \geqslant 0; u + t - X(t) \geqslant x\right\} \\ &= Pr\left\{\sup_{0\leqslant\tau\leqslant t} [X(\tau) - \tau] \leqslant u; x + X(t) - t \leqslant u\right\}. \end{aligned} \tag{5.49}$$

From equation (1.219), it is seen that the last expression is the probability that in the queueing system $M/G/1$, the waiting time at time t is at most equal to u. Using the results obtained in Sections 2.3 and 2.4, we thus find that

$$(5.50)\qquad F(t; 0, x) = \sum_{n=0}^{\infty} e^{-t} \frac{t^{n-1}}{n!} \int_{y=0}^{t-x} (t - y)\, dP_n(y),$$

and for $u \geqslant 0$,

$$(5.51)\quad F(t; u, x) = K(t + u - x, t) - \int_{\tau=0}^{t-x} F(t; 0, x)\, dK(\tau + u, \tau),$$

where we recall that

$$(5.52)\qquad dK(t + u, t) = d_x K(x, t)\,\big|_{x=t+u} = \sum_{n=0}^{\infty} e^{-t} \frac{t^n}{n!}\, d_t P_n(t + u).$$

From (5.48) it follows that the d.f. $G(t; u)$ of T is given by

$$(5.53)\qquad G(t; u) = 1 - Pr\{T(u) > t\} = 1 - F(t; u, 0).$$

Furthermore, $G(\infty; u)$ is the complement of the limiting waiting time d.f., which is known to exist if and only if $\alpha < 1$. In terms of Lundberg's security factor $\rho = \alpha^{-1}$, this means that

$$(5.54)\qquad \psi(u) = Pr\{T(u) < \infty\} \begin{cases} = 1 & \text{if } \rho \leqslant 1 \\ < 1 & \text{if } \rho > 1; \end{cases}$$

moreover, if $\rho > 1$,

$$(5.55)\qquad \psi(0) = \rho^{-1}$$

$$\psi(u) = (1 - \rho^{-1}) \int_0^{\infty} \sum_{n=0}^{\infty} e^{-t} \frac{t^n}{n!}\, d_t P_n(t + u) \qquad (u > 0).$$

Examples. (*a*) Let $P(x) = 0$ if $x < \alpha$ and $= 1$ if $x \geqslant \alpha$. Then

$$(5.56)\quad F(t; 0\ 0) = \sum_{n=0}^{N_0} e^{-t} \frac{(t - n\alpha)t^{n-1}}{n!} = e^{-t} \frac{t^{N_0}}{N_0!} + (1 - \alpha) \sum_{n=0}^{N_0-1} e^{-t} \frac{t^n}{n!},$$

and

$$(5.57)\quad F(t; u, 0) = \sum_{n=0}^{N_2} e^{-t} \frac{t^n}{n!} - e^{-t} \sum_{N_1}^{N_2} \frac{(n\alpha - u)^n}{n!} \cdot \left[\frac{(t + u - n\alpha)^{N_2-n}}{(N_2 - n)!} + (1 - \alpha) \sum_{\nu=0}^{N_2-n-1} \frac{(t + u - n\alpha)^{\nu}}{\nu!}\right],$$

where $N_0 = [t/\alpha]$, $N_1 = [u/\alpha]$, $N_2 = [(t+u)/\alpha]$, $[x]$ being the largest integer contained in x [cf. Arfwedson (1954), equation (135)]. Furthermore, if $\alpha < 1$,

$$\psi(u) = (1-\alpha)\sum_{N_1}^{\infty} e^{-(n\alpha - u)} \frac{(n\alpha - u)^n}{n!}. \tag{5.58}$$

(*b*) Let $P(x) = 1 - e^{-\rho x}$ $(0 \leqslant x < \infty)$. Here

$$1 - K(x, t) = \sum_{n=1}^{\infty} e^{-t}\frac{t^n}{n!}[1 - P_n(x)] = \sum_{n=1}^{\infty} e^{-t}\frac{t^n}{n!}\sum_{\nu=0}^{n-1} e^{-\rho x}\frac{(\rho x)^\nu}{\nu!} \tag{5.59}$$

$$= \sum_{\nu=0}^{\infty} e^{-\rho x}\frac{(\rho x)^\nu}{\nu!}\sum_{n=\nu+1}^{\infty} e^{-t}\frac{t^n}{n!} = e^{-\rho x}\int_{y=0}^{t} e^{-y}J(\rho x y)\,dy,$$

where $J(x) = \sum_{n=0}^{\infty} x^n/(n!)^2$ is a Bessel function. We have

$$F(t; 0, 0) = e^{-t} + \sum_{n=1}^{\infty} e^{-t}\frac{t^{n-1}}{n!}\int_{x=0}^{t}(t-x)e^{-\rho x}\rho^n \frac{x^{n-1}}{(n-1)!}\,dx,$$

from which we obtain

$$G(t, 0) = e^{-\rho t}\int_0^t e^{-x}J(\rho t x)\,dx + e^{-t}\rho\int_0^t e^{-\rho x}xJ'(\rho t x)\,dx. \tag{5.60}$$

The expression for $G(t, u)$ can be simplified similarly [cf. Arfwedson (1955), page 85]. Also, if $\rho > 1$,

$$\psi(u) = \left(1 - \frac{1}{\rho}\right)e^{-\rho u}\int_0^{\infty} e^{-(1+\rho)t}tJ'(\rho t^2 + \rho u t)\,dt. \tag{5.61}$$

c. The Probability of Ruin for a Negative Process

Let us consider next the case of an insurance company that deals only in ordinary whole-life annuities. Here all the claims are negative, and the process is sometimes referred to as a "negative process." If we put $\bar{X}(t) = -X(t)$, and $B(x) = 1 - P(-x)$, $0 \leqslant x < \infty$, then the distribution of $\bar{X}(t)$ is

$$K(x, t) = \sum_{n=0}^{\infty} e^{-t}\frac{t^n}{n!}B_n(x) \qquad (0 \leqslant x < \infty), \tag{5.62}$$

its Laplace-Stieltjes transform (L.S.T.) being given by

$$\int_0^{\infty} e^{-\theta x}\,d_x K(x, t) = \exp\{-t[1 - \phi(\theta)]\}, \tag{5.63}$$

where $\phi(\theta)$ is the L.S.T. of $B(x)$. Here $\alpha < 0$, and, since λ and α are of the same sign, $\lambda < 0$; without loss of generality we can take $\lambda = -1$, so that the risk reserve in this case becomes $Z(t) = u - t + \bar{X}(t)$, and the period of prosperity can be defined as

$$T(u) = \inf\,[t \mid u + \bar{X}(t) - t < 0]. \tag{5.64}$$

From Section 2.2 we now see that $T(u)$ is the busy period of the queue $M/G/1$. The results below then follow immediately. First we obtain

$$G(t; u) = Pr\{T(u) \leqslant t\} = \int_{\tau=u}^{t} \sum_{n=0}^{\infty} e^{-\tau} \frac{u\tau^{n-1}}{n!} \, dB_n(\tau - u) \tag{5.65}$$

for the distribution of T, and

$$\int_0^\infty e^{-\theta t} \, d_t G(t, u) = e^{-u\eta(\theta)} \tag{5.66}$$

for the L.S.T. of this distribution, where $\eta(\theta)$ satisfies the functional equation

$$\eta(\theta) = \theta + 1 - \phi[\eta(\theta)]. \tag{5.67}$$

Furthermore, the probability of the eventual ruin of the company is given by

$$\psi(u) = G(\infty, u) = \begin{cases} 1 & \text{if } \rho \geqslant 1 \\ e^{-Ru} & \text{if } \rho < 1, \end{cases} \tag{5.68}$$

a result due to Lundberg; here $\rho = |\alpha|^{-1}$ is Lundberg's security factor and R is the largest positive root of the equation

$$R = 1 - \phi(R). \tag{5.69}$$

Examples. (*a*) Let $B(x) = 0$ if $x < \mu$, and $= 1$ if $x \geqslant \mu$. Then $B_n(x) = 0$ if $x < n\mu$, and $= 1$ if $x \geqslant n\mu$, and

$$G(t, u) = \sum_{n=0}^{\infty} \int_u^t e^{-\tau} \frac{u\tau^{n-1}}{n!} \, dB_n(\tau - u) = \sum_{n=0}^{N} e^{-(u+n\mu)} \frac{u(u + n\mu)^{n-1}}{n!}, \tag{5.70}$$

where $N = [(t - u)/\mu]$ is the largest integer contained in $(t - u)/\mu$.

(*b*) Let $B(x) = 1 - e^{-\mu x}$ $(0 \leqslant x < \infty)$. In this case

$$dB_n(x) = e^{-\mu x}[(\mu x)^{n-1}/(n - 1)!]\mu \, dx,$$

and

$$\begin{aligned} G(t, u) &= e^{-u} + \sum_{n=1}^{\infty} \int_u^t e^{-\tau} \frac{u}{n!} \tau^{n-1} e^{-\mu(\tau-u)} \mu^n \frac{(\tau - u)^{n-1}}{(n - 1)!} \, d\tau \\ &= e^{-u} + \mu u e^{\mu u} \int_u^t e^{-(1+\mu)\tau} J'[\mu(\tau - u)\tau] \, d\tau, \end{aligned} \tag{5.71}$$

[see Arfwedson (1954), equation (152)].

d. The General Case

We now consider the general case where the claims can be positive or negative. Let us define

$$F(t; u) = 1 - G(t; u) = Pr\{T(u) > t\}; \tag{5.72}$$

then from (5.45) it follows that

$$(5.73)\qquad F(t; u) = Pr\left\{\inf_{0\leqslant\tau\leqslant t} [u + \lambda\tau - X(\tau)] \geqslant 0\right\}$$
$$= Pr\left\{\sup_{0\leqslant\tau\leqslant t} [X(\tau) - \lambda\tau] \leqslant u\right\}.$$

Thus $F(t; u)$ is the d.f. of the supremum of the process $X(\tau) - \lambda\tau$ over the interval $[0, t]$. For any separable centered infinitely divisible process $Y(t)$ Baxter and Donsker (1957) showed that

$$(5.74)\quad s\int_{t=0}^{\infty}\int_{u=0-}^{\infty} e^{-st-\theta u}\, d_u Pr\left\{\sup_{0\leqslant\tau\leqslant t} Y(\tau) < u\right\}$$
$$= \exp\left\{\int_{w=s}^{\infty}\int_{t=0}^{\infty} e^{-wt}[\psi(\theta, t) - 1]\, dt\, dw\right\}$$

by generalizing the corresponding result of Spitzer (equation (4.79)) for the discrete case. Here

$$(5.75)\qquad \psi(\theta, t) = 1 + \int_0^{\infty} (e^{-\theta y} - 1)\, d_y Pr\{Y(t) < y\}.$$

The process $Y(t) = X(t) - \lambda t$ obviously satisfies the conditions for the validity of (5.74), and therefore

$$(5.76)\quad s\int_{t=0}^{\infty}\int_{u=0-}^{\infty} e^{-st-\theta u}\, d_u F(t; u)$$
$$= \exp\left[\int_{w=s}^{\infty}\int_{t=0}^{\infty} e^{-wt}\int_0^{\infty} (e^{-\theta x} - 1)\, d_x K(x + \lambda t, t)\, dt\, dw\right].$$

The ruin problem can thus be considered to have been solved in the general case.

5.6 MODELS FOR HYDROELECTRIC SYSTEMS

It is clear that a dam (or storage reservoir of a hydroelectric system) is an inventory of type (2). Here X_n represents the random input of water into the dam, and the demand is either for electric power (expressed in terms of the volume of water required to produce it) or for water to be supplied to a city. We assume that supplementary sources exist (a thermal station or an arrangement for "borrowing" water from a nearby dam) in case the entire demand cannot be fully met, but these are available at a cost, and moreover, may be available only up to a certain limit. A formulation of the optimum storage problem along these lines was given by the French Engineer Massé (1946); Little (1955) studied the problem with reference to the Grand Coulee Dam [see also Koopmans (1958)].

More recent investigation of this problem is due to Bather [(1962, 1963)]. In 1954 Moran formulated his probability theory of a dam, which was later developed further and extended by him and several other authors [see Moran (1959)]. In the next chapter we give an account of this theory.

COMPLEMENTS AND PROBLEMS

Section 5.1

1. *Inventory model with random supply.* This is described by a critical number x^*, and the policy is effected as follows. Whenever the present stock level x is smaller than x^*, an ordering is made; if $x \geqslant x^*$ no ordering is to be done. When ordering is done, a random quantity of goods is delivered immediately. Thus

$$Z_{n+1} = \begin{cases} Z_n + X_n - \xi_n & \text{if } Z_n < x^* \\ Z_n - \xi_n & \text{if } Z_n \geqslant x^*, \end{cases} \tag{1}$$

where X_n, the amount delivered, and ξ_n, the demand, are both random variables having known distributions [see Arrow, Karlin, and Scarf (1958)].

2. *Replacements at arbitrary times.* Suppose that deliveries are made at arbitrary times, the time intervals between successive deliveries being mutually independent random variables with the common characteristic function (c.f.) $\phi(\theta)$. The warehouse has a capacity c, and is restocked completely each time the delivery is made. Demands occur in a Poisson process with mean λt, the amount demanded having a distribution with the c.f. $\psi(\theta)$. The demand is met if "physically possible," and moreover, returned material is accepted without limit, so that demand can be negative. Show that the probability that the warehouse will not become empty between one delivery and the next is given by

$$\lim_{x \to c-0} \frac{1}{\pi} \int_{\infty}^{0} \frac{\sin x\theta}{\theta} [\phi\{i\lambda[1 - \psi(\theta)]\} + \phi\{i\lambda[1 - \psi(-\theta)]\}]\, d\theta. \tag{2}$$

[Hammersley (1955)].

Section 5.2

3. The analysis of the (s, S) model given here is due to Karlin [see Arrow, Karlin, and Scarf (1958), Chapter 15].

Section 5.4

4. *Ordering cycle.* Pitt (1946) also considers a second replacement policy as follows. Orders are made regularly at the times kMa^{-1} ($k = 1, 2, \ldots$), where the number ordered is equal to the comsumption during the previous interval of length Ma^{-1}. The delivery is made after a time lag T. Discuss the stationary behavior of the stock function in this case.

Section 5.5

5. Let $F(t; u) = 1 - G(t; u)$. By considering $F(t; u)$ over the consecutive intervals $(0, dt]$ and $(dt, dt + t]$ obtain the integro-differential equation

$$\frac{\partial F}{\partial t} - \lambda \frac{\partial F}{\partial u} + F(t; u) = \int_{-\infty}^{u} F(t; u - x)\, dP(x) \tag{3}$$

with the initial condition $F(0; u) = 1$ for $u \geqslant 0$ [Arfwedson (1954)]. As Cramér (1955) has shown (3) can be solved by means of the Wiener-Hopf method. However, this does not lead to explicit results except in some particular cases.

6. Show that $\psi(u)$ satisfies the integro-differential equation

$$-\lambda\psi'(u) + \psi(u) = 1 - P(u) + \int_{-\infty}^{u} \psi(u - x)\, dP(x) \tag{4}$$

[cf. Cramér (1954)].

7. Let $N(t)$ be the number of claims during an interval $(0, t]$, and

$$F_n(t; u) = Pr\{T(u) > t; N(t) = n\}. \tag{5}$$

Show that

$$F_0(t; u) = e^{-t}P_0(u + \lambda t) \tag{6}$$

$$F_n(t; u) = \int_{\tau \geqslant 0} \int_{y=-\infty}^{u+\lambda\tau} e^{-\tau}\, d\tau\, F_{n-1}(t - \tau; u + \lambda\tau - y)\, dP(y) \qquad (n \geqslant 1), \tag{7}$$

where the upper limit for τ is t if $\lambda \geqslant 0$, and $\min(t, -u/\lambda)$ if $\lambda < 0$ [Arfwedson (1954)].

8. The special cases of positive and negative processes were considered by the author (1961).

9. *Positive process.* Show that for a positive process, the equation (3) becomes

$$\frac{\partial F}{\partial t} - \frac{\partial F}{\partial u} + F(t; u) = \int_{0}^{u} F(t; u - x)\, dP(x) \tag{8}$$

which is Takács equation for the waiting time in the queueing system $M/G/1$ (see Chapter 1).

10. Show that, for a positive process,

$$\text{(a)} \quad \int_0^\infty e^{-st}F(t; 0)\, dt = \frac{1}{\eta(s)} \tag{9}$$

$$\text{(b)} \quad \int_0^\infty \int_0^\infty e^{-st-\theta u}F(t; u)\, dt\, du = \frac{1}{\theta\eta}\frac{\eta - \theta}{s - \theta + 1 - \phi(\theta)} \tag{10}$$

$$\operatorname{Re}(s) > \theta - 1 + \phi(\theta),$$

$$\text{(c)} \quad \int_{0-}^\infty e^{-\theta u}\, du\, F(\infty; u) = \frac{(1 - \alpha)\theta}{\theta - 1 + \phi(\theta)} \tag{11}$$

where $\phi(\theta)$ is the L.S.T. of $P(x)$, and $\eta \equiv \eta(s)$ satisfies the functional equation $\eta = s + 1 - \phi[n(s)]$ [Arfwedson (1954)].

11. *Negative process.* Show that for a negative process, equation (3) gives, in the notation of Section 5.5c,

$$\frac{\partial G}{\partial t} + \frac{\partial G}{\partial u} + G(t; u) = \int_0^\infty G(t; u + x)\, dB(x). \tag{12}$$

Let $G^*(\theta; u) = \int_0^\infty e^{-\theta t}\, d_tG(t; u)$. Then from (12) we obtain

$$(1 + \theta)G^*(\theta; u) + \frac{\partial G^*}{\partial u} = \int_0^\infty G^*(\theta; u + x)\, dB(x). \tag{13}$$

Show that $G^*(\theta; u) = e^{-u\eta(\theta)}$ is the unique solution of (13) in agreement with (5.66) [Arfwedson (1955)].

12. Show that

$$G_n(t; u) = Pr\{T(u) \leqslant t; N\{T(u)\} = n\}$$
$$= \int_u^t e^{-\tau} u \frac{\tau^{n-1}}{n!} dB_n(\tau - u) \qquad (n = 0, 1, 2, \ldots)$$

(see Section 2.2).

REFERENCES

Arfwedson, G. (1954). Research in collective risk theory, part I. *Skan. Aktuar.*, **37,** 191–223.

Arfwedson, G. (1955). Research in collective risk theory, part II. *Skan. Aktuar.*, **38,** 53–100.

Arrow, K. J., S. Karlin, and H. Scarf (1958). *Studies in the Mathematical Theory of Inventory and Production.* Stanford University Press.

Bather, J. A. (1962). Optimal regulation policies for finite dams. *J. Soc. Indust. Appl. Math.*, **10,** 395–423.

Bather, J. A. (1963). The optimal regulation of dams in continuous time. *J. Soc. Indust. Appl. Math.*, **11,** 33–63.

Baxter, Glen, and M. D. Donsker (1957). On the distribution of the supremum functional for processes with stationary independent increments. *Trans. Amer. Math. Soc.*, **85,** 73–87.

Cramér, Harald (1954). On some questions connected with mathematical risk. *University of Calif. Publications in Statistics*, **2,** 99–124.

Cramér, Harald (1955). *Collective Risk Theory.* Jubilee Volume of the Skandia Insurance Co., Ab Nordiska Bokhandeln, Stockholm.

Feller, W. (1957). *An Introduction to Probability Theory and its Applications*, 2nd edition. John Wiley, New York.

Gani, J. (1957). Problems in the probability theory of storage systems. *J. Roy. Stat. Soc.*, **B19,** 181–206.

Hammersley, J. M. (1955). Storage problems. *Math. Annalen*, **128,** 475–478.

Koopmans, Tjalling C. (1958). *Water Storage Policy in a Simplified Hydroelectric System.* Cowles Foundation Paper No. 115.

Little, John D. C. (1955). The use of storage water in a hydroelectric system. *Opns. Res.*, **3,** 187–197.

Massé, P. (1946). *Les Reserves et la Regulation de l'Avenir dans la vie Economique.* Hermann, Paris.

Moran, P. A. P. (1959). *The Theory of Storage.* Methuen, London.

Pitt, H. R. (1946). A theorem on random functions with applications to a theory of provisioning. *J. London Math. Soc.*, **21,** 16–22.

Prabhu, N. U. (1961). On the ruin problem of collective risk theory. *Ann. Math. Stat.*, **32,** 757–764.

Rosenblatt, M. (1954). An inventory problem. *Econometrica*, **22,** 244–247.

Chapter 6

Moran's Model for the Dam

6.1 INTRODUCTION

Statistical treatment of problems associated with water storage systems is of recent origin. The earliest work in this field seems to be that of Gumbel (1941), which dealt with the return period of flood flows; this was later discussed by Moran (1957). Empirical work on the determination of storage capacity was done by Hurst (1951, 1956). Inventory problems arising in storage systems have been considered by Little (1955), Koopmans (1958), and Bather (1962, 1963) (see the references cited in Chapter 5). In 1954 Moran gave the first probabilistic formulation of a storage model for the dam along the following lines.

The amount of water which flows into a dam (the input) will vary from time to time and will thus have a probability distribution. Apart from a possible overflow, which may happen if the dam is of finite capacity, this water is stored, and released according to a definite rule. The purpose of the dam is to make the amount released (the output) more uniform than the input in some statistical sense; in this connection it is relevant to study the underlying stochastic process, and in particular the following problems are of some practical importance:

1. To study the situation when the process described above has reached statistical equilibrium.
2. To obtain the probability distribution of the "wet period," that is, the time taken for a given initial dam content to dry up.

The basic model considered by Moran was formulated in discrete time, so that the process occurs at discrete series of time intervals (for instance, years). The following assumptions are made.

1. The input. Let X_n be the amount of water which has flowed into the dam during the year $(n, n + 1)$ $(n = 0, 1, \ldots)$. We assume that X_0, X_1,

$X_2, \ldots$ are random variables which are mutually independent and have the same distribution. This assumption is made mainly for the sake of simplicity and seems to be reasonable in ordinary circumstances. A more realistic assumption, however, will take into account possible serial correlation among the X_n [see Bhat and Gani (1959); a review of some recent work on dams with correlated inputs is given by Prabhu (1964).

This input is assumed to occur during the "wet season," and is stored until the "dry season," when it is released: a scheme which is not entirely realistic, but again introduces a considerable simplification of theory.

2. *The overflow.* Let k be the finite capacity of the dam, and Z_n, the storage at time n, the amount of water in the dam before the input X_n flows into it. Then if $Z_n + X_n > k$, an amount $Z_n + X_n - k$ will overflow, but if $Z_n + X_n \leqslant k$, there will be no overflow; the dam now contains a quantity $\min(k, Z_n + X_n)$.

3. *The release rule.* At time $n + 1$, an amount of water m $(< k)$ if $Z_n + X_n \geqslant m$ or $Z_n + X_n$ if $Z_n + X_n < m$ is released from the dam. The release is thus $Y_n = \min(m, Z_n + X_n)$.

From these assumptions it follows that the storage function Z_n satisfies the recurrence relation

$$Z_{n+1} = \min(k, Z_n + X_n) - \min(m, Z_n + X_n) \qquad (n = 0, 1, 2, \ldots). \tag{6.1}$$

From this it is clear that the sequence of random variables $\{Z_n\}$ forms a time homogeneous Markov chain; we proceed to study this chain.

6.2 THE TRANSIENT BEHAVIOR OF Z_n IN THE DISCRETE CASE

Let us first consider the case where the inputs have a discrete probability distribution with

$$Pr\{X_n = j\} = g_j \qquad (j = 0, 1, 2, \ldots). \tag{6.2}$$

The Markov chain $\{Z_n\}$ has then a finite number of states, 0, 1, 2, ..., $k - m$. Let its transition probabilities be denoted by

$$P_{ij}^{(n)} = Pr\{Z_n = j \mid Z_0 = i\} \qquad (i, j = 0, 1, \ldots, k - m, n \geqslant 1). \tag{6.3}$$

In addition, let $P_{ij}^{(0)} = \delta_{ij}$, where $\delta_{ij} = 1$ or 0 depending on whether $i = j$ or $i \neq j$; we shall further denote $P_{ij}^{(1)} = P_{ij}$. From (6.1) we find that the transition probability matrix $P \equiv (P_{ij})$ is given by

$$
(6.4) \quad P \equiv \begin{array}{c|cccccc}
\nearrow & 0 & 1 & 2 & \cdot\ \cdot & k-m-1 & k-m \\
\hline
0 & G_m & g_{m+1} & g_{m+2} & \cdot\ \cdot & g_{k-1} & h_k \\
1 & G_{m-1} & g_m & g_{m+1} & \cdot\ \cdot & g_{k-2} & h_{k-1} \\
\cdot & \cdot & \cdot & \cdot & \cdot\ \cdot & \cdot & \cdot \\
\cdot & \cdot & \cdot & \cdot & \cdot\ \cdot & \cdot & \cdot \\
m & G_0 & g_1 & g_2 & \cdot\ \cdot & g_{k-m-1} & h_{k-m} \\
m+1 & 0 & g_0 & g_1 & \cdot\ \cdot & g_{k-m-2} & h_{k-m-1} \\
\cdot & \cdot & \cdot & \cdot & \cdot\ \cdot & \cdot & \cdot \\
\cdot & \cdot & \cdot & \cdot & \cdot\ \cdot & \cdot & \cdot \\
k-m & 0 & 0 & 0 & \cdot\ \cdot & g_{m-1} & h_m
\end{array},
$$

where $G_i = g_0 + g_1 + \cdots + g_i$, $h_i = g_i + g_{i+1} + \cdots (i \geqslant 0)$ and it is assumed that $m < \frac{1}{2}k$. It is known that the matrix $(P_{ij}^{(n)}) = P^n$ $(n \geqslant 1)$; we also have $P^0 = I$, where I is the identity matrix of order $k - m + 1$. For $n \geqslant 2$ let us write $P^n = P \cdot P^{n-2} \cdot P$; we then obtain the relation

$$(6.5) \qquad P_{ij}^{(n)} = Q_i P^{n-2} R_j \qquad (n \geqslant 2),$$

where Q_i is the ith row vector and R_j the jth column vector of P, so that

$$(6.6) \qquad \begin{aligned} Q_i &= (P_{i0}, P_{i1}, \ldots, P_{i,k-m}) \\ R_j &= (P_{0j}, P_{1j}, \ldots, P_{k-m,j})'. \end{aligned}$$

Let us now define the transform

$$(6.7) \qquad P_{ij}(z) = \sum_{n=2}^{\infty} P_{ij}^{(n)} z^n \qquad (|z| < 1);$$

from (6.5) we find that

$$(6.8) \qquad \begin{aligned} P_{ij}(z) &= z^2 Q_i \sum_{n=2}^{\infty} P^{n-2} z^{n-2} R_j \\ &= z^2 Q_i (I + zP + z^2 P^2 + \cdots) R_j \\ &= z^2 Q_i (I - zP)^{-1} R_j, \end{aligned}$$

where the existence of the inverse matrix $(I - zP)^{-1}$ is ensured if we choose z so that $\max_{i,j} |zP_{ij}| < 1$.

As an application of (6.8) let us consider the case where the inputs have a geometric distribution

$$(6.9) \qquad g_j = ab^j \qquad (j = 0, 1, 2, \ldots)$$

where $0 < a < 1$ and $b = 1 - a$, and where the release is $m = 1$. The matrix P in this case is given by

(6.10) $P \equiv$

↗	0	1	2	.	.	$k-2$	$k-1$
0	$a+ab$	ab^2	ab^3	.	.	ab^{k-1}	b^k
1	a	ab	ab^2	.	.	ab^{k-2}	b^{k-1}
2	0	a	ab	.	.	ab^{k-3}	b^{k-2}
.	.	.	.	.	.	.	.
.	.	.	.	.	.	.	.
$k-1$	0	0	0	.	.	a	b

The result (6.8) can now be written as

$$P_{ij}(z) = z^2 \sum_{\nu=0}^{j+1} ab^{j+1-\nu} A_\nu / |I - zP| \tag{6.11}$$

where A_ν is the determinant of the matrix $I - zP$ with the νth row replaced by Q_i. After some manipulation it is found that

$$P_{ij}(z) = \sum_{\nu=0}^{i-1} (az)^{i+1-\nu} b^{j+1-\nu} V_\nu(z)(1-z)^{-1} + \sum_{\nu=i}^{j+1} (az)^2 b^{j+i+2} V_\nu(z)(1-z)^{-1}, \tag{6.12}$$

where

(6.13)

$$V_0 = \frac{\lambda_1^{k-i} - \lambda_2^{k-i} - bz(\lambda_1^{k-i-1} - \lambda_2^{k-i-1})}{\lambda_1^{k+1} - \lambda_2^{k+1}}$$

$$V_\nu = \frac{[\lambda_1^{k-i} - \lambda_2^{k-i} - bz(\lambda_1^{k-i-1} - \lambda_2^{k-i-1})][\lambda_1^{\nu+2} - \lambda_2^{\nu+2} - az(\lambda_1^{\nu+1} - \lambda_2^{\nu+1})]}{(\lambda_1 - \lambda_2)(\lambda_1^{k+1} - \lambda_2^{k+1})} \quad (1 \leqslant \nu \leqslant i-1)$$

$$V_\nu = \frac{[\lambda_1^{i+1} - \lambda_2^{i+1} - az(\lambda_1^{i} - \lambda_2^{i})][\lambda_1^{k-\nu-1} - \lambda_2^{k-\nu-1} - bz(\lambda_1^{k-\nu-2} - \lambda_2^{k-\nu-2})]}{(\lambda_1 - \lambda_2)(\lambda_1^{k+1} - \lambda_2^{k+1})} \quad (i \leqslant \nu \leqslant j+1),$$

and

$$\lambda_1 = \frac{1 + \sqrt{1 - 4abz}}{2}, \qquad \lambda_2 = \frac{1 - \sqrt{1 - 4abz}}{2}. \tag{6.14}$$

6.3 STATIONARY DISTRIBUTION OF THE STORAGE

We shall be concerned with the case where m, the amount of water released at time $n + 1$, is unity. Let (g_j) be the probability distribution of X_n, as in (6.2); also, let

$$G(z) = \sum_{j=0}^{\infty} g_j z^j, \qquad |z| < 1 \tag{6.15}$$

be the probability generating function (p.g.f.) of (g_j), and

$$\rho = G'(1) = \sum_{j=0}^{\infty} j g_j \tag{6.16}$$

the mean input. The transition-matrix of the Markov chain $\{Z_n\}$ is $P \equiv \{P_{ij}\}$, where

$$P = \begin{array}{c|cccccc} \nearrow & 0 & 1 & \cdots & k-2 & k-1 \\ \hline 0 & g_0 + g_1 & g_2 & \cdots & g_{k-1} & h_k \\ 1 & g_0 & g_1 & \cdots & g_{k-2} & h_{k-1} \\ 2 & 0 & g_0 & \cdots & g_{k-3} & h_{k-2} \\ \cdot & \cdot & \cdot & \cdots & \cdot & \cdot \\ \cdot & \cdot & \cdot & \cdots & \cdot & \cdot \\ k-1 & 0 & 0 & \cdots & g_0 & h_1 \end{array} \tag{6.17}$$

where $h_i = \sum_{j=i}^{\infty} g_j$, $(i = 1, 2, \ldots, k)$. Let us assume that $g_j > 0$ for all j; the chain is then irreducible and aperiodic, so that the stationary probability distribution (u_i), $(i = 0, 1, \ldots, k - 1)$ exists, where

$$u_i = \lim_{n\to\infty} Pr\{Z_n = i\};$$

(u_i) is the unique solution of the equations

$$u_j = \sum_{i=0}^{k-1} u_i P_{ij}, \qquad (j = 0, 1, \ldots, k - 1) \tag{6.18}$$

together with $u_0 + u_1 + \cdots + u_{k-1} = 1$. We first prove the following theorem due to Moran (1956).

1. If $[u_i^{(k)}]$, $(i = 0, 1, \ldots, k - 1)$ is the stationary probability distribution of storage in a dam of capacity k, then the ratios

$$v_i = \frac{u_i^{(k)}}{u_0^{(k)}}, \qquad (i = 1, 2, \ldots, k - 1) \tag{6.19}$$

are independent of k.

2. The v_i's can be found as the coefficients of z^i in $V(z)$, where

$$V(z) = \frac{g_0(1 - z)}{G(z) - z}. \tag{6.20}$$

The first part of the theorem is easily proved; in fact, writing out the equations (6.18) in full we obtain

$$\begin{aligned} u_0 &= (g_0 + g_1)u_0 + g_0 u_1 \\ u_1 &= g_2 u_0 + g_1 u_1 + g_0 u_2 \\ \cdot &= \cdot\cdot \quad \cdot\cdot \quad \cdot\cdot \\ u_{k-2} &= g_{k-1}u_0 + g_{k-2}u_1 + \cdots + g_0 u_{k-1} \\ u_{k-1} &= h_k u_0 + h_{k-1}u_1 + \cdots + h_1 u_{k-1} \end{aligned} \tag{6.21}$$

Solving these equations successively for the ratios $v_i = u_i/u_0$, we obtain

$$\begin{aligned} v_1 &= \frac{1 - g_0 - g_1}{g_0} \\ v_2 &= \frac{1 - g_1}{g_0} v_1 + \frac{g_2}{g_0} \end{aligned} \tag{6.22}$$

and in general, the v_i's ($i = 1, 2, \ldots, k - 1$) are seen to be independent of k. Now consider the function $V(z)$ defined by (6.20). We shall first prove that $V(z)$ can be expanded as a power series which is convergent for suitable values of $|z|$. Let us first consider the case $\rho \leqslant 1$ and write

$$G(z) - z = (1 - z)\left[1 - \frac{1 - G(z)}{1 - z}\right];$$

then since

$$\frac{1 - G(z)}{1 - z} = \sum_{n=0}^{\infty} z^n \sum_{n+1}^{\infty} g_i$$

we obtain, for $|z| < 1$,

$$\left|\frac{1 - G(z)}{1 - z}\right| < \sum_{n=0}^{\infty} \sum_{n+1}^{\infty} g_i = \sum_{i=1}^{\infty} i g_i = \rho \leqslant 1,$$

so that $|G(z) - z| \neq 0$, and we have the power series expansion

$$V(z) = g_0\left[1 - \frac{1 - G(z)}{1 - z}\right]^{-1} = v_0 + v_1 z + v_2 z^2 + \cdots$$

convergent for $|z| < 1$.

Next, let $\rho > 1$. In this case there exists a positive λ such that the power series expansion

$$\frac{g_0}{G(z) - z} = c_1 + c_2 z + c_3 z^2 + \cdots \tag{6.23}$$

is valid for $|z| < \lambda$ [Knopp, (1928), page 182]. Hence it follows that $V(z)$ also possesses a power series expansion convergent for $|z| < \lambda$.

Thus whether or not $\rho \leqslant 1$, $V(z)$ has a power series expansion

$$V(z) = \frac{g_0(1 - z)}{G(z) - z} = v_0 + v_1 z + v_2 z^2 + \cdots. \tag{6.24}$$

The coefficients v_i are determined from the relation

$$g_0(1 - z) = [G(z) - z] \sum_{i=0}^{\infty} v_i z^i$$

and hence it is seen that $v_0 = 1$, and $v_1, v_2, \ldots, v_{k-1}$ satisfy the relations (6.22). Thus they are, in fact, the quantities defined in (6.19)

From this theorem, it is obvious that the general method of obtaining the stationary probability distribution (u_i) for the discrete dam of finite capacity k consists of (1) finding $V(z)$, (2) expanding $V(z)$ to obtain the v_i's, and (3) normalizing $v_0, v_1, \ldots, v_{k-1}$ to obtain a probability distribution. We proceed to do this in some particular cases.

Geometric Input. Consider, for instance, an input distribution of the geometric type

$$g_j = Pr\{X_n = j\} = ab^j, \qquad (j = 0, 1, \ldots), \tag{6.25}$$

where $0 < a < 1$ and $b = 1 - a$. The p.g.f. of X_n is then

$$G(z) = \frac{a}{1 - bz} \tag{6.26}$$

and the function $V(z)$ is given by

$$\begin{aligned} V(z) &= \frac{a(1 - z)}{a(1 - bz)^{-1} - z} = \frac{1 - bz}{1 - \rho z} \\ &= (1 - bz) \sum_{i=0}^{\infty} \rho^i z^i \left[|z| < \min\left(\frac{1}{\rho}, 1\right) \right], \end{aligned} \tag{6.27}$$

where $\rho = b/a$ is the mean input. Hence we obtain

$$v_0 = 1, \qquad v_i = \rho^i - b\rho^{i-1} = b\rho^i, \qquad (i = 1, 2, \ldots, k - 1)$$

and

$$\sum_0^{k-1} v_i = 1 + b \sum_{i=1}^{k-1} \rho^i = a \frac{1 - \rho^{k+1}}{1 - \rho}.$$

The stationary distribution in this case is therefore given by (u_i), where

$$(6.28)\quad u_0 = \frac{(1-\rho)}{a(1-\rho^{k+1})}, \qquad u_i = \frac{\rho^{i+1}(1-\rho)}{1-\rho^{k+1}}, \qquad (i = 1, 2, \ldots, k-1).$$

This is a geometric distribution, which is truncated at $Z = k - 1$, and has a modified initial term.

Negative Binomial Input. Consider next the more general case of the negative binomial input

$$(6.29)\quad g_j = Pr\{X_n = j\} = \binom{n+j-1}{j} a^n b^j, \qquad (j = 0, 1, \ldots),$$

where $0 < a < 1$, $b = 1 - a$, and n is a positive integer; the p.g.f. of X_n is then

$$(6.30)\qquad G(z) = \frac{a^n}{(1-bz)^n}$$

and the mean input is $\rho = nb/a$. We have then

$$(6.31)\qquad V(z) = \frac{a^n(1-z)}{a^n(1-bz)^{-n} - z} = \frac{a^n(1-z)(1-bz)^n}{a^n - z(1-bz)^n}.$$

Obviously, $z = 1$ is a zero of the denominator of the expression on the right-hand side of (6.31); in addition to this it has n other zeros $z_1, z_2, \ldots, z_n$. We consider here the case where $z_1, z_2, \ldots, z_n$ are all distinct and different from unity; however, the general case can be treated along similar lines. When $(1, z_1, z_2, \ldots, z_n)$ are all different, we can break up $V(z)$ into partial fractions of the form

$$(6.32)\qquad V(z) = d_0 + \sum_{p=1}^{n} \frac{d_p}{1 - z/z_p},$$

where obviously $d_0 = a^n$ and the d_p's are given by

$$(6.33)\quad d_p = \lim_{z \to z_p} \left(1 - \frac{z}{z_p}\right) V(z)$$

$$= \lim_{z \to z_p} \frac{a^n(1-z)(1-bz)^n(1-z/z_p)}{a^n - z(1-bz)^n} = \frac{a^n(1-1/z_p)}{\rho a z_p/(1-bz_p) - 1} \qquad (p = 1, 2, \ldots, n).$$

Now let λ be the least among the quantities $1, |z_1|, |z_2|, \ldots, |z_n|$; then for $|z| < \lambda$ we can express each term under the summation sign in (6.32) as a power series. Thus

$$V(z) = d_0 + \sum_{p=1}^{n} d_p \sum_{i=0}^{\infty} \left(\frac{z}{z_p}\right)^i = d_0 + \sum_{i=0}^{\infty} z^i \sum_{p=1}^{n} d_p \left(\frac{1}{z_p}\right)^i,$$

from which we obtain

$$v_0 = d_0 + \sum_{p=1}^{n} d_p = \lim_{z\to 0} V(z) = 1 \tag{6.34}$$

$$v_i = \sum_{p=1}^{n} \frac{d_p}{(z_p)^i}, \qquad (i = 1, 2, \ldots, k-1),$$

so that

$$\sum_{i=0}^{k-1} v_i = d_0 + \sum_{p=1}^{n} d_p \sum_{i=0}^{k-1} \left(\frac{1}{z_p}\right)^i = d_0 + \sum_{p=1}^{n} d_p \frac{1-(1/z_p)^k}{1-1/z_p}.$$

It follows that the stationary probabilities u_i are given by

$$u_0 = \left[d_0 + \sum_{p=1}^{n} d_p \frac{1-(1/z_p)^k}{1-1/z_p}\right]^{-1} \tag{6.35}$$

$$u_i = u_0 \sum_{p=1}^{n} d_p \left(\frac{1}{z_p}\right)^i, \qquad (i = 1, 2, \ldots, k-1).$$

Thus the stationary distribution of the dam storage here is the weighted sum of n geometric distributions, each of which is truncated at $Z = k - 1$, and has a modified initial term.

Poisson Input. Finally, we consider the case where the input has the Poisson distribution

$$g_j = Pr\{X_n = j\} = e^{-\rho} \frac{\rho^j}{j!}, \qquad (j = 0, 1, \ldots). \tag{6.36}$$

We have here

$$V(z) = \frac{e^{-\rho}(1-z)}{e^{-\rho+\rho z} - z} \tag{6.37}$$

so that the coefficients v_n in the expansion of $V(z)$ are given by

$$v_n = \frac{1}{2\pi\sqrt{-1}} \int_C \frac{e^{-\rho}(1-z)}{e^{-\rho+\rho z} - z} \frac{dz}{z^{n+1}} = \sum_p d_p, \tag{6.38}$$

where C is the circle with center at the origin and radius equal to λ [λ being appropriate to the convergence of $V(z)$ as a power series], and the d_p are the residues of the integrand within C. Thus

$$d_p = \lim_{z\to z_p} (z_p - z) \frac{e^{-\rho}(1-z)}{e^{-\rho+\rho z} - z} \cdot \frac{1}{z^{n+1}} = \frac{e^{-\rho}(1-1/z_p)}{\rho z_p - 1} \left(\frac{1}{z_p}\right)^n$$

$$(p = 1, 2, \ldots),$$

where $z_1, z_2, \ldots$ are the roots (other than unity) of the equation

$$e^{-\rho+\rho z} = z \tag{6.39}$$

within C; these roots are assumed to be distinct. Hence the stationary probabilities of the dam storage are given by

$$(6.40)\qquad \begin{aligned} u_0 &= \left[e^{-\rho} + \sum_p \frac{e^{-\rho}1-(1/z_p)^k}{\rho z_p - 1}\right]^{-1} \\ u_i &= u_0 \sum_p \frac{e^{-\rho}(1-1/z_p)}{\rho z_p - 1}\left(\frac{1}{z_p}\right)^i, \qquad (i = 1, 2, \ldots, k-1). \end{aligned}$$

6.4 THE PROBLEM OF EMPTINESS

a. Emptiness with Overflow

Let $Z_0 = i \ (1 \leqslant i \leqslant k-1)$ be the initial storage in the dam and consider the first subsequent time T_i at which the dam is empty; T_i is called the "wet period" in the dam. Two cases arise depending on whether the dam does or does not overflow during this period. In the first case we see that the random variable T_i is defined as

$$(6.41)\qquad T_i = \min\{n \mid Z_n = 0\}, \qquad Z_0 = i.$$

Let

$$(6.42)\qquad \begin{aligned} f_{i0}^{(n)} &= Pr\{T_i = n\} \\ &= Pr\{Z_r > 0 \ (r = 1, 2, \ldots, n-1); Z_n = 0 \mid Z_0 = i\} \qquad (n \geqslant 1) \end{aligned}$$

be the probability distribution of T_i; we shall obtain the p.g.f.

$$(6.43)\qquad F_i(z) = \sum_{n=1}^{\infty} f_{i0}^{(n)} z^n.$$

We have

$$(6.44)\qquad f_{i0}^{(1)} = P_{i0} = G_{m-i} \quad (i \leqslant m), \quad = 0 \ (i > m),$$

and

$$(6.45)\qquad \begin{aligned} f_{i0}^{(n)} &= \sum_{j=1}^{k-m} P_{ij} f_{j0}^{(n-1)} \\ &= \sum_{1}^{k-m-1} g_{j-i+m} f_{j0}^{(n-1)} + h_{k-i} f_{k-1,0}^{(n-1)} \qquad (n \geqslant 2). \end{aligned}$$

Let Γ be the transition matrix P (6.4) with the 0th row and 0th column removed; thus

$$(6.46)\qquad \Gamma \equiv \begin{bmatrix} g_m & g_{m+1} & \cdots & g_{k-2} & h_{k-1} \\ g_{m-1} & g_m & \cdots & g_{k-3} & h_{k-2} \\ g_{m-2} & g_{m-1} & \cdots & g_{k-4} & h_{k-3} \\ \cdot & \cdot & \cdots & \cdot & \cdot \\ \cdot & \cdot & \cdots & \cdot & \cdot \\ 0 & 0 & \cdots & g_{m-1} & h_m \end{bmatrix}.$$

Also, let $\phi^{(n)}$ be the column vector with the elements $f_{i0}^{(n)}$ $(i = 1, 2, \ldots, k - m)$. Then (6.45) can be written as

$$\phi^{(n)} = \Gamma\phi^{(n-1)} \qquad (n \geqslant 2). \tag{6.47}$$

Solving (6.47) successively for $n = 2, 3, \ldots$, we obtain

$$\phi^{(n)} = \Gamma^{n-1}\phi^{(1)} \qquad (n \geqslant 1) \tag{6.48}$$

where $\Gamma^0 = I = (\delta_{ij})$, the identity matrix of order $k - 1$. From (6.48) we obtain, in particular,

$$f_{i0}^{(n)} = \gamma_i \Gamma^{n-2}\phi^{(1)} \qquad (n \geqslant 2) \tag{6.49}$$

where $\gamma_1, \gamma_2, \ldots, \gamma_{k-1}$ are the row vectors of Γ. It follows that

$$\begin{aligned} F_i(z) &= f_{i0}^{(1)}z + z^2\gamma_i \sum_{n=2}^{\infty} z^{n-2}\Gamma^{n-2}\phi^{(1)} \\ &= G_{m-i}z + z^2\gamma_i(I - z\Gamma)^{-1}\phi^{(1)}, \end{aligned} \tag{6.50}$$

where the convergence of the infinite series is assured if we choose z so that $\max_i |zg_i| < 1$.

Since the chain $\{Z_n\}$ is finite and irreducible, the wet period $T_i < \infty$ with probability one; its mean duration is given by

$$E(T_i) = F_i'(1) = 2 - G_{m-i} + \gamma_i(I - \Gamma)^{-1}\Gamma(I - \Gamma)^{-1}\phi^{(1)}. \tag{6.51}$$

In the above results, it should be noted that $\phi^{(1)}$ is the column vector with the elements $(G_{m-1}, G_{m-2}, \ldots, G_0, 0, \ldots 0)$.

b. Emptiness before Overflow

We now consider the case where the dam does not overflow before it becomes empty. Let us define the random variable

$$T_i = \min\,(n \mid Z_n + X_n \leqslant m \quad \text{or} \quad Z_n + X_n > k); \tag{6.52}$$

$T_i + 1$ is the time the dam takes either to dry up or to overflow ($Z_{T_i+1} = 0$ or $= k - m$). Let the probability that the dam dries up at time n before overflowing be denoted by

$$g_{i0}^{(n)} = Pr\{T_i = n - 1; Z_n = 0\} \qquad (n \geqslant 1). \tag{6.53}$$

We have $g_{i0}^{(1)} = P_{i0}$ as before, and for $n \geqslant 2$,

$$\begin{aligned} g_{i0}^{(n)} = Pr\{0 < i + S_r - rm \leqslant k - m\,(r = 1, 2, \ldots, n - 1);& \\ i + S_n - nm \leqslant 0\},& \end{aligned} \tag{6.54}$$

where $S_r = X_0 + X_1 + \cdots + X_{r-1}$ $(r \geqslant 1)$. From (6.54) we obtain the recurrence relation

$$g_{i0}^{(n)} = \sum_{j=1}^{k-m} g_{j-i+m}\, g_{j0}^{(n-1)} \qquad (n \geqslant 2), \tag{6.55}$$

and proceeding as before, we find that the p.g.f. $G_i(z) \equiv \sum_{n=1}^{\infty} g_{i0}^{(n)} z^n$ is given by a formula of the type (6.50) but where now the last column in Γ is to be replaced by the vector $(g_{k-1}, g_{k-2}, \ldots, g_m)$. The probability that the dam ever dries up before overflow, given by

$$V_i = \sum_{n=1}^{\infty} g_{i0}^{(n)} = Pr\{T_i < \infty, Z_{T_i+1} = 0\} \tag{6.56}$$

is now less than one, since the event $\{T_i < \infty, Z_{T_{i+1}} = k - m\}$ (dam overflows before drying up) has a positive probability. In Section 6.3 we give a method for determining the V_i.

These results simplify to some extent when the release $m = 1$. We now have $\phi^{(1)} = (g_0, 0, \ldots, 0)$, so that (6.50) can be written as

$$F_i(z) = zg_0\delta_{i1} + g_0 z^2 \frac{|E|}{|I - z\Gamma|}, \tag{6.57}$$

where E is the matrix $(I - z\Gamma)$ with the first row replaced by γ_i. A similar simplification can be carried out in the expression for $G_i(z)$. Consider, in particular, the case of the geometric input (6.9). Here the determinants on the right-hand side of (6.57) can be evaluated without much difficulty, and we find that the p.g.f. of the wet period (with overflow) is given by

$$F_i(z) = (az)^i \frac{\lambda_1^{k-i} - \lambda_2^{k-i} - bz(\lambda_1^{k-i-1} - \lambda_2^{k-i-1})}{\lambda_1^{k} - \lambda_2^{k} - bz(\lambda_1^{k-1} - \lambda_2^{k-1})}, \tag{6.58}$$

and its mean duration by

$$E(T_i) = \begin{cases} \dfrac{i}{1-\rho} + \dfrac{\rho^{k+1}(1-\rho^i)}{(1-\rho)^2} & \text{if } \rho \neq 1 \\ \left(k - \dfrac{i-1}{2}\right) i & \text{if } \rho = 1, \end{cases} \tag{6.59}$$

$\rho = b/a$ being the mean input into the dam, and λ_1 and λ_2 being given by (6.14). For the wet period before overflow we have the p.g.f.

$$G_i(z) = (az)^i \frac{\lambda_1^{k-i+1} - \lambda_2^{k-i+1}}{\lambda_1^{k+1} - \lambda_2^{k+1}}. \tag{6.60}$$

c. The Probabilities V_i

In this section we show how the probabilities V_i can be determined explicitly in the case $m = 1$. From (6.55) it is seen that the V_i satisfy the equations

$$V_1 = \sum_{j=1}^{k-1} g_j V_j + g_0$$

$$V_i = \sum_{j=i-1}^{k-1} g_{j-i+1} V_j \qquad (i = 2, 3, \ldots, k-1).$$

These equations simplify to some extent if we note that $V_0 = 1$, $V_k = 0$; for we can then write

$$V_i = \sum_{j=i-1}^{k} g_{j-i+1} V_j \qquad (i = 1, 2, \ldots, k-1). \tag{6.61}$$

Clearly, the coefficients on the right-hand side of these equations correspond to the rows of the transition matrix P. It will now be found easiest to start at the bottom right-hand corner and work up to the left: thus

$$g_0 V_{k-2} + g_1 V_{k-1} + g_2 \cdot 0 = V_{k-1}$$

so that

$$V_{k-2} = \frac{1 - g_1}{g_0} V_{k-1},$$

and similarly

$$V_{k-3} = \frac{(1 - g_1)V_{k-2} - g_2 V_{k-1}}{g_0},$$

etc. This shows that the ratios of the quantities

$$w_i = V_{k-i} \tag{6.62}$$

are again independent of k ($w_0 = 0$, $w_k = 1$); rewriting the equations (6.61) in terms of these quantities, we obtain

$$w_i = \sum_{j=0}^{i} g_j w_{i-j+1}, \qquad (i = 1, 2, \ldots, k-1). \tag{6.63}$$

Consider the system of equations (6.63) for $i = 1, 2, \ldots$ ad infinitum, and put

$$W(z) = w_1 + w_2 z + w_3 z^2 + \cdots; \tag{6.64}$$

we have

$$\begin{aligned} zW(z) &= \sum_{i=1}^{\infty} z^i \sum_{j=0}^{i} g_j w_{i-j+1} \\ &= \sum_{j=1}^{\infty} g_j \sum_{i=j}^{\infty} w_{i-j+1} z^i + g_0 \sum_{i=1}^{\infty} w_{i+1} z^i \\ &= \sum_{j=1}^{\infty} g_j \sum_{i=1}^{\infty} w_i z^{i+j-1} + g_0 \sum_{i=2}^{\infty} w_i z^{i-1} \\ &= G(z)W(z) - g_0 w_1, \end{aligned}$$

from which we obtain the relation

$$W(z) = \frac{g_0 w_1}{G(z) - z}. \tag{6.65}$$

As in (6.23), we can prove that $W(z)$ can be expanded as a power series convergent for suitable values of $|z|$. Let $W(z)$ be expanded as in (6.64); then since $w_k = 1$, we must have

$$V_i = \frac{w_{k-i}}{w_k} \qquad (i = 1, 2, \ldots, k-1). \tag{6.66}$$

These are therefore the required solutions for the equations (6.61).

Let us now consider the particular case where the input is geometric with probabilities $g_j = ab^j$ $(j = 0, 1, 2, \ldots)$, and $G(z) = a(1 - bz)^{-1}$; then (6.65) gives

$$w_1^{-1}W(z) = \frac{a}{a(1-bz)^{-1} - z} = \frac{(1-bz)}{(1-z)(1-\rho z)} = \begin{cases} \dfrac{a}{1-\rho}\left(\dfrac{1}{1-z} - \dfrac{\rho^2}{1-\rho z}\right) & \text{if } \rho \neq 1 \\[2ex] \dfrac{1-bz}{(1-z)^2} & \text{if } \rho = 1. \end{cases} \tag{6.67}$$

Therefore

$$w_1^{-1}w_i = \begin{cases} \dfrac{a(1-\rho^{i+1})}{1-\rho} & \text{if } \rho \neq 1 \\[2ex] a(i+1) & \text{if } \rho = 1 \end{cases} \qquad (i \neq 1), \tag{6.68}$$

and hence the probabilities V_i for the geometric input are given by

$$V_i = \begin{cases} \dfrac{1-\rho^{k+1-i}}{1-\rho^{k+1}} & \text{if } \rho \neq 1 \\[2ex] 1 - \dfrac{i}{k+1} & \text{if } \rho = 1 \end{cases} \qquad (i = 1, 2, \ldots, k-1). \tag{6.69}$$

A similar procedure could be used, when the input is of a more general type, to obtain the exact expressions for the probabilities V_i. However, very often, it may suffice to know the bounds within which V_i lie, and these bounds are given by Feller [(1957); Chapter XIV, inequalities (8.11) and (8.12)]. In fact, noting that $E(X_t - 1) = \rho - 1$, where ρ is the mean input, we have that

$$\begin{aligned} &\frac{z_0^k - z_0^i}{z_0^k - 1} \leqslant V_i \leqslant 1 && \text{if } \rho < 1 \\ &\frac{z_0^i - z_0^k}{1 - z_0^k} \leqslant V_i \leqslant z_0^i && \text{if } \rho > 1 \\ &1 - \frac{i}{k} \leqslant V_i \leqslant 1 && \text{if } \rho = 1, \end{aligned} \tag{6.70}$$

where z_0 is the unique positive root (other than unity) of the equation $G(z) = z$, and $z_0 \gtrless 1$ depending on whether $\rho \lessgtr 1$.

6.5 THE CASE OF CONTINUOUS INPUTS

a. Stationary Distributions

In the last two sections we considered the case where the inputs X_n into the dam occur in discrete amounts. In practice, however, the inputs occur continuously, and a discrete distribution such as (6.2) can only lead to results which are useful approximations. Let the distribution function (d.f.) be denoted by $G(x)$, so that

$$Pr\{X_n \leqslant x\} = G(x), \tag{6.71}$$

where $G(x) = 0$ if $x \leqslant 0$. The process $\{Z_n\}$ is again a Markov chain, whose states belong to the closed interval $[0, k - m]$. To establish the existence of the limiting distribution of Z_n, we use the following argument due to Loynes (1962).

The recurrence relation (6.1) can be written as

$$Z_{n+1} = f(Z_n + X_n), \tag{6.72}$$

where the function $f(u)$ is defined as follows:

$$f(u) = \begin{cases} 0 & \text{if } u \leqslant m \\ u - m & \text{if } m < u < k. \\ k - m & \text{if } u \geqslant k \end{cases} \tag{6.73}$$

It is seen that $f(u)$ is nondecreasing and nonnegative for $u \geqslant 0$. Let us also note that since the distribution of X_n is independent of n, we can talk of the sequence $\{X_n, -\infty < n < \infty\}$ of mutually independent random variables with the d.f. (6.71). Now, for each integer N we define a sequence $\{Z_n^{(N)}, -\infty < n < \infty\}$ as follows:

$$\begin{aligned} Z_n^{(N)} &= 0 \quad \text{if } n \leqslant -N \\ Z_{n+1}^{(N)} &= f(Z_n^{(N)} + X_n) \quad \text{if } n \geqslant -N. \end{aligned} \tag{6.74}$$

We have

$$Z_n^{(N+1)} \geqslant Z_n^{(N)} \quad (-\infty < n < \infty). \tag{6.75}$$

To prove (6.75), we observe that for $n < -N$ we have $Z_n^{(N)} = 0 = Z_n^{(N+1)}$ from (6.74); for $n = -N$ we have $Z_n^{(N)} = 0$, whereas $Z_n^{(N+1)} = f(Z_{n-1}^{(N+1)} + X_{n-1}) \geqslant 0$. Thus (6.75) is true for $n \leqslant -N$. Let us assume it to be true for some n; then since $f(u)$ is nondecreasing,

$$Z_{n+1}^{(N+1)} = f(Z_n^{(N+1)} + X_n) \geqslant f(Z_n^{(N)} + X_n) = Z_{n+1}^{(N)}, \tag{6.76}$$

that is, (6.75) is true for $n + 1$. Hence (6.75) is true for all n. In particular, $Z_0^{(N+1)} \geqslant Z_0^{(N)}$; thus $\{Z_0^{(N)}\}$ is a monotone nondecreasing sequence of random variables. Therefore $Z_0^{(N)} \to Z^*$, where Z^* is a random variable which may possibly be infinite. Now let $\{Z_N^{(0)}\}$ be the sequence obtained from (6.72) with $Z_0^{(0)} = Z_0 = 0$; then since $Z_N^{(0)}$ is obtained from $Z_0^{(0)}$ in the same way as $Z_0^{(N)}$ from $Z_{-N}^{(N)}$, $Z_N^{(0)} \to Z^*$. Since $0 \leqslant Z_N^{(0)} \leqslant k - m$, it follows that $0 \leqslant Z^* \leqslant k - m$.

We have thus proved that if $Z_0 = 0$, then the limiting storage function exists as a random variable whose values belong to the closed interval $[0, k - m]$. It can be proved that if $0 < Z_0 \leqslant k - m$, then Z_n tends to the same limit Z^*. Instead of Z_n, however, we consider R_n, the content (storage plus input) of the dam at time n, after the input X_n has flowed into it; thus $R_n = Z_n + X_n$. Clearly, $\{R_n\}$ is also a Markov chain; from (6.1) its transition d.f. is found to be

$$P(x; y) = Pr\{R_{n+1} \leqslant y \mid R_n = x\} \tag{6.77}$$

$$= \begin{cases} G(y) & \text{if } x \leqslant m \\ G(y - x + m) & \text{if } m < x < k. \\ G(y - k + m) & \text{if } x \geqslant k \end{cases}$$

Then if

$$H_n(x; y) = Pr\{R_n \leqslant y \mid R_0 = x\}, \tag{6.78}$$

we have the recurrence relation

$$H_{n+1}(x; y) = \int_{t=0}^{\infty} d_t H_n(x; t) P(t; y) \qquad (n \geqslant 1). \tag{6.79}$$

It is obvious that as $n \to \infty$, $R_n \to R^* = Z^* + X_n$, where $R^* < \infty$ with probability one. Therefore $H_n(x; y) \to H(y)$, where $H(y)$ satisfies the integral equation

$$H(y) = \int_0^{\infty} dH(t) P(t; y) \qquad (0 \leqslant y < \infty). \tag{6.80}$$

It is easily seen that $H(y)$ is the unique solution of (6.80) subject to the condition $H(\infty) = 1$. Thus the stationary d.f. $H(y)$ of R_n exists and is obtained from (6.80).

Integrating the right-hand side of (6.80) by parts and using (6.77), we obtain

(6.81)

$$H(y) = -\int_m^{m+y} H(t)\, d_t G(y - t + m) \qquad \text{if } y \leqslant k - m$$

$$H(y) = G(y - k + m) - \int_m^k H(t)\, d_t G(y - t + m) \qquad \text{if } y > k - m.$$

Let

$$G^*(\theta) = \int_0^{\infty} e^{-\theta x}\, dG(x), \qquad H^*(\theta) = \int_0^{\infty} e^{-\theta y}\, dH(y) \qquad (\theta > 0) \tag{6.82}$$

be the Laplace-Stieltjes transforms (L.S.T.) of X_n and R^* respectively. Then from (6.81) we obtain

$$\int_0^\infty e^{-\theta y} H(y)\,dy = e^{-\theta(k-m)} \frac{G^*(\theta)}{\theta} + G^*(\theta)e^{\theta m} \int_m^k e^{-\theta y} H(y)\,dy$$
$$= e^{-\theta(k-m)} \frac{G^*(\theta)}{\theta} + G^*(\theta)e^{\theta m} \frac{H^*(\theta)}{\theta}$$
$$- G^*(\theta)e^{\theta m}\left[\int_0^m e^{-\theta y} H(y)\,dy + \int_k^\infty e^{-\theta y} H(y)\,dy\right]$$

from which

$$\left[1 - \frac{e^{-\theta m}}{G^*(\theta)}\right] H^*(\theta) = \int_0^m \theta e^{-\theta y} H(y)\,dy + \int_k^\infty \theta e^{-\theta y} H(y)\,dy - e^{-\theta k}$$
$$= \int_0^m (e^{-\theta u} - e^{-\theta m})\,dH(u) - \int_k^\infty (e^{-\theta k} - e^{-\theta u})\,dH(u).$$

Therefore

$$(6.83)\qquad H^*(\theta) = \frac{\displaystyle\int_0^m (e^{-\theta u} - e^{-\theta m})\,dH(u) - \int_k^\infty (e^{-\theta k} - e^{-\theta u})\,dH(u)}{1 - e^{-\theta m}/G^*(\theta)}$$

Since the right-hand side expression in (6.83) contain $H(u)$ in the range $(u \leqslant m, u \geqslant k)$ it is not evident how the result (6.83) can be used to find the solution of the integral equation (6.81). However, (6.83) yields an interesting result which is of some practical significance. We note that as $\theta \to 0+$, the numerator and denominator both tend to zero. However, $H^*(\theta)$ must tend to unity as $\theta \to 0+$, since $H(\infty) = 1$. Applying L'Hospital's rule to (6.83) we therefore obtain

$$(6.84)\qquad \int_0^m (m - u)\,dH(u) - \int_k^\infty (u - k)\,dH(u) = m - m_1,$$

where $m_1 = E(X_n)$ is the mean input $(0 < m_1 < \infty)$. To see the significance of this result, let us define Y_n to be the amount of water released from the dam at time $n + 1$. Then Y_n is a random variable such that

$$(6.85)\qquad Y_n = \begin{cases} R_n & \text{if } R_n < m \\ m & \text{if } R_n \geqslant m. \end{cases}$$

The mean release per period is therefore

$$(6.86)\qquad \bar{Y}_n = E(Y_n) = \int_0^m u\,dH_n(u) + m[1 - H_n(m)]$$
$$= m - \int_0^m (m - u)\,dH_n(u).$$

As $n \to \infty$, $\bar{Y}_n \to \bar{Y}$, where

$$\bar{Y} = m - \int_0^m (m - u)\, dH(u). \tag{6.87}$$

The overflow Ω_n during $(n, n+1)$ is also a random variable such that

$$\Omega_n = \begin{cases} R_n - k & \text{if } R_n > k \\ 0 & \text{if } R_n \leqslant k, \end{cases} \tag{6.88}$$

its mean being

$$\bar{\Omega}_n = E(\Omega_n) = \int_k^\infty (u - k)\, dH_n(u). \tag{6.89}$$

Again, $\bar{\Omega}_n \to \bar{\Omega}$, where

$$\bar{\Omega} = \int_k^\infty (u - k)\, dH(u). \tag{6.90}$$

The result (6.84) can thus be written as $\bar{Y} + \bar{\Omega} = m_1$, that is,

(6.91) (mean release per period) + (mean overflow per period)
= mean input per period.

For the storage Z_n we have

$$\begin{aligned} Pr\{Z_{n+1} = 0\} &= Pr\{Z_n + X_n \leqslant m\} \\ Pr\{Z_{n+1} = k - m\} &= Pr\{Z_n + X_n \geqslant k\} \\ Pr\{0 < Z_{n+1} \leqslant z\} &= Pr\{m < Z_n + X_n \leqslant m + z\} \\ & \qquad (0 < z < k - m) \end{aligned} \tag{6.92}$$

as a consequence of (6.1). From these relations we find that the stationary distribution of Z_n has discontinuities at $z = 0$ and $z = k - m$, given respectively by

$$F(0) = H(m), \qquad P_{k-m} = 1 - H(k). \tag{6.93}$$

whereas in the range $0 < z < k - m$, its d.f. is given by

$$F(z) = H(z + m). \tag{6.94}$$

The stationary distribution of Z_n can thus be obtained from that of R_n.

b. The Problem of Emptiness

We shall consider the problem of emptiness before overflow, the discrete version of which was considered in Section 6.4b. For $0 < u \leqslant k - m$, let $V_n(u)$ be the probability that the dam with initial storage $Z_0 = u$ becomes empty for the first time (before overflowing) at time n. Thus

$$\begin{aligned} V_n(u) &= Pr\{m < R_t \leqslant k \ (t = 0, 1, 2, \ldots, n-2); \\ & \qquad R_{n-1} \leqslant m \mid Z_0 = u\} \\ &= Pr\{0 < u + S_t - tm \leqslant k - m \ (t = 1, 2, \ldots, n-1), \\ & \qquad u + S_n - nm \leqslant 0\}, \end{aligned} \tag{6.95}$$

where $S_t = X_0 + X_1 + \cdots + X_{t-1}$ $(t \geqslant 1)$. We have

$$V_1(u) = Pr\{u + X_0 \leqslant m\} = G(m - u) \tag{6.96}$$

and for $n \geqslant 2$,

$$V_n(u) = \int_{0+}^{k-m} d_x G(x - u + m) V_{n-1}(x). \tag{6.97}$$

Adding (6.97) over $n = 2, 3, \ldots$, we obtain the integral equation

$$V(u) = G(m - u) + \int_{0+}^{k-m} d_x G(x - u + m) V(x) \tag{6.98}$$

for the probability

$$V(u) = \sum_{n=1}^{\infty} V_n(u) \tag{6.99}$$

that the dam becomes empty before it overflows.

If in the integral equation (6.97) we put

$$W(y) = V(k - y) \qquad (m \leqslant y < k) \tag{6.100}$$

it is seen that it reduces to (6.81); thus $V(y)$ can be obtained from $H(y)$, the stationary d.f. of R_n.

6.6 SOLUTIONS FOR A GAMMA-TYPE INPUT

We proceed to apply the results of the last section to the case where the input has the gamma-type distribution

$$dG(x) = \frac{\mu^p}{(p-1)!} e^{-\mu x} x^{p-1}\, dx \qquad (0 < x < \infty), \tag{6.101}$$

where $\mu > 0$ and p is a positive integer. Let us put

$$\Phi(y) = e^{-\mu y}[1 - H(k - y)] \qquad (-\infty < y \leqslant k) \tag{6.102}$$

in the integral equation (6.81); the equation then reduces to

$$\Phi(y) = e^{-\mu k} \sum_{r=0}^{p-1} \frac{\mu^r}{r!} (k - y)^r + \begin{cases} \mu^p e^{-\mu m} \displaystyle\int_0^{k-m} \Phi(t) \frac{(t - y + m)^{p-1}}{(p-1)!}\, dt & (-\infty < y \leqslant m), \\ \mu^p e^{-\mu m} \displaystyle\int_{y-m}^{k-m} \Phi(t) \frac{(t - y + m)^{p-1}}{(p-1)!}\, dt & (m < y \leqslant k), \end{cases} \tag{6.103}$$

which is a mixture of both Fredholm and Volterra types of integral equation, with the kernel $(t - y + m)^{p-1}/(p-1)!$, but owing to the presence of m in the lower limit of the integral on the right-hand side (for $m < y \leqslant k$) the known methods for solving such equations are not directly applicable. However, we note that the kernel is resolvable: in fact, we have

$$\frac{(t-y+m)^{p-1}}{(p-1)!} = \sum_{r=0}^{p-1} \frac{(-1)^r}{r!(p-r-1)!} y^r (t+m)^{p-r-1}.$$

Let us put

$$e^{-\mu k} \sum_{r=0}^{p-1} \frac{\mu^r}{r!} (k-y)^r + \mu^p e^{-\mu m} \int_0^{k-m} \Phi(t) \frac{(t-y+m)^{p-1}}{(p-1)!} dt = \sum_{r=0}^{p-1} \frac{\alpha_r}{r!} y^r,$$

where

$$\alpha_r = e^{-\mu k}(-\mu)^r \sum_{s=0}^{p-r-1} \frac{(\mu k)^s}{s!} + \mu^p e^{-\mu m}(-1)^r \times \int_0^{k-m} \Phi(t) \frac{(t+m)^{p-r-1}}{(p-r-1)!} dt \qquad (r = 0, 1, \ldots, p-1). \tag{6.104}$$

Then the equation (6.103) can be written as

$$\Phi(y) = \begin{cases} \displaystyle\sum_{r=0}^{p-1} \frac{\alpha_r}{r!} y^r & (-\infty < y \leqslant m), \\ \displaystyle\sum_{r=0}^{p-1} \frac{\alpha_r}{r!} y^r - \lambda \int_0^{y-m} \Phi(t) \frac{(y-m-t)^{p-1}}{(p-1)!} dt & (m < y \leqslant k), \end{cases} \tag{6.105}$$

where $\lambda = (-1)^{p-1}\mu^p e^{-\mu m}$. It is seen that the integral on the right-hand side of (6.105) involves $\Phi(t)$ in the range $(0, y - m)$; this enables us to solve for $\Phi(y)$ successively for the ranges $(m, 2m)$, $(2m, 3m)$, ... in terms of the unknown constants $\alpha_0, \alpha_1, \ldots, \alpha_{p-1}$. For instance, let $m < y \leqslant 2m$; then

$$\begin{aligned} \Phi(y) &= \sum_{r=0}^{p-1} \frac{\alpha_r}{r!} y^r - \lambda \int_0^{y-m} \sum_{r=0}^{p-1} \frac{\alpha_r t^r (y-m-t)^{p-1}}{r!(p-1)!} dt \\ &= \sum_{r=0}^{p-1} \frac{\alpha_r}{r} y^r - \lambda \sum_{r=0}^{p-1} \frac{\alpha_r (y-m)^{p+r}}{(p+r)!}. \end{aligned}$$

This suggests the general expression

$$\Phi(y) = \sum_{r=0}^{p-1} \alpha_r \sum_{q=0}^{n} (-\lambda)^q \frac{(y-qm)^{qp+r}}{(qp+r)!} \tag{6.106}$$

$$\left[nm < y \leqslant (n+1)m;\ n = 1, 2, \ldots, N+1,\ N+1 = \left[\frac{k}{m}\right]\right].$$

To prove that this, in fact, is the solution to (6.105) we use the method of induction. Assume that $\Phi(y)$ is given by the above expression in the range $0 < y \leqslant (n+1)m$. Then for $(n+1)m < y \leqslant (n+2)m$ we have, from (6.105),

$$\begin{aligned}\Phi(y) &= \sum_{r=0}^{p-1} \frac{\alpha_r}{r!} y^r - \lambda \sum_{r=0}^{p-1} \alpha_r \sum_{q=0}^{n} (-\lambda)^q \int_{qm}^{y-m} \frac{(t-qm)^{qp+r}(y-m-t)^{p-1}}{(qp+r)!\,(p-1)!}\,dt \\ &= \sum_{r=0}^{p-1} \frac{\alpha_r}{r!} y^r + \sum_{r=0}^{p-1} \alpha_r \sum_{q=0}^{n} (-\lambda)^{q+1} \frac{[y-(q+1)m]^{qp+p+r}}{(qp+p+r)!} \\ &= \sum_{r=0}^{p-1} \alpha_r \sum_{q=0}^{n+1} (-\lambda)^q \frac{(y-qm)^{qp+r}}{(qp+r)!}.\end{aligned}$$

Hence the result follows.

It remains to evaluate the unknown constants $\alpha_0, \alpha_1, \ldots, \alpha_{p-1}$ occurring in (6.105), so that $\Phi(y)$ will then be completely known for the entire range $(-\infty < y \leqslant k)$. These, however, are determined by (6.104). We have

$$\begin{aligned}(-1)^r \mu^p e^{-\mu m} &\int_0^{k-m} \Phi(t) \frac{(t+m)^{p-r-1}}{(p-r-1)!}\,dt \\ &= (-1)^{p+r-1} \lambda \sum_{s=0}^{p-1} \alpha_s \sum_{q=0}^{N} (-\lambda)^q \int_{qm}^{k-m} \frac{(t-qm)^{qp+s}(t+m)^{p-r-1}}{(qp+s)!\,(p-r-1)!}\,dt \\ &= \lambda \sum_{s=0}^{p-1} d_{rs}\alpha_s,\end{aligned}$$

where

$$d_{rs} = (-1)^{p+r+1} \sum_{q=0}^{N} (-\lambda)^q \int_{qm}^{k-m} \frac{(t-qm)^{qp+s}(t+m)^{p-r-1}}{(qp+s)!\,(p-r-1)!}\,dt \qquad (r, s = 0, 1, \ldots, p-1). \tag{6.107}$$

Then the equations (6.104) can be written as

$$\alpha_r - \lambda \sum_{s=0}^{p-1} d_{rs}\alpha_s = (-\mu)^r e^{-\mu k} \sum_{s=0}^{p-r-1} \frac{(\mu k)^s}{s!} \qquad (r = 0, 1, \ldots, p-1) \tag{6.108}$$

which are p linear equations in the p unknowns $\alpha_0, \alpha_1, \ldots, \alpha_{p-1}$ and have a unique solution provided that the determinant $|I - \lambda D|$ does not vanish: that is, provided that λ^{-1} is not a characteristic root of the matrix $\|d_{rs}\| = D$. Assuming this condition to be satisfied, we have the solution

$$\Phi(y) = \begin{cases} \displaystyle\sum_{r=0}^{p-1} \frac{\alpha^r}{r!} y^r & (-\infty < y \leqslant m), \\ \displaystyle\sum_{r=0}^{p-1} \alpha_r \sum_{q=0}^{n} (-\lambda)^q \frac{(y-qm)^{qp+r}}{(qp+r)!} & \\ \qquad (nm < y \leqslant (n+1)m;\ n = 1, 2, \ldots, N+1). & \end{cases} \tag{6.109}$$

To obtain the stationary distribution of the dam content R_n we note from (6.102) that

$$H(y) = 1 - e^{\mu(k-y)}\Phi(k - y),$$

which gives, if we take $k = (N + 1)m$ for convenience,

$$(6.110)\quad H(y) = \begin{cases} 1 - e^{\mu(k-y)} \sum_{r=0}^{p-1} \alpha_r \sum_{q=0}^{N-s} (-\lambda)^q \dfrac{(k - y - qm)^{qp+r}}{(qp + r)!} \\ \qquad [sm \leqslant y < (s + 1)m;\ s = 0, 1, \ldots, N - 1], \\ 1 - e^{\mu(k-y)} \sum_{r=0}^{p-1} \dfrac{\alpha_r}{r!} (k - y)^r \qquad (y \geqslant Nm) \end{cases}$$

for the stationary distribution of the dam content $Z_n + X_n$. It is seen that for large negative y, $\Phi(y)$ behaves like y^{p-1}, so that, from (6.102) $H(\infty) = 1$, as required. For the dam storage Z_n we find that the discontinuities at $z = 0$ and $z = k - m$ are given respectively by

$$(6.111)\quad F(0) = H(m) = 1 - e^{\mu(k-m)} \sum_{r=0}^{p-1} \alpha_r \sum_{q=0}^{N-1} (-\lambda)^q \frac{[(N - q)m]^{qp+r}}{(qp + r)!}$$

$$(6.112)\quad P_{k-m} = 1 - H(k) = \alpha_0$$

whereas in the range $0 < z < k - m$ its d.f. is given by

$$(6.113)\quad \begin{aligned} F(z) &= H(m + z) \\ &= 1 - e^{\mu(k-z-m)} \sum_{r=0}^{p-1} \alpha_r \sum_{q=0}^{N-s-1} \frac{[(N - q)m - z]^{qp+r}}{(qp + r)!} \\ &\qquad (sm < z \leqslant (s + 1)m;\ s = 0, 1, \ldots, N - 1). \end{aligned}$$

The mean overflow per period is given by

$$(6.114)\quad \begin{aligned} \bar{\Omega} &= \int_k^\infty (u - k)\, dH(u) = \int_k^\infty [1 - H(y)]\, dy \\ &= \sum_{r=0}^{p-1} \frac{\alpha_r}{r!} \int_k^\infty e^{\mu(k-y)} (k - y)^r\, dy = \sum_0^{p-1} \frac{(-1)^r \alpha_r}{\mu^{r+1}}, \end{aligned}$$

and the mean release per period is given by

$$\bar{Y} = m - \int_0^m (m - u)\, dH(u) = m_1 - \bar{\Omega},$$

where $m_1 = p/\mu$ is the mean input, and we have used the identity (6.84). Thus

$$(6.115)\quad \bar{Y} = \frac{p}{\mu} - \sum_0^{p-1} \frac{(-1)^r \alpha_r}{\mu^{r+1}}.$$

From (6.109) we can also obtain the probability $V(u)$ of emptiness before overflow; thus using (6.100) and (6.102) we find that

$$V(y) = 1 - e^{\mu y}\Phi(y) \tag{6.116}$$

$$= \begin{cases} 1 - e^{\mu y} \sum_{r=0}^{p-1} \alpha_r \frac{y^r}{r!} & (0 < y \leqslant m) \\ 1 - e^{\mu y} \sum_{r=0}^{p-1} \alpha_r \sum_{q=0}^{n} (-\lambda)^q \frac{(y - qm)^{qp+r}}{(qp + r)!} & \\ \qquad (nm < y \leqslant (n + 1)m,\ n = 1, 2, \ldots, N - 1). \end{cases}$$

We must have $V(0) = 1$, $V(k - m + y) = 0$ for $y > 0$. However, (6.116) gives $V(0+) = 1 - \alpha_0$ and $V(k - m - 0) > 0$, indicating that $V(y)$ has two points of discontinuity at $y = 0$ and $y = k - m$.

When $p = 1$, (6.101) reduces to the negative exponential distribution

$$dG(x) = \mu e^{-\mu x}\, dx \qquad (0 < x < \infty). \tag{6.117}$$

In this case the stationary d.f. of the dam content is given by

$$H(y) = \begin{cases} 1 - ce^{\mu(k-y)} \sum_{q=0}^{N-s} \frac{(-\lambda)^q}{q!} (k - y - qm)^q & \\ \qquad (sm \leqslant y < sm + m;\ s = 0, 1, \ldots, N - 1) \\ 1 - ce^{\mu(k-y)} \qquad (y \geqslant Nm), \end{cases} \tag{6.118}$$

where $\lambda = \mu e^{-\mu m}$, $k = (N + 1)m$, and the constant $c = \alpha_0$ can be obtained by using the fact that $H(0) = 0$. Thus

$$c = e^{-\mu k} \Big/ \sum_{q=0}^{N} \frac{(-\lambda)^q}{q!} (k - qm)^q. \tag{6.119}$$

6.7 THE CASE OF AN INFINITE DAM

a. General Results

Considerable simplification is introduced in the theory of dams if we assume the capacity of the dam to be $k = \infty$, although in practice this is unlikely to be true. The recurrence relation (6.1) becomes in this case

$$Z_{n+1} = \max(0, Z_n + X_n - m) \qquad (n = 0, 1, 2, \ldots). \tag{6.120}$$

For convenience let us assume $Z_0 = 0$; then from (6.120) we obtain

$$Z_n \sim \max(S_r - rm,\ r = 1, 2, \ldots, n), \tag{6.121}$$

when $S_r = X_0 + X_1 + \cdots + X_{r-1}$ $(r \geqslant 1)$. The storage function Z_n is thus the maximal term among the partial sums of the sequence of random variables $\{X_n - m, n = 0, 1, \ldots\}$ and can be studied by the methods developed in Chapter 4. In particular, let $0 < E(X_n) = m_1 < \infty$; then the limiting distribution of Z_n as $n \to \infty$ exists if and only if

$$m_1 < m. \tag{6.122}$$

Furthermore, for the wet period $T(u)$ defined as

$$T(u) = \min (n \mid u + S_n - nm \leqslant 0) \tag{6.123}$$

we have

$$Pr\{T(u) < \infty\}\begin{cases} = 1 & \text{if } m_1 \leqslant m \\ < 1 & \text{if } m_1 > m. \end{cases} \tag{6.124}$$

We shall now consider the details.

b. The Discrete Case

Let us first consider the case where the input X_n has a discrete distribution with the p.g.f.

$$K(\theta) = E(\theta^{X_n}), \qquad |\theta| < 1. \tag{6.125}$$

From Section 4.7 we obtain

$$\sum_0^\infty t^n E(\theta^{Z_n}) = \frac{1}{\theta^m - tK(\theta)} \prod_{r=1}^m \left(\frac{\theta - \xi_r}{1 - \xi_r}\right) \qquad (|t| < 1, |\theta| \leqslant 1), \tag{6.126}$$

where $\xi_1, \xi_2, \ldots, \xi_m$ are the roots of the functional equation

$$\xi^m = tK(\xi) \tag{6.127}$$

such that $|\xi_r| < 1$. If $m_1 < m$, then the limiting distribution of Z_n has the p.g.f.

$$U(\theta) = \frac{(m - m_1)(1 - \theta)}{K(\theta) - \theta^m} \prod_{r=1}^{m-1} \left(\frac{\theta - \zeta_r}{1 - \zeta_r}\right), \tag{6.128}$$

where $\zeta_1, \zeta_2, \ldots, \zeta_{m-1}$ are the roots of the equation

$$\zeta^m = K(\zeta) \tag{6.129}$$

within the unit circle.

Explicit results can be obtained for $m = 1$ by using the results of Section 3.6. Let

$$k_j^{(n)} = Pr\{S_n = j\} \quad (n \geqslant 1), \qquad k_j^{(1)} = k_j, \qquad k_j^{(0)} = \delta_{0j}, \tag{6.130}$$

where $\delta_{ij} = 1$ if $i = j$, and $= 0$ if $i \neq j$. Furthermore, let

$$K_j^{(n)} = Pr\{S_n \leqslant j\}. \tag{6.131}$$

The distribution of the wet period

$$T_i = \min (n \mid i + S_n - n \leqslant 0) \tag{6.132}$$

is then given by

$$g(i, n) = Pr\{T_i = n\} = \begin{cases} 0 & \text{if } n < i \\ \dfrac{i}{n} k_{n-i}^{(n)} & \text{if } n \geqslant i. \end{cases} \tag{6.133}$$

If $Z_0 = i$, then from (6.120) we obtain

$$Z_n = \max [S_r - r \, (r = 0, 1, \ldots, n - 1); i + S_n - n]. \tag{6.134}$$

Hence we find that

$$\begin{aligned} Pr\{Z_n \leqslant j \mid Z_0 = i\} &= Pr\{S_r - r \leqslant j \, (r = 0, 1, \ldots, n - 1); \\ &\qquad\qquad i + S_n - n \leqslant j\} \\ &= \sum_{\nu=i+1}^{\infty} Pr\{S_r - r \leqslant j \, (r = 0, 1, \ldots, n - 1); \\ &\qquad\qquad S_n - n = j - \nu + 1\} \\ &= \sum_{\nu=i+1}^{\infty} Pr\{S_{n-r} - (n - r) \geqslant -\nu + 1 \\ &\qquad (r = 0, 1, \ldots, n - 1); S_n - n = j - \nu + 1\} \\ &= \sum_{\nu=i+1}^{\infty} Pr\{\nu + S_r - r > 0 \, (r = 1, 2, \ldots, n - 1); \\ &\qquad\qquad \nu + S_n - n = j + 1\} \\ &= \sum_{\nu=i+1}^{\infty} \left\{ k_{n+j+1-\nu}^{(n)} - \sum_{m=1}^{n-\nu} g(\nu, n - m) k_{m+j+1}^{(m)} \right\} \end{aligned} \tag{6.135}$$

$$= K_{n+j-i}^{(n)} - \sum_{m=1}^{n-i-1} k_{m+j+1}^{(m)} \sum_{\nu=i+1}^{n-m} g(\nu, n - m). \tag{6.136}$$

Now, we have

$$\begin{aligned} g(\nu, n + 1) &= Pr\{\nu + S_r - r > 0 \, (r = 1, 2, \ldots, n); \\ &\qquad\qquad \nu + S_{n+1} - (n + 1) = 0\} \\ &= Pr\{\nu + S_r - r > 0 \, (r = 1, 2, \ldots, n - 1); \\ &\qquad \nu + S_n - n = 1; \nu + S_{n+1} - (n + 1) = 0\} \\ &= Pr\{\nu + S_r - r > 0 \, (r = 1, 2, \ldots, n - 1); \\ &\qquad\qquad \nu + S_n - n = 1\}. \end{aligned} \tag{6.137}$$

$$\begin{aligned} &Pr\{\nu + S_{n+1} - (n + 1) = 0 \mid \nu + S_n - n = 1\} \\ &= k_0 Pr\{\nu + S_r - r > 0 \, (r = 1, 2, \ldots, n - 1); \\ &\qquad\qquad \nu + S_n - n = 1\}. \end{aligned}$$

Therefore from (6.135) we find that

$$(6.138)\quad P_{i0}^{(n)} = Pr\{Z_n = 0 \mid Z_0 = i\}$$
$$= \sum_{v=i+1}^{n+1} Pr\{v + S_r - r > 0\ (r = 1, 2, \ldots, n-1);\ v + S_n - n = 1\}$$
$$= \frac{1}{k_0} \sum_{v=i+1}^{n+1} g(v, n+1).$$

Using (6.138) we can write (6.136) as

$$(6.139)\quad Pr\{Z_n \leqslant j \mid Z_0 = i\} = K_{n+j-i}^{(n)} - k_0 \sum_{m=2}^{n-i} P_{i0}^{(n-m)} k_{m+j}^{(m-1)} \qquad (j \geqslant 0).$$

For the limiting storage function we have

$$(6.140)\qquad Z_\infty = \lim_{n\to\infty} Z_n \sim \max_{r\geqslant 0} (S_r - r),$$

so that

$$(6.141)\qquad Pr\{Z_\infty \leqslant j\} = Pr\left\{\max_{r\geqslant 0} (S_r - r) \leqslant j\right\}$$
$$= Pr\{S_r - r < j + 1, \qquad (r \geqslant 0)\}$$
$$= Pr\{U_{j+1} = \infty\}.$$

Hence we obtain for $j \geqslant 0$,

$$(6.142)\quad Pr\{Z_\infty \leqslant j\} = \begin{cases} 0 & \text{if } m_1 \geqslant 1 \\ 1 - (1 - m_1)\sum_{n=0}^{\infty} k_{n+j+1}^{(n)} & \text{if } m_1 < 1. \end{cases}$$

For $j = 0$, however, we have the simpler result

$$(6.143)\qquad Pr\{Z_\infty = 0\} = \begin{cases} 0 & \text{if } m_1 \geqslant 1 \\ \dfrac{1 - m_1}{k_0} & \text{if } m_1 < 1, \end{cases}$$

using the relation (6.135).

c. The Continuous Case

Let X_n have the d.f.

$$(6.144)\qquad K(x) = Pr\{X_n \leqslant x\} \qquad (x \geqslant 0),$$

and the partial sum $S_n = X_0 + X_1 + \cdots + X_{n-1}$, the d.f.

$$(6.145)\qquad K_n(x) = Pr\{S_n \leqslant x\}, \qquad K_1(x) = K(x).$$

The recurrence relation (6.120) is the same as the one satisfied by the waiting time W_n in the queueing system $D/G/1$. Let $Z_0 = 0$; then from Section 4.5, we obtain the result

$$\sum_0^\infty t^n E(e^{-\theta Z_n}) = \exp\left[\sum_1^\infty \frac{t^n}{n} K_n(nm) + \sum_1^\infty \frac{(te^{\theta m})^n}{n!} \int_{nm}^\infty e^{-\theta x} \, dK_n(x)\right] \tag{6.146}$$

$$(|t| < 1, \ \mathrm{Re}(\theta) > 0).$$

Furthermore, if $m_1 < m$, the limiting storage function Z^* has the L.S.T. given by

$$E(e^{-\theta Z^*}) = \exp\left[-\sum_1^\infty \frac{1}{n} \int_{0-}^\infty (1 - e^{-\theta x}) \, dK_n(x + nm)\right] \tag{6.147}$$

$$[\mathrm{Re}\,(\theta) > 0].$$

Further simplifications can be made only if the form of the input distribution is known. Let us consider the special case of the gamma-type distribution

$$dK(x) = \frac{\lambda^p}{(p-1)!} e^{-\lambda x} x^{p-1} \, dx \qquad (0 < x < \infty), \tag{6.148}$$

where $\lambda > 0$ and p is a positive integer. Our model is then identical with the queueing system $D/E_p/1$, which is a special case of the system $GI/E_p/1$ considered in Section 4.8. We therefore obtain

$$\sum_0^\infty t^n E(e^{-\theta Z_n}) = \frac{1}{1-t} \prod_{r=1}^p \left(\frac{1 + \theta/\lambda}{1 + \theta/\theta_r}\right) \qquad [|t| < 1, \quad \mathrm{Re}\,(\theta) \geqslant 0], \tag{6.149}$$

where $\theta_1, \theta_2, \ldots, \theta_p$ are the roots of the equation

$$(\lambda - \theta)^p = \lambda^p t e^{-\theta m} \tag{6.150}$$

such that $\mathrm{Re}\,(\theta_r) > 0$; also, if $p < \lambda m$, then

$$E(e^{-\theta Z^*}) = \prod_{r=1}^p \left(\frac{1 + \theta/\lambda}{1 + \theta/\theta_r^0}\right) \qquad [\mathrm{Re}(\theta) \geqslant 0] \tag{6.151}$$

where $\theta_1^0, \theta_2^0, \ldots, \theta_p^0$ are the roots of the equation

$$(\lambda - \theta)^p = \lambda^p e^{-\theta m}, \qquad [\mathrm{Re}(\theta_r^0) > 0]. \tag{6.152}$$

From Chapter 4, Complement 15, we find that the d.f. $F(z)$ of Z^* is given by

$$F(z) = 1 - \sum_{r=1}^p A_r e^{-\theta_r^0 z} \qquad (z \geqslant 0), \tag{6.153}$$

where

$$A_r = \left(\frac{1 + \theta_r^0}{\lambda}\right)^p \prod_{q \neq r}^p \left(\frac{1}{1 - \theta_r^0/\theta_q^0}\right) \qquad (r = 1, 2, \ldots, p). \tag{6.154}$$

In particular, consider a negative exponential distribution for the input, that is, the distribution (6.148) with $p = 1$. Here we obtain

$$(6.155)\quad \sum_0^\infty t^n E(e^{-\theta Z_n}) = \frac{1}{1-t}\left(\frac{1+\theta/\lambda}{1+\theta/\theta_0}\right) \qquad [|t| < 1, \quad \text{Re}(\theta) \geqslant 0],$$

where θ_0 is the root of the equation $\theta = \lambda - \lambda t e^{-\theta m}$, $\text{Re}(\theta_0) > 0$. Furthermore, the d.f. $F(z)$ is given by

$$(6.156)\qquad F(z) = 1 - e^{-\mu(z+m)} \qquad (z \geqslant 0, \lambda m > 1),$$

where μ is the largest positive root of the equation $\mu = \lambda - \lambda e^{-\mu m}$.

To summarize the results of this section: for discrete inputs, the time-dependent solutions as well as the stationary solutions for Moran's storage problem are available, whereas for continuous inputs these are available only for a gamma-type distribution.

COMPLEMENTS AND PROBLEMS

Section 6.1

1. A more realistic release rule has been suggested by H. W. Holdaway; see Moran (1955) and Ghosal (1959, 1960a).

2. Consider the model in which

$$(1)\qquad Z_{n+1} = Z_n + X_n - \phi(Z_n + X_n), \qquad Z_0 = 0,$$

where the variables X_n are independent and identically distributed, and $X_n \geqslant 0$. Let $\phi(\cdot)$ satisfy the conditions

(*a*) $\max(0, u - k) \leqslant \phi(u) \leqslant u$ when $u \geqslant 0$.

(*b*) $\phi(u)$ and $u - \phi(u)$ are monotone increasing functions. Then prove that as $n \to \infty$, Z_n tends to a limit Z^* [Bather (1962)].

Section 6.2

3. The results of this section are due to Weesakul (1960).

Section 6.3

4. The results of this section are due to Prabhu (1958b) [see also Prabhu (1959)]. Earlier, Moran (1954, 1955) and Gani and Moran (1955) had obtained a few approximate solutions by numerical methods, but the only exact solution known was for the geometric input (see Complement 5).

5. *Geometric input*. Let $m \geqslant 1$ and consider the case where the input X_n has the geometric distribution.

$$(2)\qquad Pr\{X_n = j\} = ab^j \qquad (j = 0, 1, \ldots),$$

$0 < a < 1$, $b = 1 - a$. We can interpret (2) as the probability that j "trials" will be required before a release can occur. If we take the time variable to be T, the number of these trials, and ζ_n to be the amount of water in the dam (overflow included) at time $T = n$ (nth trial), then we get a sequence $\{\zeta_n, n = 0, 1, \ldots\}$ of random variables with the values $(0, 1, 2, \ldots, k)$. Clearly, $\{\zeta_n\}$ is a Markov chain with the transition probabilities

$$\begin{aligned} &P_{i0} = a \quad \text{if } 0 \leqslant i \leqslant m; \qquad P_{i,i-m} = a \quad \text{if } m \leqslant i \leqslant k \\ &P_{i,i+1} = b \quad \text{if } 0 \leqslant i \leqslant k-1; \qquad P_{kk} = b \end{aligned} \tag{3}$$

and $P_{ij} = 0$ for all other combinations of i and j. The stationary distribution $\{\pi_j\}$ of ζ_n can be obtained from (3). The stationary distribution of Z_n is given by $\{u_j\}$, where $u_0 = \pi_0 + \pi_1 + \cdots + \pi_m$, $u_j = \pi_{j+m}$ $(j = 1, 2, \ldots, k - m)$ [Moran (1955)]. When $m = 1$, this solution reduces to (6.28).

6. Let $m \geqslant 1$ and $H_j = Pr\{R^* \leqslant j\}$ be the stationary d.f. of the dam content. Show that the H_j $(j \geqslant 0)$ satisfy the equations

$$\begin{aligned} H_i &= \sum_{m}^{i+m} H_\nu g_{i-\nu+m} \qquad \text{if } 0 \leqslant i < k - m \\ H_i &= (g_0 + g_1 + \cdots + g_{i-k+m}) + \sum_{m}^{k-1} H_\nu g_{i-\nu+m} \qquad \text{if } i \geqslant k - m. \end{aligned} \tag{4}$$

In particular, if the input X_n has the negative binomial distribution

$$Pr(X_n = j\} = \binom{p+j-1}{j} a^p b^j \qquad (j = 0, 1, 2, \ldots), \tag{5}$$

where $0 < a < 1$, $b = 1 - a$, and p is a positive integer, show that

$$H_i = \begin{cases} 1 - b^{-(k-i)} \displaystyle\sum_{r=0}^{p-1} \binom{k-i+r-1}{r} \alpha_r & (k - i \leqslant m) \\ 1 - b^{-(k-i)} \displaystyle\sum_{r=0}^{p-1} \alpha_r \sum_{q=0}^{n} (-\lambda)^q \binom{k-i+qm+r-1}{qp+r} & \\ \qquad (nm < k - i \leqslant nm + m, n = 1, 2, \ldots N), & \end{cases} \tag{6}$$

where $\lambda = (-1)^{p-1} a^p b^m$, $k = Nm + u$, $0 \leqslant u < m$ [Ghosal (1962)].

Section 6.4

7. The results of Section 6.4a and 6.4b due to Weesakul (1961). The simplified result for the V_i in Section 6.4b is due to Prabhu (1958b).

8. If $m \geqslant 1$ and the input has the geometric distribution (2), show that

$$V_i = 1 - \alpha b^{-i} \sum_{q=0}^{n} (-\lambda)^q \binom{i-qm-1}{q} \qquad (nm < i \leqslant nm + m, \quad n = 0, 1, \ldots, N) \tag{7}$$

where $\lambda = ab^m$,

$$\alpha = b^k \Big/ \sum_{q=0}^{N+1} (-\lambda)^q \binom{k-qm-1}{q}, \tag{8}$$

and $k = (N + 1)m + u$, $0 \leqslant u < m$ [Ghosal (1960b)].

Section 6.5

9. The integral equation (6.81) for $H(y)$ is essentially due to Moran (1954). The stationary d.f. $F(z)$ if Z_n satisfies the equation

$$
(9) \quad
\begin{aligned}
F(z) &= -\int_0^{z+m} F(t)\, dG(z - t + m) \qquad (0 \leqslant z < k - 2m) \\
F(z) &= G(z - k + 2m) - \int_0^{z+m} F(t)\, dG(z - t + m) \\
&\qquad\qquad\qquad (k - 2m \leqslant z \leqslant k - m),
\end{aligned}
$$

with the condition $F(k - m) = 1$.

10. The integral equation (6.98) for $V(y)$ is due to Ghosal (1960b), who also noted the relation (6.100).

Section 6.6

11. The solution for $H(y)$ for gamma-type input (6.101) is due to Prabhu (1958a). Earlier, the solution for the negative exponential input had been obtained by Moran (1955) by a different technique.

12. The result (6.116) is due to Ghosal (1960b).

13. *Problems of optimization.* Optimization problems in a dam subject to Moran's model have been considered by Prabhu (1960) and Avi-Itzhak and Ben-Tuvia (1963). Jarvis (1963) has applied Moran's model to the Ord River Project in Western Australia. Bather (1962) has considered optimal regulation policies for models of type (1).

Section 6.7

14. The result (6.133) is the discrete time version of Kendall's (1957) result for the wet period in the continuous time model [see also Gani (1958)].

15. The results (6.138) and (6.139) are due to Yeo (1961), whose methods are different from the combinatorial methods of Chapter 3. See also Yeo (1960).

16. The integral equation (6.81) for the stationary d.f. $H(y)$ of the dam content $R_n = Z_n + X_n$ becomes for the infinite dam

$$
(10) \qquad H(y) = -\int_m^{m+y} H(t)\, d_t G(y - t + m) \qquad (y \geqslant 0).
$$

The result (6.122) implies that if $m_1 < m$, then (10) has a unique solution which is nonnegative, nondecreasing, and such that $H(\infty) = 1$.

17. Use (10) to prove that in statistical equilibrium (11) mean release per period = mean input per period.

18. From (6.156) [or solving (10)] prove that for the negative exponential input, the stationary d.f. of R_n is given by

$$
(12) \qquad dH(y) = \mu e^{-\mu y}\, dy \qquad (0 < y < \infty).
$$

Now, consider the following problem: Suppose that the stationary distribution of R_n is given by

$$
(13) \qquad dH(y) = h_1(y)\, dy \qquad (0 < y < m),
$$

whereas in the range $y \geqslant m$, it is the negative exponential

$$dH(y) = h_1(m)e^{-\mu(y-m)} \qquad (y \geqslant m,\ \mu > 0). \tag{14}$$

What sort of input distributions will give rise to a distribution of the above type for R_n? Gani and Prabhu (1957) proved that several input distributions with negative exponential tails for $x > m$ will result in such a distribution.

REFERENCES

Avi-Itzhak, B., and S. Ben-Tuvia (1963). A problem of optimizing a collecting reservoir system. *Opns. Res.*, **11,** 122–136.

Bhat, B. R., and J. Gani (1959). On the independence of yearly inputs in dams. *O.N.R. Report.*

Feller, W. (1957). *An Introduction to Probability Theory and its Applications*, 2nd edition. John Wiley, New York.

Gani, J. (1958). Elementary methods in an occupancy problem of storage. *Math. Ann.*, **136,** 454–465.

Gani, J. and P. A. P. Moran (1955). A solution of dam equations by Monte Carlo methods. *Aust. J. Appl. Sci.*, **6,** 267–273.

Gani, J. and N. U. Prabhu (1957). Stationary distributions of the negative exponential type for the infinite dam. *J. Roy. Stat. Soc.*, **B19,** 342–351.

Ghosal, A. (1959). On the continuous analogue of Holdaway's problem for the finite dam. *Aust. J. Appl. Sci.*, **10,** 365–370.

Ghosal, A. (1960a). Problem of emptiness in Holdaway's finite dam. *Cal. Stat. Assoc. Bull.*, **9,** 111–116.

Ghosal, A. (1960a). Emptiness in the finite dam. *Ann. Math. Stat.*, **31,** 803–808.

Ghosal, A. (1962). Finite dam with negative binomial input. *Aust. J. Appl. Sci.*, **13,** 71–74.

Gumbel, E. J. (1941). The return period of flood flows. *Ann. Math. Stat.*, **12,** 163–190.

Hurst, H. E. (1951). Long term storage capacity of reservoirs. *Trans. Amer. Soc. Civ. Engrs.*, **116.**

Hurst, H. E. (1956). Methods of using long term storage in reservoirs. *Inst. Civ. Engrs.*, London, Paper 6059.

Jarvis, C. L. (1963). *An Application of Moran's Theory of Dams to the Ord River Project.* M.Sc. Thesis, The University of Western Australia.

Kendall, D. G. (1957). Some problems in the theory of dams. *J. Roy. Stat. Soc.*, **B19,** 207–212.

Knopp, K. (1928). *Theory and Applications of Infinite Series.* Blackie and Son, London and Glasgow.

Loynes, R. M. (1962). The stability of a queue with non-independent interarrival and service times. *Proc. Cam. Phil. Soc.*, **58,** 497–520.

Moran, P. A. P. (1954). A probability theory of dams and storage systems. *Aust. J. Appl. Sci.*, **5,** 116–124.

Moran, P. A. P. (1955). A probability theory of dams and storage systems: modifications of the release rules. *Aust. J. Appl. Sci.*, **6,** 117–130.

Moran, P. A. P. (1956). A probability theory of dams with a continuous release. *Quart. J. of Math.* (Oxford, 2), **7,** 130–137.

Moran, P. A. P. (1957). The statistical treatment of flood flows. *Trans. Amer. Geophys. Union*, **38,** 519–523.

Prabhu, N. U. (1958a). On the integral equation for the finite dam. *Quart. J. Math.* (Oxford, 2), **9,** 183–188.

Prabhu, N. U. (1958b). Some exact results for the finite dam. *Ann. Math. Stat.*, **29,** 1234–1243.

Prabhu, N. U. (1959). Application of generating functions to a problem in finite dam theory. *Aust. J. Math.*, **1,** 116–120.

Prabhu, N. U. (1960). A problem in optimum storage. *Cal. Stat. Assoc. Bull.*, **10,** 35–40.

Prabhu, N. U. (1964). Time-dependent results in storage theory. *J. Appl. Prob.*, **1,** 1–46.

Weesakul, B. (1960). The explicit time dependent solution for a finite dam with geometric inputs. *Aust. Math. Soc. Summer Research Inst. Report.*

Weesakul, B. (1961). First emptiness in a finite dam. *J. Roy. Stat. Soc.*, **B23,** 343–351.

Yeo, G. F. (1960). The time-dependent solution for a dam with geometric inputs. *Aust. J. Appl. Sci.*, **11,** 434–442.

Yeo, G. F. (1961). The time-dependent solution for an infinite dam with discrete additive inputs. *J. Roy. Stat. Soc.*, **B23,** 173–179.

Chapter 7

Continuous Time Storage Processes

7.1 INTRODUCTION

Some continuous time inventory models have already been discussed in Chapter 5. The stochastic processes underlying these models were found to be more complex in nature than those in discrete time, the latter being sequences of (dependent) random variables. More powerful techniques would therefore be required to analyze these continuous time stochastic processes.

In this chapter we consider continuous time models arising as extensions of Moran's discrete time dam model described in Chapter 6. The initial attempts to set up such a model were by using limiting methods. Moran (1955), considering a discrete time dam model in which the input during $(t, t + 1)$ has a geometric distribution, recasts his problem along the lines indicated in Chapter 6, Complement 5. By a suitable limiting procedure he then obtains a model in which the "input" $Z(s)$ flows in continuously at a steady unit rate, and the release (of h) occurs in a Poisson process with parameter λ. It is clear that the deficit $k - Z(s)$ in this dam (k being its capacity) is equivalent to the content of a dam in continuous time defined as follows. (1) The input is a simple Poisson process with parameter λ, each input having the magnitude $h < k$. (2) Any excess over k overflows. (3) The release is continuous and occurs at a unit rate except when the dam is empty, when it ceases. This latter model was discussed by Gani (1955). However, it escaped both Moran and Gani that these two models, although formulated in different terms and having apparently different solutions, were essentially the same, and, in fact, analogous to the queueing system $M/D/1$. In Section 7.2 we discuss Gani's model and give some further results obtained by Gani and Prabhu (1959a, 1959b).

Later, Moran (1956) considered a discrete time model in which the units of time as well as amount of water are equal to n^{-1}, and the input during such a time unit is a random variable with the characteristic function (c.f.)

$[1 - n\rho(e^{i\theta/n} - 1)]^{-1/n}$. Letting $n \to \infty$ in this model, he obtained a continuous time model in which the input $X(t)$ during an interval $(0, t]$ has a gamma distribution; the c.f. of the limiting distribution of the dam content was then obtained as the limit as $n \to \infty$ of the corresponding c.f. in the discrete model. These results are given in Section 7.3.

Limiting procedures of the type just described are cumbersome and obscure the essential features of the basic stochastic processes. A systematic attempt to set up continuous time storage models was therefore made by Gani and Prabhu, Kendall, and others; the following is a brief summary of their results.

1. The input process. Our first task would obviously be a reasonably realistic specification of the input into a dam (or a store). In the discrete time model it was assumed that the inputs during the intervals $(t, t+1]$ $(t = 0, 1, 2, \ldots)$ were mutually independent and identically distributed random variables. If we denote by X_n the total input during an interval $(0, n]$, then $\{X_n, n = 0, 1, 2, \ldots\}$ is a sequence of partial sums of mutually independent and identical random variables. The natural generalization of such an input in the continuous time case would therefore be a process $X(t)$ $(t \geqslant 0)$ with stationary and independent increments (time-homogeneous additive process). Such a process is known to be infinitely divisible, that is, the input during an interval $(0, t]$ can be expressed as the sum of inputs during the subintervals $(0, t/n]$, $(t/n, 2t/n]$, $\ldots$, $([(n-1)/n]t, t]$ for every positive integer n. This again is in agreement with our concept of inputs into a dam. In our case $X(t) \geqslant 0$, and we shall assume that the mean input is finite; for the purpose of analyzing the process, we shall assume further that $X(t)$ is separable and centered. It is known that such a process $X(t)$ has a c.f. of the form

$$E[e^{i\theta X(t)}] = e^{t\phi(\theta)} \tag{7.1}$$

where $\phi(\theta)$ is given by

$$\phi(\theta) = \int_0^\infty (e^{i\theta x} - 1)\, dL(x), \tag{7.2}$$

where the function $L(x)$ is continuous to the right, nondecreasing, and is such that $L(\infty) = 0$. From (7.1) and (7.2) it may be proved that almost all sample functions of $X(t)$ have right- and left-hand limits at every t and that they increase only by jumps, the number of jumps in $(0, t]$ of magnitude $\geqslant x \geqslant 0$ being a random variable having a Poisson distribution with mean $-tL(x)$.

As examples of such an input let us consider the following.

(*a*) *The compound Poisson input.* Let $B(x)$ be a distribution function (d.f.) with $B(x) = 0$ for $x \leqslant 0$ and $B(\infty) = 1$, and let $\psi(\theta)$ be the corresponding c.f. Let $0 < \lambda < \infty$, and put $L(x) = \lambda B(x) - \lambda$ $(x \geqslant 0)$; then $L(x)$ is seen to satisfy the conditions stated above [note that $L(0) = -\lambda > -\infty$]. We have $\phi(\theta) = \lambda\psi(\theta) - \lambda$ and the c.f. (7.1) is therefore given by

$$E[e^{i\theta X(t)}] = e^{-\lambda t[1-\psi(\theta)]} \tag{7.3}$$

The process $X(t)$ thus has a compound Poisson distribution. Here $X(t)$ increases by jumps whose magnitudes have the d.f. $B(x)$ $(x \geqslant 0)$, there being finitely many jumps in every finite interval since $L(0) > -\infty$. The input considered by Moran (1955) and Gani (1955) (already referred to) is a special case of this with $B(x) = 0$ for $x < h$, and $= 1$ for $x \geqslant h$.

(*b*) *The gamma input.* Let $0 < \rho < \infty$, and put

$$L(x) = -\int_x^\infty e^{-x/\rho}\,\frac{dx}{x} \qquad (x > 0); \tag{7.4}$$

$L(x)$ is of the required type, and $L(0) = -\infty$. We have

$$\begin{aligned}\phi(\theta) &= \int_0^\infty (e^{i\theta x} - 1)e^{-x/\rho}\,\frac{dx}{x}\\ &= \int_0^\infty \frac{e^{-(1/\rho - i\theta)x} - e^{-x/\rho}}{x}\,dx = \log\frac{1/\rho}{1/\rho - i\theta}\\ &= -\log(1 - \rho i\theta)\end{aligned} \tag{7.5}$$

and

$$E[e^{i\theta X(t)}] = e^{-t\log(1-\rho i\theta)} = (1 - \rho i\theta)^{-t}, \tag{7.6}$$

which shows that $X(t)$ has a gamma distribution. Here the process increases by jumps such that

$$Pr\{x < dX(t) < x + dx\} = \frac{e^{-x/\rho}}{x}\,dx\,dt + o(dt) \qquad (x > 0), \tag{7.7}$$

where $dX(t) = X(t + dt) - X(t)$; however, since $L(0) = -\infty$, there may be an infinity of such jumps in a finite interval. This is the process considered by Moran (1956). Gani and Prabhu (1963) have treated the more general case where $dL(x) = \xi(x)\,dx$, and

$$\phi(\theta) = \int_0^\infty (e^{i\theta x} - 1)\xi(x)\,dx; \tag{7.8}$$

their results are described in Sections 7.6 to 7.8.

2. *Specification of the storage process.* Now suppose that the input into a dam has been specified by (7.1) and (7.2). For simplicity we assume that the dam has infinite capacity. Let the release be continuous and at a unit rate except when the dam is empty. If $Z(t)$ denotes the content of the dam at time t, it is then clear that $Z(t)$ satisfies the relation

$$Z(t + dt) = Z(t) + dX(t) - (1 - r)\,dt \tag{7.9}$$

where $r\,dt$ $(0 \leqslant r \leqslant 1)$ is that part of the interval $(t, t + dt]$ during which the dam is empty. More correctly, we may write

$$Z(t) = Z(0) + X(t) - t + \int_0^t \zeta(\tau)\,d\tau, \tag{7.10}$$

where $\zeta(t)$ is a random variable such that $\zeta(t) = 1$ if $Z(t) = 0$, and $= 0$ if $Z(t) > 0$, so that the integral in (7.10) gives the length of the dry period in the dam during $(0, t]$.

In the discrete time model the storage function Z_n is given by

$$Z_n = \max\,[\max_{0\leqslant k\leqslant n}(Y_n - Y_k), Z_0 + Y_n], \tag{7.11}$$

where $Y_n = X_n - nm$ is the net input (input minus the amount demanded for consumption) during an interval $(0, n)$ [cf., equation (6.121)]. It is therefore natural to ask whether the analogous formula

$$Z(t) = \max\,\{\sup_{0\leqslant\tau\leqslant t}[Y(t) - Y(\tau)], Z(0) + Y(t)\} \tag{7.12}$$

holds for the continuous storage process $Z(t)$. For the case where $Z(0) = 0$ and $X(t)$ has a compound Poisson distribution, this was proved by Reich for the waiting time process in the queueing system $M/G/1$ (see Chapter 1). Gani and Pyke (1960) extended this result to the case where $Z(0) \geqslant 0$ and the net input $Y(t)$ belongs to a wide class of infinitely divisible processes. In the case where $Y(t) = X(t) - t$, jumps of positive or negative magnitudes occur in the process $X(t)$ in such a way that $L(0) > -\infty$ [cf. (7.2)], they suggest (7.12) as a constructive definition of the storage process $Z(t)$ (Section 7.9). Such a definition fails when $L(0) = -\infty$ as in the case of gamma input; however Gani and Pyke have proved that the process defined by (7.12) is a limit with probability one of a corresponding sequence of discrete time storage processes (Section 7.4). Later, Kingman (1963) established (7.12) directly in this case without recourse to discrete time analogues.

3. *Analysis of the storage process.* As in the queueing system an important role in the analysis of a storage system is played by the "wet period," that is, the time taken by the dam with a given initial content to dry up. For a system in which the input is a time homogeneous additive process, Kendall (1957) obtained the L.S.T. as well as the fr.f. of the wet period; these results are described in Section 7.5.

The process $Z(t)$ as defined by (7.9) is easily seen to be a Markov process of the mixed type. The L.S.T. of the limiting distribution of $Z(t)$ as $t \to \infty$ was obtained by Downton, Lindley, and Smith [see discussion in Kendall

(1957)]. The transient behavior of the process when the input is specified by (7.1) and (7.8) was studied by Gani and Prabhu (1963) see Sections 7.6 to 7.8.

In the remainder of this chapter we study some more general storage processes.

7.2 THE DAM WITH POISSON INPUT

a. The Differential Equation of the Process

We first consider a model in which the dam has a finite capacity k, the release is continuous at unit rate except when the dam is empty, and the input is of Poisson type such that during an interval $(t, t + dt]$ an input $dX(t)$ of either h units or no units flows into the dam with probabilities

$$(7.13)\qquad \begin{aligned} Pr\{dX(t) = h\} &= \lambda\, dt + o(dt) \\ Pr\{dX(t) = 0\} &= 1 - \lambda\, dt + o(dt), \end{aligned}$$

respectively. It is seen from (7.13) that the input $X(t)$ in $(0, t]$ has the d.f.

$$(7.14)\qquad K(x, t) = Pr\{X(t) \leqslant x\} = \sum_{r=0}^{[x/h]} e^{-\lambda t} \frac{(\lambda t)^r}{r!}$$

and the Laplace-Stieltjes transform

$$(7.15)\qquad E\{e^{-\theta X(t)}\} = e^{-\lambda t(1-e^{-\theta h})} \qquad [\mathrm{Re}\,(\theta) > 0],$$

where $[x/h]$ is the largest integer contained in x/h. It is clear from (7.15) that $X(t)$ is a time homogeneous additive process. The content $Z(t)$ of the dam at time t is defined for $t \geqslant 0$ by the equation

$$(7.16)\qquad Z(t + dt) = \min\,[k, Z(t) + dX(t)] - (1 - r)\, dt,$$

where $r\, dt$ $(0 \leqslant r \leqslant 1)$ is that part of the interval $(t, t + dt]$ during which the dam is empty and $\min\,[k, Z(t) + dX(t)]$ indicates that there will be an overflow whenever $Z(t) + dX(t) > k$, leaving only the amount k in the dam.

From (7.16) it follows that $Z(t)$ is a time homogeneous Markov process. Let us denote its transition d.f. by

$$(7.17)\qquad \begin{aligned} F(z, t) &\equiv F(z_0; z, t) \\ &= Pr\{Z(t) \leqslant z \mid Z(0) = z_0\} \qquad (0 \leqslant z \leqslant k, t \geqslant 0). \end{aligned}$$

When $k = \infty$, this dam model is easily seen to be analogous to the queueing system $M/D/1$, and we obtain the differential equation

$$(7.18)\qquad \frac{\partial F}{\partial t} - \frac{\partial F}{\partial z} = -\lambda F(z, t) + \lambda F(z - h, t) \qquad (0 \leqslant z < \infty)$$

as a special case of Takács' integro-differential equation† for the d.f. $F(z, t)$ in the system $M/G/1$ (Section 1.9) with the service time distribution given by

$$B(v) = \begin{cases} 0 & \text{if } v < h \\ 1 & \text{if } v \geqslant h. \end{cases} \tag{7.19}$$

For the dam with capacity $k < \infty$, so that $0 \leqslant Z(t) \leqslant k$, it is easy to see that $F(z, t)$ satisfies (7.18) for all $0 \leqslant z < k$; to verify whether (7.18) also holds at $z = k$, let us observe that

$$Pr\{k - dt < Z(t + dt) \leqslant k\} = Pr\{k - h < Z(t) \leqslant k\}\lambda\, dt + o(dt). \tag{7.20}$$

Using the fact $F(z, t)$ is differentiable with respect to t, and remembering that $F(k, t) = F(k, t + dt) = 1$, we obtain from (7.20),

$$1 - F(k - dt, t) = \lambda\, dt[1 - F(k - h, t)] + dt \frac{\partial}{\partial t} F(k - dt, t) + o(dt). \tag{7.21}$$

This shows that $F(z, t) \to 1$ as $z \to k - 0$. Thus there is no concentration of probability at $z = k$, and moreover, the left derivative of $F(z, t)$ with respect to z exists at $z = k$; we may therefore write

$$\frac{\partial}{\partial t} F(k, t) - \frac{\partial}{\partial z} F(k, t) = -\lambda + \lambda F(k - h, t), \tag{7.22}$$

the derivative $(\partial/\partial z)F(k, t)$ being taken on the left and $(\partial/\partial t)F(k, t)$ being written for the sake of uniformity, although it is known to be zero.

Thus, for the finite dam, the d.f. $F(z, t)$ satisfies the equation (7.18) in the range $0 \leqslant z \leqslant k$ and is subject to the condition $F(z, t) = 1$ for $z \geqslant k$.

b. The Limiting Distribution of $Z(t)$

It is difficult to see how the differential equation (7.18) can be solved to obtain $F(z, t)$ for the finite dam. However, let us consider the limiting d.f.

$$F^*(z) = \lim_{t \to \infty} F(z_0; z, t) \qquad (0 \leqslant z \leqslant k). \tag{7.23}$$

Assuming that it exists independently of the initial content $Z(0) = z_0$, it is seen to satisfy the equation

$$\frac{dF^*}{dz} = \lambda F^*(z) - \lambda F^*(z - h) \tag{7.24}$$

† See, however, the remarks following equation (1.222).

analogous to (7.18) in which $\partial F/\partial t$ has been put equal to zero. To solve (7.24), we first consider the range $0 \leqslant z < h$; the equation (7.24) reduces in this range to

$$\frac{\partial F^*}{\partial z} = \lambda F^*(z), \tag{7.25}$$

which gives

$$F^*(z) = F^*(0)e^{\lambda z} \qquad (0 \leqslant z < h). \tag{7.26}$$

In the next range $h \leqslant z < 2h$ the equation (7.24) gives

$$\frac{dF^*}{dz} = \lambda F^*(z) - \lambda F^*(0)e^{\lambda(z-h)}, \tag{7.27}$$

so that

$$F^*(z) = Ae^{\lambda z} - \lambda F^*(0)e^{\lambda(z-h)}(z-h), \tag{7.28}$$

where A is a constant. Now using the property that $F^*(z)$ is continuous at $z = h$, we obtain from (7.26) and (7.28)

$$F^*(0)e^{\lambda h} = Ae^{\lambda h}, \tag{7.29}$$

and therefore (7.28) can be written as

$$F^*(z) = F^*(0)[e^{\lambda z} - e^{\lambda(z-h)}\lambda(z-h)] \qquad (h \leqslant z < 2h). \tag{7.30}$$

Proceeding in this manner we obtain

$$F^*(z) = F^*(0)\sum_{r=0}^{[z/h]} e^{\lambda(z-rh)}\frac{(-\lambda)^r}{r!}(z-rh)^r \qquad (0 \leqslant z \leqslant k). \tag{7.31}$$

To determine the unknown probability $F^*(0)$ we use the condition $F^*(k) = 1$; we thus obtain

$$F^*(0) = \left[\sum_{r=0}^{[k/h]} e^{\lambda(k-rh)}\frac{(-\lambda)^r}{r!}(k-rh)^r\right]^{-1}. \tag{7.32}$$

The limiting d.f. of the content $Z(t)$ of the dam with finite capacity k is thus the corresponding d.f. for the infinite dam truncated at k and suitably scaled so that $F^*(k) = 1$. However, it must be noted that the d.f. for the infinite dam exists if and only if $\lambda h < 1$, whereas for the finite dam (7.31) holds whether or not $\lambda h < 1$.

c. The Transition D.F. for the Infinite Dam

Let us now return to the differential equation (7.18) for $F(z, t)$ and consider the case of the infinite dam. Although the solution derived in Section 2.4, for the general case of an arbitrary service time distribution $dB(v)$ holds in this case, the following alternative method of solving (7.18) is much more direct and is therefore of some interest. First let us note from equation (2.39) that the probability of emptiness of the dam at time t is given by

$$F(0, t) \equiv F(z_0; 0, t) = \sum_{r=0}^{n} e^{-\lambda t} \frac{\lambda^r}{r!} t^{r-1}(t - rh), \tag{7.33}$$

where $[(t - z_0)/h] = n$. Now we carry out the transformation

$$u = z + t, \qquad t = t \tag{7.34}$$

in (7.18) and let $F(z, t) \to H(u, t)$. Then $H(u, t) = 0$ for $u < t$, $t \geqslant 0$, and $H(u, t) \leqslant 1$ for all $u \geqslant t \geqslant 0$; moreover, $H(u, t) \to 1$ as $u \to \infty$, so that it is itself a d.f. Furthermore, $H(u, t)$ will be continuous in $t < u < \infty$, but will have a discontinuity $G(t, t) = F(0, t)$ at $u = t$. The equation (7.18) transforms into

$$\frac{\partial}{\partial t} H(u, t) = -\lambda H(u, t) + \lambda H(u - h, t) \qquad (t \leqslant u < \infty). \tag{7.35}$$

This can be written as

$$\frac{\partial}{\partial t} H(u, t)e^{\lambda t} = \lambda H(u - h, t)e^{\lambda t},$$

from which we obtain

$$H(u, t)e^{\lambda t} = A - \lambda \int_t^{u-h} H(u - h, \tau)e^{\lambda \tau}\, d\tau, \tag{7.36}$$

where it is understood that the integral vanishes if $u - h < t$. To evaluate A we put $u = t$ in (7.36) and find that

$$A = H(u, u)e^{\lambda u} = F(0, u)e^{\lambda u}. \tag{7.37}$$

Substituting (7.37) in (7.36) we obtain

$$H(u, t) = F(0, u)e^{-\lambda(t-u)} - \lambda \int_t^{u-h} H(u - h, \tau)e^{-\lambda(t-\tau)}\, d\tau. \tag{7.38}$$

For $t \leqslant u < t + h$ equation (7.38) gives

$$H(u, t) = F(0, u)e^{-\lambda(t-u)}. \tag{7.39}$$

For $t + h \leqslant u < t + 2h$, we substitute (7.39) for $H(u, t)$ inside the integral in (7.38) and find that

$$\begin{aligned} H(u, t) &= F(0, u)e^{-\lambda(t-u)} - \lambda \int_t^{u-h} F(0, u - h)e^{-\lambda(\tau-u+h)}e^{-\lambda(t-\tau)}\, d\tau. \\ &= F(0, u)e^{-\lambda(t-u)} + F(0, u - h)e^{-\lambda(t-u+h)}\lambda(t - u + h) \\ &\qquad\qquad (t + h \leqslant u < t + 2h). \end{aligned} \tag{7.40}$$

This suggests the general result

$$(7.41)\quad H(u, t) = \sum_{r=0}^{n} F(0, u - rh)e^{-\lambda(t-u+rh)}\frac{\lambda^r}{r!}(t - u + rh)^r$$
$$(t + nh \leqslant u < t + nh + h).$$

To prove this we use induction. For, assuming (7.41) to be true for $t + nh \leqslant u < t + nh + h$, we find from (7.38) that for $t + nh + h \leqslant u < t + nh + 2h$,

$$\begin{aligned}H(u, t) &= F(0, u)e^{-\lambda(t-u)} \\ &\quad -\lambda\sum_{r=0}^{n}\int_t^{u-rh-h} F(0, u - rh - h)e^{-\lambda(\tau-u+rh+h)}e^{-\lambda(t-\tau)} \\ &\qquad\qquad \times \frac{\lambda^r}{r!}(\tau - u + rh + h)^r\,d\tau \\ &= F(0, u)e^{-\lambda(t-u)} \\ &\quad -\sum_{r=1}^{n+1} F(0, u - rh)e^{-\lambda(t-u+rh)}\frac{\lambda^r}{(r-1)!}\int_t^{u-rh}(\tau - u + rh)^{r-1}\,d\tau \\ &= F(0, u)e^{-\lambda(t-u)} + \sum_{r=1}^{n+1} F(0, u - rh)e^{-\lambda(t-u+rh)}\frac{\lambda^r}{r!}(t - u + rh)^r \\ &= \sum_{r=0}^{n+1} F(0, u - rh)e^{-\lambda(t-u+rh)}\frac{\lambda^r}{r!}(t - u + rh)^r.\end{aligned}$$

We have thus proved (7.41) for $n + 1$.

From (7.41) we obtain $F(z, t)$ explicitly as

$$(7.42)\qquad F(z, t) = \sum_{r=0}^{[z/h]} F(0, z + t - rh)e^{-\lambda(rh-z)}\frac{\lambda^r}{r!}(rh - z)^r,$$

where $F(0, t)$ is itself given by (7.33). This expression for $F(z, t)$ is slightly different from the one which would arise from the general solution obtained for the system $M/G/1$.

7.3 AN INPUT OF THE GAMMA TYPE

Let us consider a dam of infinite capacity and assume that the input $X(t)$ during an interval $(0, t]$ has the gamma distribution given by

$$\begin{aligned}(7.43)\quad k(x, t)\,dx &= Pr\{x < X(t) < x + dx\} \\ &= e^{-x/\rho}\frac{(x/\rho)^{t-1}}{\Gamma(t)}\frac{dx}{\rho} \qquad (0 < x < \infty,\quad t > 0).\end{aligned}$$

The c.f. of this distribution is given by

$$E\{e^{i\theta X(t)}\} = \int_0^\infty e^{i\theta x} e^{-x/\rho} \frac{(x/\rho)^{t-1}}{\Gamma(t)} \frac{dx}{\rho} = (1 - \rho i\theta)^{-t}, \tag{7.44}$$

and the mean input during $(0, t]$ is found to be ρt. The release from the dam is continuous and occurs at a unit rate except when it is empty. Let $Z(t)$ be the content of this dam at time t.

To study the behavior of the continuous time process $Z(t)$ we consider a discrete time dam model in which (1) during the time interval $(t, t + 1]$ an input X_t flows into the dam, and (2) the release at time $t + 1$ is unity except when the dam is empty. Let X_t have a discrete distribution with the c.f. $\phi(\theta) = E(e^{i\theta X_t})$. Then if Z_t denotes the storage function at time t, the limiting distribution of Z_t as $t \to \infty$ exists if and only if $0 < \rho = E(X_t) < 1$, and from equation (6.128), the c.f. of this distribution is found to be

$$\psi(\theta) = \frac{(1 - \rho)(e^{i\theta} - 1)}{e^{i\theta} - \phi(\theta)}. \tag{7.45}$$

Now, let the units of time as well as amount of water be n^{-1} and assume that the input X_t during $(t/n, (t + 1)/n]$ has the negative binomial distribution with the c.f.

$$\phi_n(\theta) = E(e^{i\theta X_t}) = a^{1/n}(1 - be^{i\theta/n})^{-1/n},$$

where $a = (1 + n\rho)^{-1}$, $b = n\rho(1 + n\rho)^{-1}$, so that $b(na)^{-1} = \rho$ is the mean input during this interval. We can write

$$\phi_n(\theta) = [1 - n\rho(e^{i\theta/n} - 1)]^{-1/n}. \tag{7.46}$$

The total input during the interval $(0, T/n]$ has therefore the c.f.

$$[\phi_n(\theta)]^T = \{1 - n\rho(e^{i\theta/n} - 1)\}^{-T/n}, \tag{7.47}$$

since the inputs over the intervals $\left(0, \frac{1}{n}\right], \left(\frac{1}{n}, \frac{2}{n}\right], \ldots$ are independently distributed. In (7.47) let $T \to \infty$ as $n \to \infty$ in such a way that $T/n \to t$ (fixed); then

$$[\phi_n(\theta)]^T = [1 - \rho i\theta + o(1)]^{-T/n} \to (1 - \rho i\theta)^{-t}, \tag{7.48}$$

which is the c.f. (7.44) of the gamma-type input (7.43). The c.f. of the storage function Z_t, measured in units of n^{-1}, is given by

$$\psi_n(\theta) = \frac{(1 - \rho)(e^{i\theta/n} - 1)}{e^{i\theta/n} - \phi_n(\theta)}. \tag{7.49}$$

The numerator of the last expression is

$$(1-\rho)\left(\frac{i\theta}{n}+\frac{1}{2}\frac{i^2\theta^2}{n^2}+\cdots\right), \tag{7.50}$$

whereas the denominator is

(7.51)

$$\begin{aligned}
e^{i\theta/n} &- [1-n\rho(e^{i\theta/n}-1)]^{-1/n} \\
&= \left(1+\frac{i\theta}{n}+\frac{1}{2}\frac{i^2\theta^2}{n^2}+\cdots\right) \\
&\quad -\left[1+\frac{1}{n}n\rho(e^{i\theta/n}-1)+\frac{1}{n}\left(\frac{1}{n}+1\right)\frac{n^2\rho^2}{2}(e^{i\theta/n}-1)^2\right. \\
&\quad \left.+\frac{1}{n}\left(\frac{1}{n}+1\right)\left(\frac{1}{n}+2\right)\frac{n^3\rho^3}{3!}(e^{i\theta/n}-1)^3+\cdots\right] \\
&= \left(\frac{i\theta}{n}+\frac{1}{2}\frac{i^2\theta^2}{n^2}+\cdots\right) \\
&\quad -\left[\rho\left(\frac{i\theta}{n}+\frac{1}{2}\frac{i^2\theta^2}{n^2}+\cdots\right)+\frac{\rho^2}{2}(n+1)\left(\frac{i\theta}{n}+\frac{1}{2}\frac{i^2\theta^2}{n^2}+\cdots\right)^2\right. \\
&\quad \left.+\frac{\rho^3}{3!}(n+1)(2n+1)\left(\frac{i\theta}{n}+\frac{1}{2}\frac{i^2\theta^2}{n^2}+\cdots\right)^3+\cdots\right] \\
&= \frac{i\theta}{n}-\frac{1}{n}\left[\rho i\theta+\frac{1}{2}(\rho i\theta)^2+\frac{1}{3}(\rho i\theta)^3+\cdots\right]+o\left(\frac{1}{n}\right) \\
&= \frac{i\theta}{n}+\frac{1}{n}\log(1-\rho i\theta)+o\left(\frac{1}{n}\right).
\end{aligned}$$

Substituting (7.50) and (7.51) in (7.49) we find that as $n \to \infty$, $\psi_n(\theta) \to \psi(\theta)$, where

$$\psi(\theta) = \frac{(1-\rho)i\theta}{i\theta+\log(1-\rho i\theta)} \qquad (0<\rho<1); \tag{7.52}$$

this is therefore the c.f. of the limiting distribution of the continuous time process $Z(t)$ as $t \to \infty$. The corresponding d.f. $F(z)$ can be obtained by inverting this c.f. In particular, the probability that the dam will be empty is given by

$$F(0) = \lim_{\theta\to\infty}\psi(\theta) = 1-\rho, \tag{7.53}$$

whereas for $z > 0$,

$$F(z) - \tfrac{1}{2}F(0) = \frac{1}{2\pi}\int_{-\infty}^{\infty}\frac{(1-\rho)(1-e^{-i\theta z})}{i\theta+\log(1-\rho i\theta)}\,d\theta. \tag{7.54}$$

7.4 THE CONTENT OF A DAM AS THE SUPREMUM OF AN INFINITELY DIVISIBLE PROCESS

For each $n \geqslant 1$, let us define a discrete time storage process $\{Z_k^{(n)}, k \geqslant 0\}$ as follows. Let the time unit be 2^{-n}, and let us suppose that the net input $U_k^{(n)}$ during $[k2^{-n}, (k+1)2^{-n}]$ is given by

$$(7.55) \qquad U_k^{(n)} = Y[(k+1)2^{-n}] - Y(k2^{-n})$$

where $Y(t)$ is a separable, entered, infinitely divisible process with $Y(0) = 0$; the random variables $U_k^{(n)}$ $(k \geqslant 0)$ are therefore independent and identically distributed for each n. Let us denote $Y_k^{(n)} = Y(k2^{-n})$, then we can write (7.55) as

$$(7.56) \qquad U_k^{(n)} = Y_{k+1}^{(n)} - Y_k^{(n)} \qquad (k \geqslant 0).$$

The content $Z_k^{(n)}$ is defined by the relations

$$(7.57) \qquad Z_0^{(n)} = z_0, \qquad Z_{k+1}^{(n)} = \max(0, Z_k^{(n)} + U_k^{(n)}) \qquad (k \geqslant 0),$$

as in equation (6.120). From (7.57) we obtain

$$(7.58) \qquad Z_k^{(n)} = \max[0, U_{k-1}^{(n)} + U_{k-2}^{(n)} + \cdots + U_r^{(n)}\ (r = 0, 1, \ldots, k-1), \\ z_0 + U_{k-1}^{(n)} + U_{k-2}^{(n)} + \cdots + U_0^{(n)}]$$

Now from (7.56) we have

$$U_{k-1}^{(n)} + U_{k-2}^{(n)} + \cdots + U_0^{(n)} = \sum_{i=0}^{k-1} [Y_{i+1}^{(n)} - Y_i^{(n)}] = Y_k^{(n)},$$

so that

$$(7.59) \qquad U_{k-1}^{(n)} + U_{k-2}^{(n)} + \cdots + U_r^{(n)} \\ = [U_{k-1}^{(n)} + U_{k-2}^{(n)} + \cdots + U_0^{(n)}] - [U_{r-1}^{(n)} + U_{r-2}^{(n)} + \cdots + U_0^{(n)}] \\ = Y_k^{(n)} - Y_r^{(n)}.$$

We can therefore write

$$(7.60) \qquad Z_k^{(n)} = \max\left[\max_{0 \leqslant r \leqslant k}(Y_k^{(n)} - Y_r^{(n)}), z_0 + Y_k^{(n)}\right].$$

We now define a process $Z^{(n)}(t)$ in continuous time $t \geqslant 0$ and depending on a parameter n, as follows.

$$(7.61) \qquad Z^{(n)}(t) = Z_k^{(n)} \quad \text{for} \quad k2^{-n} \leqslant t < (k+1)2^{-n} \qquad (k \geqslant 0).$$

In view of (7.60) we can write for $t \geqslant 0$

$$(7.62) \qquad Z^{(n)}(t) = \max\left\{\max_{0 \leqslant r \leqslant [t2^n]}(Y_{[t2^n]}^{(n)} - Y_{r-}^{(n)}), z_0 + Y_{[t2^n]}^{(n)}\right\}.$$

We now investigate the behavior of this process $Z^{(n)}(t)$ as $n \to \infty$. Since the process $Y(t)$ is separable, we find that as $n \to \infty$

$$(7.63) \qquad \max_{0 \leqslant r \leqslant [t2^n]} \{Y^{(n)}_{[t2^n]} - Y^{(n)}_{r-}\} = \max_{0 \leqslant r \leqslant [t2^n]} [Y([t2^n]\,2^{-n}) - Y(r2^{-n}-)] \to \sup_{0 \leqslant \tau \leqslant t} [Y(t) - Y(\tau-)]$$

with probability one, whereas since $Y(t)$ is centered

$$(7.64) \qquad Y^{(n)}_{[t2^n]} = Y[[t2^n]2^{-n}] \to Y(t),$$

also with probability one. From (7.63) and (7.64) it follows that with probability one

$$(7.65) \qquad Z^{(n)}(t) \to Z(t) \quad \text{as} \quad n \to \infty,$$

where

$$(7.66) \qquad Z(t) = \max \left\{ \sup_{0 \leqslant \tau \leqslant t} [Y(t) - Y(\tau-)],\, z_0 + Y(t) \right\}.$$

We have thus obtained a continuous time storage process $Z(t)$ defined by (7.66) as a limit (with probability one) of a sequence of storage processes in discrete time. Observe that since the net input $Y(t) = X(t) - t$, where $X(t)$ is the actual input, we can write (7.66) as

$$(7.67) \quad Z(t) = \max \left\{ \sup_{0 \leqslant \tau \leqslant t} [X(t) - X(\tau-) - (t - \tau)],\, z_0 + X(t) - t \right\}.$$

Since $X(t)$ is time homogeneous, $X(t) - X(\tau-) \sim X(t - \tau+)$, and from (7.67) we find that $Z(t)$ has the same distribution as

$$(7.68) \qquad \max \left[\sup_{0 \leqslant \tau \leqslant t} (X(\tau) - \tau),\, z_0 + X(t) - t \right],$$

which reduces to

$$(7.69) \qquad \sup_{0 \leqslant \tau \leqslant t} [X(\tau) - \tau]$$

if $Z(0) = 0$. Now, for any separable centered infinitely divisible process $Y(t)$, Baxter and Donsker (1957) have shown that

$$(7.70) \quad s \int_{t=0}^{\infty} \int_{u=0-}^{\infty} e^{-st-\theta u}\, d_u Pr\left\{ \sup_{0 \leqslant \tau \leqslant t} Y(\tau) < u \right\} = \exp \int_{w=s}^{\infty} \int_{t=0}^{\infty} e^{-wt}[\psi(\theta, t) - 1]\, dt\, dw,$$

where

$$\psi(\theta, t) = 1 + \int_0^\infty (e^{-\theta y} - 1)\, d_y Pr\{Y(t) < y\}. \tag{7.71}$$

In the present case $Y(t) = X(t) - t$, and therefore if $Z(0) = 0$, the distribution of $Z(t)$ is given by

$$s\int_{t=0}^\infty \int_{u=0-}^\infty e^{-st-\theta u}\, d_y Pr\{Z(t) < u\} = \exp \int_{w=s}^\infty \int_{t=0}^\infty e^{-wt} \int_{x=0}^\infty (e^{-\theta x} - 1)\, d_x K(t + x, t), \tag{7.72}$$

where $K(x, t) = Pr\{X(t) \leqslant x\}$ is the d.f. of the input process $X(t)$.

7.5 THE WET PERIOD IN A DAM

Suppose that the input $X(t)$ into the dam during an interval $(0, t]$ is a time homogeneous additive process such that†

$$Pr\{x < X(t) < x + dx\} = k(x, t)\, dx \qquad (x \geqslant 0, t \geqslant 0) \tag{7.73}$$

and

$$E[e^{-\theta X(t)}] = \int_0^\infty e^{-\theta x} k(x, t)\, dx = e^{-t\xi(\theta)} \qquad [\mathrm{Re}\,(\theta) > 0], \tag{7.74}$$

where $\xi(\theta)$ is a function of a specified type. Let $E[X(t)] = \rho t < \infty$; then $\xi(\theta) = \rho\theta + o(\theta)$ as $\theta \to 0+$. Let the release from the dam be continuous and at a unit rate except when the dam is empty. Let $Z(t)$ denote the content of the dam at time t. Now suppose that the initial content of the dam is $Z(0) = u > 0$, and let $T \equiv T(u)$ be the first subsequent time at which the dam runs dry, so that $Z(T) = 0$; then the duration T of this wet period T is a random variable. Thus

$$T(u) = \inf\,[t \mid Z(t) = 0], \qquad Z(0) = u; \tag{7.75}$$

this can also be written as

$$T(u) = \inf\,[t \mid u + X(t) - t \leqslant 0]. \tag{7.76}$$

We shall study the properties of $T(u)$.

Clearly, $T(u) \geqslant u$, and

$$T(u) = u + T[X(u)]. \tag{7.77}$$

It is obvious that $T(u)$ is itself additive in the parameter u, so that

$$E[e^{-\theta T(u)}] = e^{-u\eta(\theta)} \qquad [\mathrm{Re}\,(\theta) > 0], \tag{7.78}$$

† For an example of such a process see Hasofer (1964).

where the function $\eta(\theta)$ is to be obtained. From (7.77) we find that

$$E[e^{-\theta T(u)}] = e^{-\theta u}E\{e^{-\theta T[X(u)]}\} = e^{-\theta u}E[e^{-X(u)\eta(\theta)}] = e^{-\theta u - u\xi[\eta(\theta)]}, \tag{7.79}$$

where we have used (7.74); thus $\eta(\theta)$ satisfies the functional equation

$$\eta(\theta) = \theta + \xi[\eta(\theta)]. \tag{7.80}$$

Proceeding as in Section 2.2, we find that (7.80) has a unique root such that $\eta(\infty) = \infty$, and moreover, that $\eta(0+) = 0$ or ζ depending on whether $\rho < 1$ or $\geqslant 1$, where ζ is the largest positive root of the equation

$$\zeta = \xi(\zeta). \tag{7.81}$$

Hence it follows that the probability that the dam with an initial content u eventually runs dry is given by

$$Pr\{T(u) < \infty\} = \begin{cases} 1 & \text{if } \rho \leqslant 1 \\ e^{-u\zeta} & \text{if } \rho > 1. \end{cases} \tag{7.82}$$

The d.f. of $T(u)$ can be obtained by inverting the Laplace transform (7.78). However, it can be explicitly obtained in the following way. Let us first observe that the relation

$$\frac{d}{d\theta}[e^{-(t+s)\xi(\theta)}] = (t+s)e^{-(t+s)\xi(\theta)}[-\xi'(\theta)] = \frac{t+s}{t}e^{-s\xi(\theta)}\frac{d}{d\theta}[e^{-t\xi(\theta)}] \quad (t > 0, s > 0) \tag{7.83}$$

gives

$$\frac{t}{t+s}\int_0^\infty e^{-\theta x}xk(x, t+s)\,dx = \int_0^\infty e^{-\theta x}\,dx\int_0^x yk(y, t)k(x-y, s)\,dy;$$

that is,

$$\int_0^\infty e^{-\theta x}\left[\frac{tx}{t+s}k(x, t+s)\,dx - \int_0^x yk(y, t)k(x-y, s)\,dy\right] = 0 \tag{7.84}$$

for all $\theta > 0$. This implies the important result

$$\int_0^x yk(y, t)k(x-y, s)\,dy = \frac{tx}{t+s}k(x, t+s). \tag{7.85}$$

Now let

$$G(u, t) = Pr[T(u) \leqslant t] \quad (t \geqslant u > 0) \tag{7.86}$$

be the d.f. of $T(u)$. From the functional equation (7.77) we obtain

$$G(u, t) = Pr\{T[X(u)] \leqslant t - u\} = \int_0^{t-u} k(x, u)G(x, t - u)\, dx;$$

that is, $G(u, t)$ satisfies the integral equation

$$G(u, t) = \int_0^{t-u} k(x, u)G(x, t - u)\, dx. \tag{7.87}$$

We assert that if a function $G(u, t)$ is defined as follows:

$$G(u, t) = \begin{cases} 0 & \text{if} \quad t \leqslant u \\ \displaystyle\int_u^t \frac{u}{\tau} k(\tau - u, \tau)\, d\tau & \text{if} \quad t > u, \end{cases} \tag{7.88}$$

then $G(u, t)$ is a solution of (7.87). We have, in fact,

$$\begin{aligned} \int_0^{t-u} k(x, u)G(x, t - u)\, dx &= \int_{x=0}^{t-u} k(x, u)\, dx \int_{\tau=x}^{t-u} \frac{x}{\tau} k(\tau - x, \tau)\, d\tau \\ &= \int_{\tau=0}^{t-u} \frac{d\tau}{\tau} \int_{x=0}^{\tau} xk(x, u)k(\tau - x, \tau)\, dx \\ &= \int_0^{t-u} \frac{d\tau}{\tau} \cdot \frac{u\tau}{u + \tau} k(\tau, u + \tau) \qquad \text{from} \quad (7.85) \\ &= \int_u^t \frac{u}{\tau} k(\tau - u, \tau)\, d\tau = G(u, t), \end{aligned} \tag{7.89}$$

which proves our assertion. If we leave the question of uniqueness of the integral equation (7.87) open, it follows that the d.f. of $T(u)$ is given by (7.88). Incidentally, we have proved that $T(u)$ has a fr.f. $g(u, t)$ given by

$$\frac{\partial}{\partial t} G(u, t) = g(u, t) = \frac{u}{t} k(t - u, t). \tag{7.90}$$

The above results yield the following useful identities:

$$\int_u^\infty k(t - u, t)\, dt = (1 - \rho)^{-1} \qquad (u > 0, \rho < 1), \tag{7.91}$$

$$\int_{0+}^\infty k(t, t)\, dt = \rho(1 - \rho)^{-1} \qquad (\rho < 1). \tag{7.92}$$

The first of these is an immediate consequence of (7.78) and (7.90). We have

$$\int_u^\infty e^{-\theta t}\frac{u}{t}\,k(t-u,t)\,dt = e^{-u\eta(\theta)} \qquad (u > 0); \tag{7.93}$$

differentiating (7.93) with respect to θ under the integral sign and putting $\theta = 0$, we find that

$$\int_u^\infty k(t-u,t)\,dt = \lim_{\theta\to 0+} e^{-u\eta(\theta)}\eta'(\theta) = (1-\rho)^{-1}, \tag{7.94}$$

as desired. To prove (7.92) we recall that $T(u)$ is the first passage time of the process $Y(t) = u + X(t) - t$ from u (> 0) to 0; since $Y(t)$ is a time-homogeneous Markov process with the transition fr.f. $k(t+y-u,t)$, we obtain

$$g(u,t) + \int_{0+}^{t-u} g(u,t-\tau)k(\tau,\tau)\,d\tau = k(t-u,t) \qquad (t \geqslant u > 0) \tag{7.95}$$

by a direct enumeration of the paths from u to 0 in the process $Y(t)$. Integrating (7.95) over $u \leqslant t < \infty$, we obtain

$$\begin{aligned}\int_u^\infty k(t-u,t)\,dt &= \left[1 + \int_{0+}^\infty k(t,t)\,dt\right]\int_u^\infty g(u,t)\,dt \\ &= \left[1 + \int_{0+}^\infty k(t,t)\,dt\right] Pr\{T(u) < \infty\},\end{aligned} \tag{7.96}$$

or, using (7.82) and (7.91),

$$(1-\rho)^{-1} = 1 + \int_{0+}^\infty k(t,t)\,dt \qquad (\rho < 1), \tag{7.97}$$

which leads to (7.92).

In the special case of a gamma-type input considered in Section 7.3, we have from (7.43)

$$k(x,t) = e^{-x/\rho}\frac{x^{t-1}}{\rho^t\Gamma(t)} \qquad (0 \leqslant x < \infty, t > 0) \tag{7.98}$$

for the fr.f. of $X(t)$, and

$$\int_0^\infty e^{-\theta x}k(x,t)\,dx = (1+\rho\theta)^{-t} = e^{-t\log(1+\rho\theta)} \tag{7.99}$$

for its Laplace transform. Thus the process $X(t)$ is of the type considered in this section, and the above results are applicable in this case. The fr.f. of the wet period $T(u)$ is

$$g(u,t) = \frac{ue^{-(t-u)/\rho}(t-u)^{t-1}}{\rho^t\Gamma(t+1)} \qquad (t \geqslant u > 0). \tag{7.100}$$

For large t, applying Stirling's approximation to $\Gamma(t+1)$ in (7.100), we obtain

$$g(u,t) \sim \begin{cases} \exp\left[u\left(\frac{1}{\rho}-1\right) - t\left(\frac{1}{\rho}-1+\log\rho\right)\right]\frac{u}{\sqrt{2\pi t^3}} & \text{if} \quad \rho < 1 \\ \frac{u}{\sqrt{2\pi t^3}} \qquad \text{if} \quad \rho = 1. \end{cases} \tag{7.101}$$

7.6 INTEGRO-DIFFERENTIAL EQUATION FOR THE DAM PROCESS

a. Specification of the Process

Let the input into the dam during a time interval $(0, t]$ be denoted by $X(t)$. We assume that $X(t)$ is a time-homogeneous, nonnegative, infinitely divisible process with a continuous distribution having finite mean and variance. Let $K(x, t)$ be the d.f. of $X(t)$; then its L.S.T. is given by

$$E[e^{-\theta X(t)}] = \int_0^\infty e^{-\theta x}\, d_x K(x,t) = e^{-t\xi(\theta)} \qquad [\mathrm{Re}\,(\theta) > 0], \tag{7.102}$$

$$\xi(\theta) = \int_0^\infty (1 - e^{-\theta u})\lambda(u)\, du, \tag{7.103}$$

where $\lambda(u) \geqslant 0$ is finite for $u > 0$, but $\lambda(u) \to \infty$ as $u \to 0$. From the general theory of such processes it is known that during a time interval $(t, t+dt]$, a jump $dX(t)$ of magnitude $u < dX(t) \leqslant u + du$ occurs in a Poisson process with parameter $\lambda(u)\, du$ $(u > 0)$. The probability of such a jump in $(t, t+dt]$ is therefore

$$\begin{aligned} dK(u, dt) &= Pr\{u < dX(t) \leqslant u + du\} \\ &= \lambda(u)\, du\, dt + o(dt). \end{aligned} \tag{7.104}$$

Furthermore, we have for $t > 0$,

$$Pr\{X(t) = 0\} = K(0, t) = \exp\left[-t\int_0^\infty \lambda(u)\, du\right], \tag{7.105}$$

and this is zero, since $\lambda(u) \to \infty$ as $u \to 0$. The mean and variance of the process per unit time are respectively

$$\rho = \int_0^\infty u\lambda(u)\, du < \infty, \qquad \sigma^2 = \int_0^\infty u^2\lambda(u)\, du < \infty. \tag{7.106}$$

For $t = 0$, it follows from (7.102) that $K(x, 0) = 1$ $(x \geqslant 0)$ and from the continuity property of the transform

$$\lim_{t\to 0} K(x,t) = 1 \qquad (x > 0). \tag{7.107}$$

The fr.f. of $x(t)$ is given by

$$\frac{d}{dx} K(x, t) = k(x, t) \qquad (0 \leqslant x < \infty, t > 0). \tag{7.108}$$

As a particular case, let

$$\lambda(u) = \frac{1}{u} e^{-u/\rho} \qquad (u > 0); \tag{7.109}$$

then

$$\begin{aligned} \xi(\theta) &= \int_0^\infty (1 - e^{-\theta u}) e^{-u/\rho} \frac{du}{u} \\ &= \int_0^\infty \frac{e^{-u/\rho} - e^{-u(\theta+1/\rho)}}{u} du = \log(1 + \rho\theta), \end{aligned} \tag{7.110}$$

and

$$E[e^{-\theta X(t)}] = e^{-t \log(1+\rho\theta)} = (1 + \rho\theta)^{-t}. \tag{7.111}$$

Thus the input process resulting from (7.109) is of the gamma type considered in Section 7.3. From (7.106) it is easily verified that the mean and variance of this process are equal to ρ and ρ^2 respectively.

Returning to the general case, let us suppose that the input into the dam is specified by equations (7.102) to (7.108). The release is assumed to be continuous and at a unit rate except when the dam is empty. The dam content $Z(t)$ at any time can then be represented by the equation

$$Z(t + dt) = Z(t) + dX(t) - (1 - r)\, dt, \tag{7.112}$$

where $r\,dt$ $(0 \leqslant r \leqslant 1)$ is that part of the interval $(t, t + dt)$ during which the dam is empty. From (7.112) it is clear that $Z(t)$ is a time-homogeneous Markov process. Let us denote its transition d.f. by

$$F(z, t) \equiv F(z_0; z, t) = Pr\{Z(t) \leqslant z \mid Z(0) = z_0\}; \tag{7.113}$$

$F(z, t)$ is a point function, nondecreasing, and everywhere continuous to the right in z such that $0 \leqslant F(z, t) \leqslant 1$. We may assume that $F(z, t)$ has the following properties:

1. $F(z, t) = 0$ for $z < \max(0, z_0 - t)$,
2. $\lim_{z \to \infty} F(z, t) = 1$;
3. $F(z, t)$ is differentiable with respect to t for all values of z.

b. The Integro-Differential Equation for $F(z, t)$

We now derive the integro-differential equation for the transition d.f. $F(z, t)$. In order to do this we consider a discrete time model in which

(1) the units of time and input are both equal to Δ; (2) the inputs $X(\Delta)$ over the time intervals $(n\Delta, n\Delta + \Delta)$ are independent and have the probability distribution

$$Pr\{X(\Delta) = 0\} = e^{-\lambda\Delta}$$

(7.114) $$Pr\{X(\Delta) = i\Delta\} = (1 - e^{-\lambda\Delta})\frac{\lambda_i}{\lambda} \qquad (i \geqslant 1),$$

where

(7.115) $$\lambda_i \equiv \lambda_i(\Delta), \qquad \lambda \equiv \lambda(\Delta) = \sum_1^\infty \lambda_i,$$

and

(7.116) $$\begin{aligned} 0 &< \rho(\Delta) \equiv E[X(\Delta)] < \infty, \\ 0 &< \sigma^2(\Delta) \equiv E[X(\Delta)]^2 - \rho^2(\Delta) < \infty; \end{aligned}$$

and (3) the release is Δ at the end of each time interval, except when the dam is empty. The storage function $Z(n\Delta)$ at time $n\Delta$ in this dam satisfies the relation

(7.117) $$Z(n\Delta + \Delta) = \max\,[0, Z(n\Delta) + X(\Delta) - \Delta];$$

this yields the identity

(7.118) $$Z(n\Delta) = \max\,[X(m\Delta) - m\Delta\ (0 \leqslant m \leqslant n), z_0 + X(n\Delta) - n\Delta],$$

where $z_0 = Z(0)$ and $X(n\Delta)$ is the total input during $(0, n\Delta)$. As $\Delta \to 0$, $Z(n\Delta)$ in the above equation will tend with probability one to the continuous time storage function $Z(t)$ defined by (7.67). The difference equation for the d.f. of $Z(n\Delta)$ then tends to the required integro-differential equation for $F(z, t)$.

To study the limiting behavior of this discrete model, we assume that as $\Delta \to 0$ and $i\Delta \to u$,

(7.119) $$\frac{\lambda_i}{\Delta} \to \lambda(u), \quad \lambda(\Delta) \to \infty \qquad \text{but} \quad \lambda\Delta \to 0,$$

and

(7.120) $$\frac{\rho(\Delta)}{\Delta} \to \rho \qquad (0 < \rho < \infty), \qquad \frac{\sigma^2(\Delta)}{\Delta} \to \sigma^2 \qquad (0 < \sigma^2 < \infty).$$

From these assumptions it follows that

(7.121) $$\begin{aligned} Pr\{X(\Delta) = i\Delta\} &= \frac{1 - e^{-\lambda\Delta}}{\lambda\Delta}\lambda_i\Delta \sim \lambda(u)\,\delta u\,\delta t, \\ Pr\{X(n\Delta) = 0\} &= e^{-\lambda n\Delta} \to 0 \qquad \text{as} \quad \Delta \to 0,\ n\,\Delta \to t. \end{aligned}$$

Furthermore, for the L.S.T. $\phi(\theta, \Delta)$ of $X(\Delta)$ we find that

$$\text{(7.122)} \quad \begin{aligned} \log \phi(\theta, \Delta) &= \log \left[e^{-\lambda\Delta} + \left(\frac{1 - e^{-\lambda\Delta}}{\lambda}\right) \sum \lambda_i e^{-i\theta\Delta} \right] \\ &= \log \left[1 - \left(\frac{1 - e^{-\lambda\Delta}}{\lambda}\right) \sum \lambda_i (1 - e^{-i\theta\Delta}) \right] \\ &= -\Delta\xi(\theta, \Delta) + o(\Delta), \end{aligned}$$

where

(7.123)

$$\xi(\theta, \Delta) = \sum_1^\infty \lambda_i (1 - e^{-i\theta\Delta}) \to \int_0^\infty \lambda(u)(1 - e^{-\theta u})\, du = \xi(\theta) \qquad \text{(say)}.$$

The transform of $X(n\Delta)$ is therefore given by

$$\text{(7.124)} \qquad \phi(\theta, n\Delta) = \exp\left[-n\Delta\xi(\theta, \Delta) + o(\Delta)\right] \to e^{-t\xi(\theta)}.$$

From (7.121) and (7.124), we see that the input $X(n\Delta)$ in the discrete model tends to the continuous time process $X(t)$ described in Section 7.6a. We also remark that the assumptions (7.119) and (7.120) imply (7.77), so that the ρ and σ^2 of this section are, in fact, the mean and variance per unit time of the continuous process.

Now consider the d.f. $F(j\Delta, n\Delta)$ of $Z(n\Delta)$; from (7.117) we see that for $j > 0$,

(7.125)

$$F(j\Delta - \Delta, n\Delta + \Delta) = F(j\Delta, n\Delta)e^{-\lambda\Delta} + \sum_{i=1}^\infty F(j\Delta - i\Delta, n\Delta)(1 - e^{-\lambda\Delta}) \frac{\lambda_i}{\lambda}.$$

This can be written as

$$\text{(7.126)} \quad \begin{aligned} &[F(j\Delta - \Delta, n\Delta + \Delta) - F(j\Delta - \Delta, n\Delta)] \\ &\qquad - [F(j\Delta, n\Delta) - F(j\Delta - \Delta, n\Delta)] \\ &\qquad = \Delta\left(\frac{1 - e^{-\lambda\Delta}}{\lambda\Delta}\right) \sum_1^\infty \lambda_i [F(j\Delta - i\Delta, n\Delta) - F(j\Delta, n\Delta)]. \end{aligned}$$

Suppose that

$$\text{(7.127)} \qquad \Delta \to 0, \qquad j\Delta \to z, \qquad i\Delta \to u, \qquad n\Delta \to t,$$

then $F(j\Delta, n\Delta) \to F(z, t)$, the d.f. of $Z(t)$. If we divide (7.126) by Δ and take limits as $\Delta \to 0$, a heuristic argument suggests that $\partial F/\partial z$ exists and is finite for all $z > 0$ and finally leads to the integro-differential equation

$$\text{(7.128)} \quad \frac{\partial}{\partial t} F(z, t) - \frac{\partial}{\partial z} F(z, t) = \int_0^\infty [F(z - u, t) - F(z, t)]\lambda(u)\, du \qquad (z > 0).$$

For a rigorous derivation of (7.128), however, further justification of the limiting process would be needed.

At $j = 0$, we have the relation similar to (7.125)

$$F(0, n\Delta + \Delta) = F(\Delta, n\Delta)e^{-\lambda\Delta}, \tag{7.129}$$

which can be written as

$$F(0, n\Delta + \Delta) - F(0, n\Delta) - [F(\Delta, n\Delta) - F(0, n\Delta)] = (e^{-\lambda\Delta} - 1)F(\Delta, n\Delta). \tag{7.130}$$

Dividing by Δ and letting $\Delta \to 0$, this leads to

$$\frac{\partial}{\partial z} F(z, t) = \infty \qquad \text{at} \quad z = 0 \tag{7.131}$$

since $\lambda(\Delta) \to \infty$. Thus the equation (7.128) may be regarded as being also satisfied at $z = 0$. Since $F(0, t)$ is continuous to the right at $z = 0$, it may be obtained as

$$F(0, t) = \lim_{z\to 0+} F(z, t). \tag{7.132}$$

To the properties (1) to (3) of $F(z, t)$ we might therefore add the following.

4. $F(z, t)$ is continuous in the range $0 < z < \infty$, but has a discontinuity $F(0, t)$ at $z = 0$, this being the probability of emptiness of the dam.

5. $F(z, t)$ has a unique derivative at all points z in the range except for $z = 0$, where the right derivative $(\partial/\partial z)F(0, t) = \infty$. Subject to the suitable interpretation of $(\partial/\partial z)F(z, t)$ at $z = +0$, however, the integro-differential equation (7.128) for $F(z, t)$ may be regarded as valid for all values of $0 \leqslant z < \infty$.

7.7 THE TRANSITION D.F. OF $Z(t)$

In this section we shall obtain an explicit expression for the transition d.f. $F(z_0; z, t)$ of $Z(t)$. Clearly, $F(z_0; z, t) = K(t + z - z_0, t)$ for $0 \leqslant t \leqslant z_0$, $z \geqslant z_0 - t$, and therefore we need consider only the case where $0 \leqslant z_0 < t$, $z \geqslant 0$. Let

$$\psi(\theta, t) = \int_{0-}^{\infty} e^{-\theta z}\, d_z F(z, t) \qquad [\mathrm{Re}\,(\theta) > 0] \tag{7.133}$$

be the L.S.T. of the distribution of $Z(t)$. We have

$$\int_{0+}^{\infty} e^{-\theta z} \frac{\partial F}{\partial z}\, dz = \int_{0-}^{\infty} e^{-\theta z}\, d_z F(z, t) - F(0, t) = \psi(\theta, t) - F(0, t), \tag{7.134}$$

and, assuming differentiation under integration to be justified,

$$\int_{0+}^{\infty} e^{-\theta z} \frac{\partial F}{\partial t}\, dz = \frac{\partial}{\partial t} \int_{0+}^{\infty} e^{-\theta z} F(z, t)\, dz = \frac{\partial}{\partial t} \frac{\psi(\theta, t)}{\theta}. \tag{7.135}$$

Taking transforms with respect to z of both sides of the equation (7.128) and using (7.134), (7.135), and (7.103), we obtain

$$\begin{aligned}\frac{1}{\theta}\frac{\partial}{\partial t}\psi(\theta, t) - \psi(\theta, t) + F(0, t) &= \int_{0+}^{\infty} e^{-\theta z}\, dz \int_0^{\infty} [F(z-u, t) - F(z, t)]\lambda(u)\, du \\ &= \int_{0+}^{\infty} \lambda(u)\, du \int_0^{\infty} e^{-\theta z}[F(z-u, t) - F(z, t)]\, dz \\ &= \int_{0+}^{\infty} \lambda(u)\, du (e^{-\theta u} - 1)\frac{\psi(\theta, t)}{\theta} \\ &= -\frac{\psi(\theta, t)}{\theta}\xi(\theta),\end{aligned}$$

or

$$\frac{\partial}{\partial t}\psi(\theta, t) + [\xi(\theta) - \theta]\psi(\theta, t) = -\theta F(0, t), \tag{7.136}$$

a differential equation for the L.S.T. $\psi(\theta, t)$. To solve this we multiply both sides of (7.136) by $e^{[\xi(\theta)-\theta]t}$ and write the resulting equation as

$$\frac{\partial}{\partial t}\psi(\theta, t)e^{[\xi(\theta)-\theta]t} = -\theta F(0, t)e^{[\xi(\theta)-\theta]t}; \tag{7.137}$$

on integrating (7.137) we obtain

$$\psi(\theta, t)e^{[\xi(\theta)-\theta]t} = A - \theta\int_0^t F(0, \tau)e^{[\xi(\theta)-\theta]\tau}\, d\tau, \tag{7.138}$$

where

$$A = \psi(\theta, 0) = e^{-\theta z_0}. \tag{7.139}$$

Substituting (7.139) in (7.138) and simplifying, we obtain the result

$$\psi(\theta, t) = e^{-t\xi(\theta)+\theta(t-z_0)} - \theta\int_0^t F(0, t-\tau)e^{-[\xi(\theta)-\theta]\tau}\, d\tau, \tag{7.140}$$

which determines $\psi(\theta, t)$ uniquely in terms of $F(0, t)$. To invert this L.S.T., we proceed as in Section 2.4, making use of the identities

$$\int_{z_0-t}^{\infty} e^{-\theta z}K(t + z - z_0, t)\, dz = \theta^{-1}e^{-t\xi(\theta)+\theta(t-z_0)}, \tag{7.141}$$

$$\int_{-\tau}^{\infty} e^{-\theta z}k(\tau + z, \tau)\, dz = e^{-\tau\xi(\theta)+\theta\tau}, \tag{7.142}$$

which follow from (7.102). We thus obtain the relation

$$F(z, t) = K(t + z - z_0, t) - \int_0^{t-z_0} F(0, t-\tau)k(\tau + z, \tau)\, d\tau \tag{7.143}$$

and also the identity

$$\int_z^{t-z_0} F(0, t-\tau)k(\tau - z, \tau)\, d\tau = K(t - z - z_0, t) \qquad (0 < z \leqslant t - z_0). \tag{7.144}$$

Since $F(0, t) = \lim_{z\to 0+} F(z, t)$ it follows from (7.143) that the probability of emptiness $F(0, t)$ of the dam satisfies the integral equation

$$F(0, t) + \int_0^{t-z_0} F(0, t-\tau)k(\tau, \tau)\, d\tau = K(t - z_0, t). \tag{7.145}$$

From the corresponding formula in the discrete time case it seems likely that $F(0, t)$ is given by

$$F(0, t) = \begin{cases} 0 & \text{if } t < z_0 \\ \displaystyle\int_{z_0}^{t} g(u, t)\, du & \text{if } t \geqslant z_0. \end{cases} \tag{7.146}$$

To verify that (7.146) is indeed the solution of (7.145) we integrate the identity (7.95) over $z_0 \leqslant u \leqslant t$ and find that

$$\int_{z_0}^{t} g(u, t)\, du + \int_{z_0}^{t} du \int_{0+}^{t-u} g(u, t-\tau)k(\tau, \tau)\, d\tau = \int_{z_0}^{t} k(t-u, t)\, du$$

or

$$\int_{z_0}^{t} g(u, t)\, du + \int_{0+}^{t-z_0} k(\tau, \tau)\, d\tau \int_{z_0}^{t-\tau} g(u, t-\tau)\, du = K(t - z_0, t) \qquad (t \geqslant z_0). \tag{7.147}$$

On comparing (7.147) with (7.145) we see that (7.146) is the required solution for $F(0, t)$ (it is obviously the unique nonnegative solution). The Laplace transform of $F(0, t)$ is given by

$$\begin{aligned} F^*(s) &= \int_{z_0}^{\infty} e^{-st}F(0, t)\, dt = \int_{z_0}^{\infty} e^{-st}\, dt \int_{z_0}^{t} g(u, t)\, du \\ &= \int_{z_0}^{\infty} du \int_{u}^{\infty} e^{-st}g(u, t)\, dt = \int_{z_0}^{\infty} e^{-u\eta(s)}\, du \\ &= \frac{e^{-z_0\eta(s)}}{\eta(s)}. \end{aligned} \tag{7.148}$$

Since $F(0, t)$ has now been determined, our inversion of (7.140) is complete, and we have thus obtained an expression (7.143) for the transition d.f. $F(z, t)$ of $Z(t)$ for $0 \leqslant z_0 < t$, $z \geqslant 0$; clearly, this is valid also for $0 \leqslant t \leqslant z_0$, $z \geqslant z_0 - t$.

7.8 LIMITING DISTRIBUTION OF $Z(t)$

We now investigate the limiting behavior of $F(z, t)$ as $t \to \infty$. Proceeding as in Section 2.7, we can prove that $\lim_{t\to\infty} F(z, t) = F^*(z)$ exists independently of the initial content $Z(0) = z_0$, and that $F^*(z) \equiv 0$ if $\rho \geqslant 1$, where ρ is the mean input per unit time. To evaluate the limiting d.f. $F^*(z)$ in the case $\rho < 1$, we first note from (7.148) that

$$(7.149)\quad F^*(0) = \lim_{t\to\infty} F(0, t) = \lim_{s\to 0+} sF^*(s) = \begin{cases} 0 & \text{if} \quad \rho \geqslant 1 \\ 1 - \rho & \text{if} \quad \rho < 1. \end{cases}$$

We need two further results. The first is the inequality

$$(7.150)\quad \int_0^\infty k(t + z, t)\, dt \leqslant (1 - \rho)^{-1} \qquad (-\infty < z < \infty, \rho < 1).$$

For $z < 0$ we have equality, as in (7.91), whereas for $z = 0$, from (7.92), we find that the integral in (7.150) has the value $\rho(1 - \rho)^{-1} < (1 - \rho)^{-1}$. For $z > 0$ we find from (7.143) that

$$(7.151)\quad \begin{aligned} 1 \geqslant K(t + z, t) &\geqslant \int_0^t F(0, t - \tau) k(\tau + z, \tau)\, d\tau \\ &\geqslant F(0, t) \int_0^t k(\tau + z, \tau)\, d\tau \end{aligned}$$

since $F(0, t) \equiv F(0; 0, t)$ is monotone nonincreasing [cf. remarks following equation (2.86)]. Letting $t \to \infty$ in (7.151) and using (7.149) we obtain (7.150) for $z > 0$ and $\rho < 1$.

The second result we need is that

$$(7.152)\quad \lim_{t\to\infty} K(t + z - z_0, t) = 1 \qquad (\rho < 1).$$

To prove (7.152) we observe that

$$(7.153)\quad \mathrm{Var}\,[X(t)] = \sigma^2 t = \int_0^\infty (x - \rho t)^2 k(x, t)\, dx > 0;$$

for large t we can take $z > -(1 - \rho)t$ without loss of generality, and obtain from (7.153) the inequality

$$\sigma^2 t \geqslant \int_{t+z}^\infty (x - \rho t)^2 k(x, t)\, dx \geqslant [z + (1 - \rho)t]^2 \int_{t+z}^\infty k(x, t)\, dx,$$

or

$$(7.154)\quad 0 \leqslant 1 - K(t + z, t) \leqslant \frac{t\sigma^2}{[z + (1 - \rho)t]^2}.$$

The result (7.152) now follows from (7.154) as $t \to \infty$.

We shall now obtain $F^*(z)$ by letting $t \to \infty$ in (7.143). In order to do this we choose $T < t$, and write (7.143) as

$$F(z, t) = K(t + z - z_0, t) - I_1 - I_2, \tag{7.155}$$

where

$$\begin{aligned} I_1 &= \int_0^T F(0, t - \tau)k(\tau + z, \tau)\, d\tau \\ I_2 &= \int_T^{t-z_0} F(0, t - \tau)k(\tau + z, \tau)\, d\tau. \end{aligned} \tag{7.156}$$

In this, let first t and then $T \to \infty$; then

$$I_1 \to \int_0^T (1 - \rho)k(\tau + z, \tau)\, d\tau \to (1 - \rho)\int_0^\infty k(\tau + z, \tau)\, d\tau, \tag{7.157}$$

and

$$I_2 \leqslant \int_T^{t-z_0} k(\tau + z, \tau)\, d\tau \to 0, \tag{7.158}$$

since by (7.150), $k(t + z, t)$ is integrable over $(0 < t < \infty)$. Using (7.152), (7.157), and (7.158) in (7.155) it follows that the limiting d.f. $F^*(z)$ is given by

$$F^*(z) = 1 - (1 - \rho)\int_0^\infty k(t + z, t)\, dt \qquad (\rho < 1). \tag{7.159}$$

The L.S.T. of the limiting distribution of $Z(t)$ can also be obtained from the results of Section 7.7. For, let

$$\psi^*(\theta, z) = \int_0^\infty e^{-st}\psi(\theta, t)\, dt \tag{7.160}$$

be the Laplace transform of $\psi(\theta, t)$; from (7.140) and (7.148) we then find that

$$\begin{aligned} \psi^*(\theta, s) &= \int_0^\infty \exp\{-[s + \xi(\theta) - \theta]t - \theta z_0\}\, dt \\ &\quad -\theta\int_0^\infty \exp\{-[\xi(\theta) - \theta]\tau\}\, d\tau \int_\tau^\infty e^{-st}F(0, t - \tau)\, dt \\ &= \frac{e^{-\theta z_0}}{s - \theta + \xi(\theta)} - \theta\int_0^\infty \exp\{-[\xi(\theta) - \theta]\tau\}e^{-s\tau - z_0\eta(s)}\frac{d\tau}{\eta(s)} \\ &= \frac{e^{-\theta z_0} - \theta e^{-z_0\eta(s)}/\eta(s)}{s - \theta + \xi(\theta)} \qquad (\operatorname{Re}[s - \theta + \xi(\theta)] > 0). \end{aligned} \tag{7.161}$$

As $t \to \infty$, $\psi(\theta, t) \to \Psi(\theta)$, where

$$\Psi(\theta) = \lim_{s\to 0+} s\psi^*(\theta, s) = \frac{\theta}{\theta - \xi(\theta)} \lim_{s\to 0+} \frac{se^{-z_0\eta(s)}}{\eta(s)} \tag{7.162}$$

$$= \begin{cases} 0 & \text{if } \rho \geqslant 1 \\ \dfrac{\theta(1-\rho)}{\theta - \xi(\theta)} & \text{if } \rho < 1, \end{cases}$$

which is the required L.S.T. of the limiting distribution.

7.9 A MODEL WITH RANDOM OUTPUT

We now describe a more general storage model considered by Gani and Pyke (1960). Let $Y(t)$ be the net input during a time interval $(0, t]$. We assume that $Y(t)$ is a separable infinitely divisible process which can be represented as the difference of two infinitely divisible nonnegative processes; such a process is centered. Let us assume further that $Y(t)$ has a finite mean. Then the c.f. of the process $Y(t)$ is given by

$$E[e^{i\theta Y(t)}] = e^{t\phi(\theta)}, \tag{7.163}$$

where

$$\phi(\theta) = -i\theta + \left(\int_{-\infty}^{0-} + \int_{0}^{\infty}\right)(e^{i\theta x} - 1)\, dL(x), \tag{7.164}$$

where the function $L(x)$ is continuous to the right, nondecreasing in both $(-\infty, 0)$ and $[0, \infty)$, and is such that $L(\pm\infty) = 0$. The term $-i\theta$ in (7.164) indicates that $Y(t)$ contains a deterministic term $-t$; thus the net input is of the form $Y(t) = X_1(t) - X_2(t) - t$ $[X_1(t) \geqslant 0,\ X_2(t) \geqslant 0]$, where $X_1(t)$ is the actual input, and the random component $X_2(t)$ and the deterministic component t together constitute the output. From the general theory of additive processes it follows that almost all sample functions of $Y(t) + t$ have right- and left-hand limits at every t and that they increase or decrease only by jumps, the number of jumps in $(0, t]$ of magnitude $\geqslant x \geqslant 0$ $(\leqslant x < 0)$ being a random variable having a Poisson distribution with mean $-tL(x)$ $[tL(x)]$. Let us assume that $L(0) > -\infty$; then in any finite interval $(0, t]$, only a finite number of positive jumps occur, and moreover,

$$Pr\{\text{no jumps of positive magnitude occur in } (0, t]\} = e^{-\lambda t} \tag{7.165}$$

where $\lambda = -L(0)$.

For a net input process defined above we define a storage process $Z(t)$ $(t \geqslant 0)$ as

$$Z(t) = \max\left\{\sup_{0\leqslant\tau\leqslant t} [Y(t) - Y(\tau-)],\ z_0 + Y(t)\right\}, \tag{7.166}$$

where $Z(0) = z_0 \geqslant 0$. To understand the physical significance of this analytical definition we construct two sequences $\{\tau_k\}$, $\{T_k\}$ $(k \geqslant 1)$ and a function $Z(t)$ as follows. Let

$$\begin{aligned} \tau_1 &= \inf\,[t \geqslant 0 \mid z_0 + Y(t) \leqslant 0] \\ T_1 &= \sup\,[t \geqslant \tau_1 \mid \text{no jumps of positive magnitude in } (\tau_1, t]] \end{aligned} \tag{7.167}$$

$$Z(t) = \begin{cases} z_0 + Y(t) & \text{if } 0 \leqslant t < \tau_1 \\ 0 & \text{if } \tau_1 \leqslant t < T_1 \\ Y(T_1+) - Y(T_1-) & \text{if } t = T_1, \end{cases} \tag{7.168}$$

and for $k > 1$,

$$\begin{aligned} \tau_k &= \inf\,[t \geqslant T_{k-1} \mid Z(T_{k-1}) + Y(t) \leqslant 0] \\ T_k &= \sup\,[t \geqslant \tau_k \mid \text{no jumps of positive magnitude in } (\tau_k, t]] \end{aligned} \tag{7.169}$$

$$Z(t) = \begin{cases} Y(t) - Y(T_{k-1}) & \text{if } T_{k-1} < t < \tau_k \\ 0 & \text{if } \tau_k \leqslant t < T_k \\ Y(T_k+) - Y(T_k-) & \text{if } t = T_k. \end{cases} \tag{7.170}$$

The interpretation of this second function $Z(t)$ defined by (7.167) to (7.170) as a storage function is as follows. The initial content of the dam is $Z(0) = z_0$, and the content at time t is $z_0 + Y(t)$ so long as $z_0 + Y(t) > 0$, where $Y(t)$ is the net input during $(0, t]$. If $z_0 + Y(t) \leqslant 0$ at time τ_1, then for $t \geqslant \tau_1$, $Z(t) = 0$ until a jump of positive magnitude occurs, say at T_1; the magnitude of this jump is then the dam content at T_1. The procedure then repeats itself. It is clear that τ_1, $\tau_2 - T_1$, $\tau_3 - T_2, \ldots$ are the successive wet periods in the dam, and $T_k - \tau_k$ $(k \geqslant 1)$ the successive dry periods; since the process $Y(t)$ is separable, these are well-defined random variables and therefore the process $Z(t)$ defined in terms of these random variables is also well defined.

We shall now show that the definition (7.166) of the process $Z(t)$ is, in fact, equivalent to the above constructive definition. Let us first observe that since only a finite number of positive jumps occur in a finite interval, $T_k \to \infty$ as $k \to \infty$. Now put $\tau_0 = T_0 = 0$, and for each $t > 0$, define $k(t)$ by $T_{k(t)} \leqslant t < T_{k(t)+1}$. Furthermore, set $\tau_0 = T_0 = 0$, and $Y(T_0-) = -z_0$. Then with probability one we can write (7.166) as

$$Z(t) = \max\left\{\max_{1 \leqslant k \leqslant k(t)} \sup_{T_{k-1} < \tau \leqslant T_k} [Y(t) - Y(\tau-)],\ \sup_{T_{k(t)} < \tau \leqslant t} [Y(t) - Y(\tau-)],\ Y(t) - Y(T_0-)\right\}. \tag{7.171}$$

Now since $Y(t)$ is nonincreasing in (τ_k, T_k), we have

$$(7.172)\qquad \sup_{T_{k-1}<\tau\leqslant T_k} [Y(t) - Y(\tau-)] = Y(t) - \inf_{T_{k-1}<\tau\leqslant T_k} Y(\tau-)$$

$$= Y(t) - \inf_{\tau_k<\tau\leqslant T_k} Y(\tau-)$$

$$= Y(t) - Y(T_k-)$$

for $1 \leqslant k \leqslant k(t)$, and similarly,

$$(7.173)\qquad \sup_{T_{k(t)}<\tau\leqslant t} [Y(t) - Y(\tau-)] = Y(t) - Y(T_{k(t)}-),$$

with probability one. Using (7.172) and (7.173) we can write (7.171) as

$$(7.174)\qquad Z(t) = \max_{0\leqslant k\leqslant k(t)} [Y(t) - Y(T_k-)].$$

However, we have $Y(T_k-) \leqslant Y(T_{k-1}-)$, so that the maximal term among $Y(t) - Y(T_k-)$ $[0 \leqslant k \leqslant k(t)]$ is the last one. Thus

$$(7.175)\qquad Z(t) = Y(t) - Y(T_{k(t)}-) \qquad (t \geqslant 0),$$

which is equal to $Z(t)$ defined by (7.167) to (7.170). [In the above discussion we have assumed that $t < \tau_{k(t)+1}$, but if $t \geqslant \tau_{k(t)+1}$ (7.173), and hence $Z(t)$ will reduce to zero.]

As in Section 7.4, the distribution of $Z(t)$ can be obtained at least for the case where $Z(0) = 0$ by using the formula due to Baxter and Donsker (1957).

7.10 MODELS WITH RANDOM LINEAR INPUTS AND OUTPUTS

a. Introduction

Miller (1963) has studied storage models in which the input and the output occur at a unit rate over random intervals of time. More specifically, these models may be described as follows. Let $Z(t)$ be the storage level at time t, and assume that $Z(0) = 0$; $Z(t)$ increases and decreases alternately over random intervals of time, denoted by $\{v_i\}$ and $\{u_i\}$ respectively. The rates of increase and decrease are respectively $+1$ and -1. The random variables $\{v_i\}$, $\{u_i\}$ are assumed to be independent; the v_i are identically distributed, with the d.f. $B(x)$, and the u_i are also identically distributed with the d.f. $A(x)$ $(0 \leqslant x < \infty)$. If $Z(t) = 0$ for some $t > 0$, it remains at zero until the end of the current period of decrease. For convenience let us assume that the initial period is an interval of decrease, say u_0. We then have

$$Z(t) = 0 \quad \text{for} \quad 0 \leqslant t \leqslant u_0. \tag{7.176}$$

Let $t_0 = u_0$, $t_n = u_0 + \sum_{i=1}^{n} (v_i + u_i)$ $(n \geqslant 1)$; then

(7.177)
$$Z(t + \Delta t) = \begin{cases} Z(t) + \Delta t & \text{for} \quad t_n \leqslant t < t + \Delta t \leqslant t_n + v_{n+1} \\ \max\,[0, Z(t) - \Delta t] & \text{for} \quad t_n + v_{n+1} \leqslant t \leqslant t_{n+1} \end{cases}$$
$$(n = 0, 1, 2, \ldots).$$

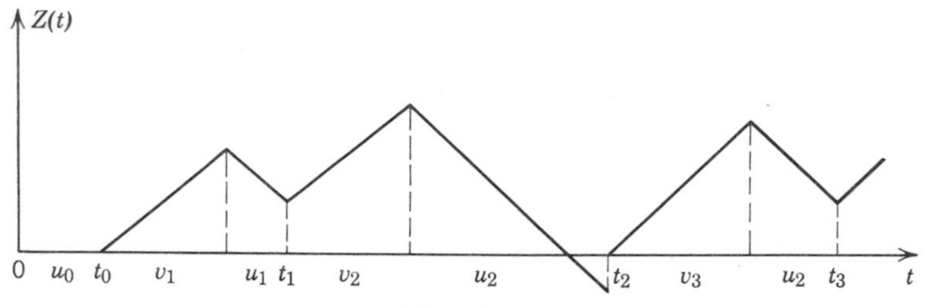

Figure 7.1

A typical realization of $Z(t)$ is shown in Figure 7.1.

In the general case where the d.f.'s $A(x)$ and $B(x)$ are arbitrary, it is clear from (7.177) that the process $Z(t)$ is non-Markovian. However, two important observations can be made. The first one concerns the random variables $Z_n = Z(t_n)$ $(n = 0, 1, \ldots)$; $\{Z_n\}$ is a Markov chain imbedded in the process $Z(t)$. In fact, we have from (7.176) and (7.177)

$$Z_0 = 0, \qquad Z_n = \max\,(0, Z_{n-1} + v_n - u_n) \qquad (n \geqslant 1). \tag{7.178}$$

so that

$$Z_n \sim \max_{0 \leqslant r \leqslant n} (S_r), \tag{7.179}$$

where $S_0 = 0$, $S_r = v_r - u_r$ $(r = 1, 2, \ldots)$. The distribution of Z_n is of the type already discussed in Chapter 4.

Our second observation concerns the "nonempty" period T in the storage system, defined by

$$T = \inf\,[t > t_0 \mid Z(t) = 0]. \tag{7.180}$$

Clearly,

$$T = \sum_{1}^{N-1} (v_i + u_i) + v_N + u_N', \tag{7.181}$$

where

(7.182)
$$\begin{aligned} N &= \min\,[n > 0 \mid Z_n = 0] \\ &= \min\,[n > 0 \mid (v_1 + v_2 + \cdots + v_n) \\ &\qquad - (u_1 + u_2 + \cdots + u_n) \leqslant 0], \end{aligned}$$

and u_N' is such that

$$(v_1 + v_2 + \cdots + v_N) - (u_1 + u_2 + \cdots + u_{N-1} + u_N') = 0.$$

Thus $T = 2T_1$, where $T_1 = v_1 + v_2 + \cdots + v_N$. However, comparison with the results of Section 4.3 shows that T_1 is the busy period in the queueing system $GI/G/1$ with the interarrival times $\{v_i\}$ and service times $\{u_i\}$. Since the distribution of T_1 is known, the problem of the nonempty period in Miller's storage model can be considered to have been solved.

b. The System with Negative Exponential Intervals of Decrease

Let us now consider the particular case of the preceding model in which

(7.183) $$dA(x) = \lambda e^{-\lambda x}\,dx, \qquad dB(x) = b(x)\,dx \qquad (0 \leqslant x < \infty).$$

Since the process $Z(t)$ is non-Markovian, the method of analysis of the system is based on the use of supplementary variables. For $t \geqslant 0$ let us define a random variable $Y(t)$ by

(7.184) $$Y(t) = \begin{cases} 0 & \text{if } 0 \leqslant t \leqslant t_0 \\ t - t_n & \text{if } t_n \leqslant t < t_{n+1} \end{cases} \qquad (n = 0, 1, \ldots).$$

Thus $Y(t)$ is the amount of time which has elapsed since the beginning of the preceding interval of increase. In terms of the renewal process $\{t_n\}$, $Y(t)$ is the age of the article in use at time t and its distribution can be found using (7.183); it is seen that $Y(t)$ has a fr.f. If the state of the system is specified by $Z(t)$, $Y(t)$, and whether $Z(t)$ is increasing or decreasing, it is obvious that the process becomes Markovian. Let

(7.185) $$F_+(x, y, t)\,dy = Pr[Z(t) \leqslant x, y \leqslant Y(t) \leqslant y + dy, Z(t) \text{ is increasing}] \qquad (x > 0,\ y \geqslant 0),$$

(7.186) $$F_-(x, t) = Pr[Z(t) \leqslant x, Z(t) \text{ is nonincreasing}] \qquad (x \geqslant 0).$$

The function $F_-(x, t)$ has a discontinuity at $x = 0$, $F_-(0, t)$ being the discrete probability of the store being empty at time t. Let us assume that $F_-(x, t)$ and $F_+(x, y, t)$ have continuous partial derivatives with respect to $x, y, t > 0$. The forward Kolmogorov equations of the process can then be found by using (7.177). Let $f^*(y)$ be the conditional fr.f. of v_i on the hypothesis that $v_i \geqslant y$, so that

(7.187)
$$\begin{aligned} f^*(y)\,dy &= Pr\{y \leqslant v_i \leqslant y + dy \mid v_i \geqslant y\} \\ &= \frac{b(y)\,dy}{1 - B(y)}; \end{aligned}$$

we then find that

$$(7.188)\quad Pr\{Z(t) \text{ stops increasing in } (t, t+dt] \mid Z(t) \text{ is increasing at } t, \text{ and } Y(t) = y\}$$
$$= Pr\{y \leqslant v_i \leqslant y + dt \mid v_i \geqslant y\} = f^*(y)\, dt.$$

The corresponding probability for a decrease is $\lambda\, dt$ independently of the value of $Y(t)$, that is,

$$(7.189)\quad Pr\{Z(t) \text{ stops decreasing in } (t, t+dt] \mid Z(t) \text{ is decreasing at } t\} = \lambda\, dt,$$

on account of the Markovian property of the negative exponential distribution. Considering $Z(t)$ over the infinitesimal interval $[t, t + dt]$, we find that

$$(7.190)\quad F_+(x, y, t+dt) = \{1 - f^*(y - dt)\, dt\}F_+(x - dt, y - dt, t) + o(dt) \quad (x > 0, y > 0)$$

and

$$(7.191)\quad F_-(x, t + dt) = (1 - \lambda\, dt)F_-(x + dt, t) + \int_0^\infty dy F_+(x + dt, y, t) f^*(y)\, dt + o(dt) \quad (x \geqslant 0).$$

Expanding both sides of (7.190) and (7.191) in terms of the partial derivatives with respect to x, y, t (whose existence has been assumed) and letting $dt \to 0$, we obtain the equations

$$(7.192)\quad \left(\frac{\partial}{\partial x} + \frac{\partial}{\partial y} + \frac{\partial}{\partial t}\right)F_+(x, y, t) = -f^*(y)F_+(x, y, t) \quad 0 < y < \min(x, t),$$

and

$$(7.193)\quad \frac{\partial}{\partial t}F_-(x, t) - \frac{\partial}{\partial x}F_-(x, t) = -\lambda F_-(x, t) + \int_0^\infty F_+(x, y, t) f^*(y)\, dy \quad (x, t > 0).$$

The boundary conditions are

$$(7.194)\quad \begin{aligned} F_+(x, y, 0) &= 0 \quad \text{for } x \geqslant 0, y \geqslant 0, \\ F_-(x, 0) &= 1 \quad \text{for } x \geqslant 0, \end{aligned}$$

$$(7.195)\quad F_+(x, 0, t) = \lambda F_-(x, t).$$

The conditions (7.194) are a consequence of our definition of $Z(t)$, whereas (7.195) can be established by considering $Z(t)$ in the interval $[t - dt, t]$, where $t = t_n$ is a point of increase; thus we obtain

$$F_+(x, 0, t)\, dt = F_-(x + dt, t - dt)\lambda\, dt, \tag{7.196}$$

which in the limit as $dt \to 0$ yields (7.195).

To solve the differential equation (7.192) we carry out the transformation

$$\begin{aligned} x' = x - y, \qquad y' &= y, \qquad t' = t - y; \\ F_+(x, y, t) &\to G(x', y', t'); \end{aligned} \tag{7.197}$$

the equation (7.192) then reduces to the simple equation

$$\frac{\partial G}{\partial y} = -f^*(y')G = -\frac{b(y')}{1 - B(y')}G,$$

whose solution is easily found to be

$$G(x', y', t') = A[1 - B(y')]. \tag{7.198}$$

To evaluate A, we use the boundary condition (7.195); thus

$$A = G(x', 0, t') = F_+(x', 0, t') = \lambda F_-(x', t'),$$

so that

$$G(x', y', t') = \lambda[1 - B(y')]F_-(x', t'). \tag{7.199}$$

Since $F_+(x, y, t) = G(x - y, y, t - y)$, (7.199) gives

$$F_+(x, y, t) = \lambda[1 - B(y)]F_-(x - y, t - y); \tag{7.200}$$

the solution of (7.192) has thus been obtained in terms of $F_-(x, y)$.

Substituting (7.200) in (7.193) we obtain

(7.201)

$$\frac{\partial}{\partial t}F_-(x, t) - \frac{\partial}{\partial x}F_-(x, t) = -\lambda F_-(x, t) + \lambda\int_0^\infty F_-(x - y, t - y)b(y)\, dy,$$

an integro-differential equation similar to Takács' equation for the waiting time in the queueing system $M/G/1$ (see Chapter 2). To solve (7.201) we use L.S.T.'s. Let

$$\psi(\theta) = \int_0^\infty e^{-\theta x}\, dB(x) \tag{7.202}$$

$$\Phi_-(\theta, s) = \int_{t=0}^\infty \int_{x=0-}^\infty e^{-\theta x - st}\, d_x F_-(x, t)\, dt \tag{7.203}$$

for suitable values of θ, s. We then have

$$\int_{t=0}^{\infty}\int_{x=0}^{\infty} e^{-\theta x-st}F_{-}(x,t)\,dt\,dx = \frac{\Phi_{-}(\theta,s)}{\theta}, \tag{7.204}$$

$$\begin{aligned}\int_{t=0}^{\infty}\int_{x=0}^{\infty} & e^{-\theta x-st}\frac{\partial}{\partial t}F_{-}(x,t)\,dt\,dx \\ &= \left[e^{-st}\int_0^{\infty} e^{-\theta x}F_{-}(x,t)\,dx\right]_0^{\infty} + s\int_0^{\infty}\int_0^{\infty} e^{-\theta x-st}F_{-}(x,t)\,dt\,dx \\ &= -\frac{1}{\theta}+\frac{s\Phi_{-}(\theta,z)}{\theta},\end{aligned} \tag{7.205}$$

since $F_{-}(x, 0) = 1$, and

$$\begin{aligned}\int_{t=0}^{\infty}\int_{x=0}^{\infty} & e^{-\theta x-st}\frac{\partial}{\partial x}F_{-}(x,t)\,dt\,dx \\ &= \int_0^{\infty} e^{-st}\,dt\left\{\left[e^{-\theta x}F_{-}(x,t)\right]_0^{\infty} + \theta\int_0^{\infty} e^{-\theta x}F_{-}(x,t)\,dx\right\} \\ &= -F_{-}^{*}(0,s)+\Phi_{-}(\theta,s),\end{aligned} \tag{7.206}$$

where

$$F_{-}^{*}(0,s) = \int_0^{\infty} e^{-st}F_{-}(0,t)\,dt. \tag{7.207}$$

Moreover,

$$\begin{aligned}\int_{t=0}^{\infty}\int_{x=0}^{\infty} & e^{-\theta x-st}\int_{y=0}^{\infty} F_{-}(x-y,t-y)b(y)\,dy\,dt\,dx \\ &= \int_{y=0}^{\infty} b(y)\,dy\int_{t=y}^{\infty}\int_{x=y}^{\infty} e^{-\theta x-st}F_{-}(x-y,t-y)\,dt\,dx \\ &= \int_0^{\infty} b(y)e^{-\theta y-sy}\,\frac{\Phi_{-}(\theta,s)}{\theta}\,dy = \psi(\theta+s)\,\frac{\Phi_{-}(\theta,s)}{\theta}.\end{aligned} \tag{7.208}$$

Taking transforms with respect to x, t of both sides of (7.201) and using (7.204) to (7.208), we obtain

$$-\frac{1}{\theta}+\frac{s}{\theta}\Phi_{-}(\theta,s)+F_{-}^{*}(0,s)-\Phi_{-}(\theta,s) = -\lambda\frac{\Phi_{-}(\theta,s)}{\theta}+\lambda\psi(\theta+s)\frac{\Phi_{-}(\theta,s)}{\theta},$$

from which we find that

$$\Phi_{-}(\theta,s) = \frac{1-\theta F_{-}^{*}(0,s)}{s-\theta+\lambda-\lambda\psi(\theta+s)}. \tag{7.209}$$

To evaluate the unknown transform $F_{-}^{*}(0, s)$ occurring in (7.209) we proceed as follows. In view of the remarks at the end of Section 7.10a, we find that the nonempty period T in this system is given by $T = 2T^*$, where T^* is the busy period in the queueing system $M/G/1$. From Section 2.2, it follows that the L.S.T. $\Gamma(\theta) = E(e^{-\theta T})$ satisfies the functional equation

$$\Gamma(\theta) = \psi[2\theta + \lambda - \lambda\Gamma(\theta)] \tag{7.210}$$

with $\Gamma(\infty) = \infty$. Now if the d.f. of T is denoted by $G(x)$, then we have

$$\begin{aligned} F_-(0, t) &= Pr\{Z(t) = 0\} \\ &= 1 - A(t) + \int_{\tau_1=0}^{t} \int_{\tau_2=0}^{t-\tau_1} dA(\tau_1)\, dG(\tau_2) F_-(0, t - \tau_1 - \tau_2) \\ &= e^{-\lambda t} + \int_0^t \int_0^{t-\tau_1} \lambda e^{-\lambda\tau_1} dG(\tau_2) F_-(0, t - \tau_1 - \tau_2). \end{aligned} \tag{7.211}$$

Taking Laplace transforms of both sides of (7.211) with respect to t, we obtain

$$F_-^*(0, s) = \frac{1}{s + \lambda} + \frac{\lambda}{s + \lambda} \Gamma(s) F_-^*(0, s),$$

which gives the required transform as

$$F_-^*(0, s) = \frac{1}{s + \lambda - \lambda\Gamma(s)}. \tag{7.212}$$

The transform (7.209) is then completely determined. The transform of

$$\Phi_+(\theta, \omega, s) = \int_{t=0}^{\infty} \int_{x=0}^{\infty} \int_{y=0}^{\infty} e^{-\theta x - \omega y - st} d_x F_+(x, y, t)\, dt\, dy \tag{7.213}$$

can also be obtained from (7.209) and (7.200). Thus

$$\begin{aligned} \Phi_+(\theta, \omega, s) &= \int_0^{\infty} \int_0^{\infty} \int_0^{\infty} e^{-\theta x - \omega y - st} \lambda[1 - B(y)] \\ &\qquad \times F_-(x - y, t - y)\, dt\, dx \\ &= \int_0^{\infty} dy e^{-\omega y} \lambda[1 - B(y)] e^{-\theta y - sy} \Phi_-(\theta, s) \\ &= \lambda\Phi_-(\theta, s) \frac{1 - \psi(\theta + \omega + s)}{\theta + \omega + s}. \end{aligned} \tag{7.214}$$

The limiting distribution of $Z(t)$ as $t \to \infty$, assuming that it exists, can be found from (7.209) and (7.214). Let us assume that $0 = 1/\mu = -\psi'(0) < \infty$, and put $\rho = \lambda\mu^{-1}$; then (7.210) gives $\Gamma(0+) = 1$ or < 1 depending on whether $\rho \leqslant 1$ or $\rho > 1$, and $-\Gamma'(0) = 2/\mu(1 - \rho)$ if $\rho < 1$, and $= \infty$ if $\rho = 1$. Therefore from (7.212) we obtain

$$\lim_{t \to \infty} F_-(0, t) = \lim_{s \to 0+} sF_-^*(0, s) = \begin{cases} (1 - \rho)/(1 + \rho) & \text{if } \rho < 1 \\ 0 & \text{if } \rho \geqslant 1. \end{cases} \tag{7.215}$$

Using (7.215) we obtain from (7.209) and (7.214),

$$\text{(7.216)}\quad \lim_{t\to\infty}\int_0^\infty e^{-\theta x}\,d_xF_-(x,t)=\lim_{s\to 0+} s\Phi_-(\theta,s)$$
$$=\begin{cases}\dfrac{1-\rho}{1+\rho}\dfrac{\theta}{\theta-\lambda+\lambda\psi(\theta)} & \text{if } \rho<1\\ 0 & \text{if } \rho\geqslant 1,\end{cases}$$

$$\text{(7.217)}\quad \lim_{t\to\infty}\int_0^\infty\int_0^\infty e^{-\theta x-\omega y}\,d_xF_+(x,y,t)\,dy$$
$$=\begin{cases}\dfrac{\lambda(1-\rho)\theta[1-\psi(\theta+\omega)]}{(1+\rho)(\theta+\omega)[\theta-\lambda+\lambda\psi(\theta)]} & \text{if } \rho<1\\ 0 & \text{if } \rho\geqslant 1\end{cases}$$

for the limiting transforms of $F_-(x, t)$ and $F_+(x, y, t)$ as $t \to \infty$. Thus if $\rho \geqslant 1$, the storage function $Z(t)$ increases indefinitely as $t \to \infty$, whereas if $\rho < 1$, it has a limiting distribution whose transforms are indicated above. It may be noted that the result corresponding to the case $\rho < 1$ in (7.216) is analogous to the Pollaczek-Khintchine formula (see Section 2.7) for the queueing system $M/G/1$.

7.11 THE CASE OF ORDERED INPUTS

a. The Transition D.F.

It occurs frequently in practice that the input into a dam varies seasonally, so that its distribution during the annual wet season is different from the one during the dry season. A model of a dam with such an input has been considered by Gani (1961, 1962a). The content $Z(t)$ of the dam in this model at time $t \geqslant 0$ is defined by the equation

$$\text{(7.218)}\qquad Z(t+dt)=Z(t)+dX(t)-(1-r)\,dt,$$

where $r\,dt$ $(0 \leqslant r \leqslant 1)$ is the time during $(t, t + dt]$ that the dam is empty, and the input $X(t)$ during a time interval $(0, t]$ is given by

$$\text{(7.219)}\quad X(t)=\left[\frac{N(t)+1}{2}\right]\alpha_1+\left[\frac{N(t)}{2}\right]\alpha_2\qquad(\alpha_1\neq\alpha_2,\ \alpha_1>0,\ \alpha_2>0),$$

$N(t)$ being a Poisson process with mean λt. The interpretation of (7.219) is that inputs of constant sizes α_1, α_2 arrive consecutively in that order in a Poisson process with mean λt. The process $Z(t)$ defined in this manner is not Markovian; we therefore introduce the supplementary variable $N(t)$ in the specification of the process at time t. Accordingly, let

$$\text{(7.220)}\quad \begin{aligned}F_1(z_0;z,t)&=Pr\{Z(t)\leqslant z;\ N(t)\text{ odd}\mid Z(0)=z_0\}\\ F_2(z_0;z,t)&=Pr\{Z(t)\leqslant z;\ N(t)\text{ even}\mid Z(0)=z_0\}.\end{aligned}$$

Each of the functions F_1 and F_2 has properties similar to those of the transition d.f. $F(z_0; z, t)$ of the dam with a simple Poisson input described in Section 7.2. In particular, we have the following:

$$\begin{aligned} &F_1(z_0; z, t) = 0 \quad \text{for} \quad z < \max(0, z_0 + \alpha_1 - t) \\ &F_2(z_0; z, t) = 0 \quad \text{for} \quad z < \max(0, z_0 - t), \end{aligned} \tag{7.221}$$

and

$$\begin{aligned} &F_1(z_0; z, 0) = 0 \quad \text{for} \quad z \geqslant 0. \\ &F_2(z_0; z, 0) = \begin{cases} 0 & \text{for} \quad z < z_0 \\ 1 & \text{for} \quad z \geqslant z_0. \end{cases} \end{aligned} \tag{7.222}$$

Furthermore, it is found that F_1 and F_2 satisfy the differential equations

$$\begin{aligned} &\left(\frac{\partial}{\partial t} - \frac{\partial}{\partial z}\right) F_1(z_0; z, t) = -\lambda F_1(z_0; z, t) + \lambda F_2(z_0; z - \alpha_1, t) \\ &\left(\frac{\partial}{\partial t} - \frac{\partial}{\partial z}\right) F_2(z_0; z, t) = -\lambda F_2(z_0; z, t) + \lambda F_1(z_0; z - \alpha_2, t) \\ &\qquad\qquad\qquad\qquad\qquad\qquad\qquad\qquad (z \geqslant 0, t \geqslant 0). \end{aligned} \tag{7.223}$$

The transition d.f. $F(z_0; z, t)$ of $Z(t)$ is given by

$$F(z_0; z, t) = F_1(z_0; z, t) + F_2(z_0; z, t), \tag{7.224}$$

so that F can be obtained if F_1 and F_2 can be determined from (7.223).

It is easily seen from the definition of $Z(t)$ that

$$\begin{aligned} &F_1(z_0; z, t) = \sum_{r=0}^{w_1} e^{-\lambda t} \frac{(\lambda t)^{2r+1}}{(2r+1)!} \quad \text{for} \quad z \geqslant z_0 + \alpha_1 - t \geqslant 0 \\ &F_2(z_0; z, t) = \sum_{r=0}^{w_2} e^{-\lambda t} \frac{(\lambda t)^{2r}}{(2r)!} \quad \text{for} \quad z \geqslant z_0 - t \geqslant 0, \end{aligned} \tag{7.225}$$

where

$$w_1 = \left(\frac{t + z - z_0 - \alpha_1}{\alpha_1 + \alpha_2}\right), \qquad w_2 = \left(\frac{t + z - z_0}{\alpha_1 + \alpha_2}\right). \tag{7.226}$$

In view of (7.221) it remains to obtain F_1 and F_2 for $t > z_0 + \alpha_1$, $z \geqslant 0$. In order to do this we put $u = z + t$, $t = t$ in (7.223), and let $F_i(z_0; z, t) \to H_i(u, t)$ $(i = 1, 2)$ (the variable z_0 in the H_i has been suppressed for convenience); the equations (7.223) then reduce to

$$\begin{aligned} &\frac{\partial}{\partial t} H_1(u, t) = -\lambda H_1(u, t) + \lambda H_2(u - \alpha_1, t) \\ &\frac{\partial}{\partial t} H_2(u, t) = -\lambda H_2(u, t) + \lambda H_1(u - \alpha_2, t) \qquad (u \geqslant t \geqslant 0). \end{aligned} \tag{7.227}$$

From (7.227) we obtain

$$
\begin{aligned}
H_1(u, t) &= F_1(0, u)e^{-\lambda(t-u)} - \lambda\int_t^{u-\alpha_1} H_2(u - \alpha_1, \tau)e^{-\lambda(t-\tau)}\, d\tau \\
H_2(u, t) &= F_2(0, u)e^{-\lambda(t-u)} - \lambda\int_t^{u-\alpha_2} H_1(u - \alpha_2, \tau)e^{-\lambda(t-\tau)}\, d\tau,
\end{aligned}
\tag{7.228}
$$

where the integrals vanish if the lower limit exceeds the upper limit. Thus

$$
H_i(u, t) = F_i(0, u)e^{-\lambda(t-u)} \qquad (t \leqslant u < t + \alpha_i,\ i = 1, 2).
\tag{7.229}
$$

Let $u \geqslant t + \alpha_1$ and in the first of the equations (7.228) substitute for $H_2(u, t)$ from the second; we then obtain after some simplification

$$
\begin{aligned}
H_1(u, t) = {} & F_1(0, u)e^{-\lambda(t-u)} + F_2(0, u - \alpha_1)e^{-\lambda(t-u+\alpha_1)} \\
& \times \lambda(t - u + \alpha_1) + \int_t^{u-\alpha_1-\alpha_2} H_1(u - \alpha_1 - \alpha_2, \tau) \\
& \times \lambda^2 e^{-\lambda(t-\tau)}(\tau - t)\, d\tau \qquad (u \geqslant t + \alpha_1).
\end{aligned}
\tag{7.230}
$$

For $t + \alpha_1 \leqslant u < t + \alpha_2$, (7.230) gives

$$
\begin{aligned}
H_1(u, t) = {} & F_1(0, u)e^{-\lambda(t-u)} \\
& + F_2(0, u - \alpha_1)e^{-\lambda(t-u+\alpha_1)}\lambda(t - u + \alpha_1).
\end{aligned}
\tag{7.231}
$$

From (7.230), using (7.229) and (7.231) we can obtain $H_1(u, t)$ in the range $t + \alpha_1 + \alpha_2 \leqslant u < t + 2\alpha_1 + \alpha_2$; proceeding in this manner we obtain

$$
\begin{aligned}
H_1(u, t) = {} & \sum_{k=0}^{[\frac{n-1}{2}]} F_1(0, u - k\alpha_1 - k\alpha_2)e^{-\lambda(t-u+k\alpha_1+k\alpha_2)} \\
& \times \frac{\lambda^{2k}}{(2k)!}(t - u + k\alpha_1 + k\alpha_2)^{2k} \\
& + \sum_{k=1}^{[\frac{n}{2}]} F_2(0, u - k\alpha_1 - \overline{k-1}\alpha_2)e^{-\lambda(t-u+k\alpha_1+\overline{k-1}\alpha_2)} \\
& \times \frac{\lambda^{2k-1}}{(2k-1)!}(t - u + k\alpha_1 + \overline{k-1}\alpha_2)^{2k-1} \\
& \left\{t + \left[\frac{n}{2}\right]\alpha_1 + \left[\frac{n-1}{2}\right]\alpha_2 \leqslant u < t \right. \\
& \left. + \left[\frac{n+1}{2}\right]\alpha_1 + \left[\frac{n}{2}\right]\alpha_2,\ n = 1, 2, \ldots\right\}.
\end{aligned}
\tag{7.232}
$$

Reverting to the original variables (z, t), we find that

$$(7.233)\quad F_1(z_0; z, t) = \sum_{k=0}^{[\frac{n-1}{2}]} F_1(0, t + z - k\alpha_1 - k\alpha_2)e^{\lambda(z-k\alpha_1-k\alpha_2]}$$

$$\times \frac{\lambda^{2k}}{(2k)!}(z - k\alpha_1 - k\alpha_2)^{2k}$$

$$+ \sum_{k=1}^{[\frac{n}{2}]} F_2(0, t + z - k\alpha_1 - \overline{k-1}\alpha_2)e^{\lambda(z-k\alpha_1-\overline{k-1}\alpha_2)}.$$

$$\times \frac{(-\lambda)^{2k-1}}{(2k-1)!}(z - k\alpha_1 - \overline{k-1}\alpha_2)^{2k-1}$$

$$\left(\left[\frac{n}{2}\right]\alpha_1 + \left[\frac{n-1}{2}\right]\alpha_2 \leqslant z < \left[\frac{n+1}{2}\right]\alpha_1 + \left[\frac{n}{2}\right]\alpha_2,\ n = 1, 2, \ldots\right),$$

and that F_2 is given by an expression similar to the above but with F_1 and F_2, α_1 and α_2 interchanged.

b. The Probabilities of Emptiness

The expression (7.233) contains the probabilities $F_i(z_0; 0, t)$ $(i = 1, 2)$ of emptiness of the dam at time t; to determine these we first consider the random variables

$$(7.234)\quad \begin{aligned} T_1 &= \inf\,[t \mid z + X(t) - t \leqslant 0;\ \text{first input is } \alpha_1], \\ T_2 &= \inf\,[t \mid z + X(t) - t \leqslant 0;\ \text{first input is } \alpha_2], \end{aligned}$$

which are the durations of wet periods initiated by a dam content $Z(0) = z$, the first input being α_1 and α_2 respectively. It is clear that T_1 and T_2 take values of the form

$$(7.235)\quad \begin{aligned} T_1 &= z + \left[\frac{n+1}{2}\right]\alpha_1 + \left[\frac{n}{2}\right]\alpha_2 \\ T_2 &= z + \left[\frac{n}{2}\right]\alpha_1 + \left[\frac{n+1}{2}\right]\alpha_2 \qquad (n = 0, 1, 2, \ldots); \end{aligned}$$

let $g_1(z, t)$ and $g_2(z, t)$ be the corresponding probabilities. We have then

$$g_i(z, t) = e^{-\lambda z} \qquad (i = 1, 2) \qquad \text{if} \quad t = z, \tag{7.236}$$

and for $t > z$,

$$\begin{aligned} g_1(z, t) = {} & \sum_{k=1}^{[\frac{n}{2}]} e^{-\lambda z} \frac{(\lambda z)^{2k}}{(2k)!} g_1(k\alpha_1 + k\alpha_2, t - z) \\ & + \sum_{k=1}^{[\frac{n+1}{2}]} e^{-\lambda z} \frac{(\lambda z)^{2k-1}}{(2k-1)!} g_2(k\alpha_1 + \overline{k-1}\alpha_2, t - z) \end{aligned} \tag{7.237}$$

and a similar relation for $g_2(z, t)$. Let

$$\phi_i(\theta, z) = E(\theta^{T_i}) \qquad (i = 1, 2) \qquad (0 \leqslant \theta \leqslant 1) \tag{7.238}$$

be the p.g.f.'s of T_1 and T_2. Then (7.237) gives

$$\begin{aligned} \phi_1(\theta, z) &= \sum_{n=0}^{\infty} \theta^{z_1 + [\frac{n+1}{2}]\alpha_1 + [\frac{n}{2}]\alpha_2} g_1\left(z, z + \left[\frac{n+1}{2}\right]\alpha_1 + \left[\frac{n}{2}\right]\alpha_2\right) \\ &= \theta^z f(0, z) + \sum_{k=1}^{\infty} f(2k, z)\phi_1(\theta, k\alpha_1 + k\alpha_2) \\ &\qquad + \sum_{k=1}^{\infty} f(2k-1, z)\phi_2(\theta, k\alpha_1 + \overline{k-1}\alpha_2) \end{aligned} \tag{7.239}$$

and similarly,

$$\begin{aligned} \phi_2(\theta, z) = {} & \theta^z f(0, s) + \sum_{k=1}^{\infty} f(2k, z)\phi_2(\theta, k\alpha_1 + k\alpha_2) \\ & + \sum_{k=1}^{\infty} f(2k-1, z)\phi_1(\theta, k\alpha_2 + \overline{k-1}\alpha_1), \end{aligned} \tag{7.240}$$

where $f(r, z) = e^{-\lambda z}(\lambda z)^r/r!$ $(r = 0, 1, 2, \ldots)$. Now let A be the column vector with the elements $\theta^{z_r} f(0, z_r)$ $(r = 1, 2, \ldots)$ and Φ the column vector

$$\Phi = [\phi_1(\theta, z_1), \phi_2(\theta, z_2), \phi_1(\theta, z_3), \phi_2(\theta, z_4), \ldots], \tag{7.241}$$

where

$$\begin{aligned} z_{2j} &= \left[\frac{j+1}{2}\right]\alpha_1 + \left[\frac{2j+1}{4}\right]\alpha_2 \\ z_{2j-1} &= \left[\frac{2j+1}{4}\right]\alpha_1 + \left[\frac{j+1}{2}\right]\alpha_2 \qquad (j = 1, 2, \ldots). \end{aligned} \tag{7.242}$$

Furthermore, let B be the matrix (b_{rs}) $(r, s = 1, 2, \ldots)$, where

$$(7.243)\quad b_{2j-1,s} = \begin{cases} 0 & \text{if } s = 4m-3, 4m \\ \theta^{z_{2j-1}} f(2m-1, z_{2j-1}) & \text{if } s = 4m-2 \\ \theta^{z_{2j-1}} f(2m, z_{2j-1}) & \text{if } s = 4m-1 \end{cases}$$

$$(7.244)\quad b_{2j,s} = \begin{cases} \theta^{z_{2j}} f(2m-1, z_{2j}) & \text{if } s = 4m-3 \\ 0 & \text{if } s = 4m-2, 4m-1 \\ \theta^{z_{2j}} f(2m, z_{2j}) & \text{if } s = 4m \quad (m = 1, 2, \ldots). \end{cases}$$

We can then write the equations (7.239) and (7.240) as $\Phi = A + B\Phi$, or

$$(7.245)\qquad (I - B)\Phi = A.$$

Now $\sum_{s=1}^{\infty} b_{rs} = \theta^{z_r}[1 - f(0, z_r)] < \theta^{z_r} \leqslant 1$ for $0 \leqslant \theta \leqslant 1$, so the inverse $(I - B)^{-1}$ exists and we may write $(I - B)^{-1} = I + \sum_{0}^{\infty} B^n$. Hence

$$(7.246)\qquad \Phi = A + \sum_{0}^{\infty} (B^n A)$$

gives the solution of (7.239) and (7.240). The problem of first emptiness can thus be considered to have been formally solved.

Now let us define the two probabilities $g_{11}(z, t)$ and $g_{12}(z, t)$ for $t = z + [(n+1)/2]\alpha_1 + [n/2]\alpha_2$ as follows:

$$(7.247)\qquad g_{11}(z, t) = \begin{cases} 0 & \text{if } n \text{ is even} \\ g_1(z, t) & \text{if } n \text{ is odd,} \end{cases}$$

$$(7.248)\qquad g_{12}(z, t) = \begin{cases} g_1(z, t) & \text{if } n \text{ is even} \\ 0 & \text{if } n \text{ is odd.} \end{cases}$$

Clearly,

$$(7.249)\qquad g_1(z, t) = g_{11}(z, t) + g_{12}(z, t).$$

Gani then proves by combinatorial methods that

$$(7.250)\qquad F_1(z_0; 0, t) = \sum_{n=0}^{\infty} g_{11}\left(t - \left[\frac{n+1}{2}\right]\alpha_1 - \left[\frac{n}{2}\right]\alpha_2, t\right)$$

and similarly for $F_2(z_0; 0, t)$.

COMPLEMENTS AND PROBLEMS

Section 7.1

1. Lindley and Smith have considered alternative specifications of the input process $X(t)$, and obtained the result (7.162) for the L.S.T. of the limiting distribution of $Z(t)$ by heuristic arguments [see the discussion in Kendall (1957)].

2. Consider the deterministic input $X(t) = \frac{1}{2}t$. Then from (7.10) we obtain

$$Z(t) = Z(0) - \tfrac{1}{2}t + \int_0^t \zeta(\tau)\,d\tau. \tag{1}$$

This gives $Z'(t) = -\frac{1}{2} + \zeta(t)$ for almost all t. At a point t such that $\zeta(t) = 1$, we have $Z(t) = 0$, $Z'(t) = \frac{1}{2}$, which contradicts the fact that $Z(t) \geqslant 0$. Thus $\zeta(t) = 0$ for almost all t, and

$$Z(t) = Z(0) - \tfrac{1}{2}t, \tag{2}$$

which is again a contradiction. Thus the specification (7.10) breaks down in this case [Kingman (1963)]. Kingman therefore suggests the modified formulation

$$Z(t) = Z(0) + Y(t) + \int_0^t \zeta(\tau)\,dY_{-}(\tau) \tag{3}$$

where $Y(t)$ is the net input during $(0, t]$, and $Y_{-}(t)$ is the total negative variation of $Y(t)$ in $(0, t]$. If $Y(t)$ is a right continuous function of bounded variation in every finite subinterval of $t \geqslant 0$ which has no downward jumps and satisfies $Y(0) = 0$, then the unique nonnegative measurable solution of (3) is given by (7.12).

3. Consider the case where there is a flow

$$V(t) = \int_{-\infty}^t e^{-\alpha(t-u)}\,dY(u), \tag{4}$$

where increments $dY(u)$ of size x, $x + dx$ occur in the time interval u, $u + du$ at rate $\nu e^{-x/\beta}\,dx/\beta$ $(0 < x < \infty)$. The total input $X(t)$ into the dam during $(0, t]$ is then given by

$$X(t) = \int_0^t V(\tau)\,d\tau. \tag{5}$$

Show that for large t,

$$E\{e^{\theta X(t)}\} \sim e^{\nu t\theta\beta/\alpha - \theta\beta}, \tag{6}$$

which indicates that $X(t)$ is an additive process with mean $\nu\beta t/\alpha$ and $2\nu\beta^2 t/\alpha^2$ [Bartlett; see the discussion in Kendall (1957)].

Section 7.2

4. Consider a dam of infinite capacity with inputs specified by (7.13). Since inputs occur in amounts of h, it is clear that the dam with an initial content z_0

will become empty only at times $z_0, z_0 + h, z_0 + 2h, \ldots$. Therefore the wet period $T(z_0) \equiv z_0 + Nh$, where N is a random variable defined by

$$N = \min (n \mid X_0 + S_n - n \leqslant 0) \tag{7}$$

$$S_n = X_1 + X_2 + \cdots + X_n \qquad (n \geqslant 1), \tag{8}$$

$X_0, X_1, X_2, \ldots$ being mutually independent random variables with Poisson distributions, X_0 having the mean λz_0, and X_n $(n \geqslant 1)$ the mean λh. From Section 3.2 we have

$$Pr\{N = n \mid X_0 = i\} = \frac{i}{n} e^{-\lambda nh} \frac{(\lambda nh)^{n-i}}{(n-i)!} \qquad (n \geqslant i > 1), \tag{9}$$

so that

$$\begin{aligned} g(z_0, z_0 + nh) &= Pr\{T(z_0) = z_0 + nh\} = Pr\{N = n\} \\ &= \sum_{i=1}^{n} Pr\{X_0 = i\} Pr\{N = n \mid X_0 = i\} \\ &= \sum_{i=1}^{n} e^{-\lambda z_0} \frac{(\lambda z_0)^i}{i!} \frac{i}{n} e^{-\lambda nh} \frac{(\lambda nh)^{n-i}}{(n-i)!} \\ &= e^{-\lambda(z_0 + nh)} \frac{\lambda^n}{n!} z_0 (z_0 + nh)^{n-1} \qquad (n \geqslant 1), \end{aligned} \tag{10}$$

a result which agrees with equation (2.15). For a proof based on the method of truncated polynomials, see Gani (1958). The result (7.33) follows from (10) by a combinatorial argument [see Gani and Prabhu (1959b)].

5. Gani (1962b) has considered the case of a nonhomogeneous Poisson input.

Section 7.3

6. Write the result (7.52) as a L.S.T.; then

$$\Psi(\theta) = E(e^{-\theta Z^*}) = \frac{(1 - \rho)\theta}{\theta - \log(1 + \rho\theta)} \qquad (\theta > 0), \tag{11}$$

where $Z^* = \lim_{t \to \infty} Z(t)$ is the limiting storage function. Prove that

$$g(x) = \frac{1}{\rho} \int_x^{\infty} e^{-u/\rho} \frac{du}{u}. \tag{12}$$

is a fr.f. in $(0 < x < \infty)$, with the Laplace transform

$$\int_0^{\infty} e^{-\theta x} g(x)\, dx = \frac{1}{\rho\theta} \log(1 + \rho\theta) \qquad (\theta > 0).$$

Deduce that if $\rho < 1$, then Z^* has the same distribution as

$$V = X_1 + X_2 + \cdots + X_N, \tag{13}$$

where $X_1, X_2, \ldots$ is a sequence of independent random variables, each having the fr.f. $g(x)$, and N is a random variable independent of the X_n and having the geometric distribution $(1 - \rho)\rho^N$ $(N = 0, 1, 2, \ldots)$ [Kendall (1957)]. A second method of inverting $\Psi(\theta)$ is due to Daniels (see Complement 16).

7. Put $W = (1 - \rho)Z^*$, then from (11) the L.T. of W is found to be

$$E(e^{-\theta W}) = \frac{(1-\rho)^2\theta}{(1-\rho)\theta - \log[1 + (\rho - \rho^2)\theta]} \tag{14}$$

$$\to (1 + \tfrac{1}{2}\theta)^{-1} \quad \text{as} \quad \rho \to 1 - 0.$$

Deduce that

$$\lim_{p \to 1-0} Pr\{W > w\} = e^{-2w} \tag{15}$$

[Kendall (1957)].

8. The Pollaczek-Khintchine formula for the L.S.T. of the limiting waiting time d.f. in the queueing system $M/G/1$ is given by

$$\phi(\theta) = \frac{(1-\rho)\theta}{\theta - \lambda + \lambda\psi(\theta)}, \tag{16}$$

where $\psi(\theta)$ is the L.S.T. of the service time distribution [see equation (2.101)]. Consider the particular case where the service time is Erlangian, so that $\psi(\theta) = (1 + \rho\theta)^{-p}$, and $p = \lambda^{-1}$, and consequently,

$$\phi(\theta) = \frac{(1-\rho)\theta}{\theta - \dfrac{1}{p}[1 - (1 + \rho\theta)^{-p}]}. \tag{17}$$

Show that as $p \to 0$, $\phi(\theta) \to \Psi(\theta)$, where $\Psi(\theta)$ is given by (10). Note that the fr.f. corresponding to the L.S.T. $[1 - (1 + \rho\theta)^{-p}]/p\,\rho\theta$ is given by

$$g_p(x) = \frac{1}{p\rho}\int_x^\infty e^{-y/p}\frac{y^{p-1}}{\rho^p\Gamma(p)}\,dy, \tag{18}$$

and that as $p \to 0$, $g_p(x) \to g(x)$, where $g(x)$ is given by (12) [Foster; see the discussion in Kendall (1947)].

9. Consider once again the Pollaczek-Khintchine formula (16). By any limiting procedure such that $-\lambda\psi'(0) = \rho$ (fixed), and

$$\lim_{\lambda \to \infty} [\lambda - \lambda\psi(\theta)] = -t^{-1}\log E[e^{-\theta X(t)}] \tag{19}$$

independently of t, we obtain (7.162) as the limit of $\phi(\theta)$ as $\lambda \to \infty$ [Downton (1957)].

Section 7.5

10. Consider the gamma-type input defined by (7.43).

(*a*) Show that the mean and variance of the wet period $T(u)$ are given by

$$E[T(u)] = \frac{u}{1-\rho}, \qquad \mathrm{Var}[T(u)] = \frac{u\rho^2}{(1-\rho)^3}; \tag{20}$$

(b) If $\rho - 1$ is small and positive, then the root of the equation (7.81) is approximately $\zeta \sim 2(\rho - 1)$, and the probability that the dam with an initial content u will never dry up is given approximately by

$$Pr\{T(u) = \infty\} \sim 1 - e^{-2u(\rho-1)} \tag{21}$$

(c) If $\rho = 1$, show that the asymptotic distribution of $T(u)/u^2$ as $u \to \infty$ is given by

$$\frac{e^{-1/2t}}{\sqrt{2\pi t^3}}\,dt \qquad (0 < t < \infty); \tag{22}$$

[Kendall (1957)].

11. *First passage times.* Consider a dam of infinite capacity, specified in Section 7.6. Let us define the first passage times

$$T \equiv T(z_0; z) = \begin{cases} \inf\,[t \mid Z(t) \leqslant z; Z(0) = z_0] & \text{if} \quad z < z_0. \\ \inf\,[t \mid Z(t) \geqslant z; Z(0) = z_0] & \text{if} \quad z > z_0. \end{cases} \tag{23}$$

In particular, if $z_0 > 0$, $T(z_0; 0)$ is the wet period in the dam. In the general case, let us assume that T has a fr.f. $h(z_0; z, t)$, and let

$$h^*(z_0; z, \theta) = \int_0^\infty e^{-\theta t} h(z_0; z, t)\,dt \tag{24}$$

denote its Laplace transform. Show that

$$h^*(z_0; z, \theta) = \frac{\rho^*(z_0; z', \theta)}{\rho^*(z_0; z', \theta)}, \tag{25}$$

where either $z_0 < z < z'$ or $z_0 > z > z'$ and

$$\rho(z_0; z, t) = \begin{cases} F(z_0; 0, t) & \text{for} \quad z = 0 \\ \dfrac{\partial}{\partial z} F(z_0; z, t) & \text{for} \quad z > 0, \end{cases} \tag{26}$$

$$\rho^*(z_0; z, \theta) = \int_0^\infty e^{-\theta t} \rho(z_0; z, t)\,dt. \tag{27}$$

In particular, let us choose $z' = 0$ and $z_0 > z$; then

$$\begin{aligned} h^*(z_0; z, \theta) &= \frac{\rho^*(z_0; 0, \theta)}{\rho^*(z; 0, \theta)} = \frac{e^{-z_0\eta(\theta)}}{\eta(\theta)} \Big/ \frac{e^{-z\eta(\theta)}}{\eta(\theta)} \\ &= e^{-(z_0 - z)\eta(\theta)} \qquad (z_0 > z > 0). \end{aligned} \tag{28}$$

It follows that

$$h(z_0; z, t) = g(z_0 - z, t) \qquad (t \geqslant z_0 - z > 0). \tag{29}$$

Thus the probability of first passage from z_0 to z is the same as the probability of first passage from $z_0 - z$ to 0. [Gani and Prabhu (1963).]

12. Suppose that the dam has finite capacity k and that the input $X(t)$ has the moment generating function (m.g.f.) $E\{e^{\theta X(t)}] = e^{t\xi(\theta)}$. Let us define

$$\begin{aligned} T \equiv T(u) &= \inf\,[t \mid Z(t) = 0 \quad \text{or} \quad Z(t) = k], \qquad Z(0) = u \\ &= \inf\,[t \mid u + X(t) - t \leqslant 0 \quad \text{or} \quad u + X(t) - t \geqslant k] \\ &= \inf\,[t \mid Y(t) \leqslant -u \quad \text{or} \quad Y(t) \geqslant k - u], \end{aligned} \tag{30}$$

where $Y(t) = X(t) - t$. Show that

$$E[e^{\theta_0 Y(T+)}] = 1, \tag{31}$$

where θ_0 is the nonzero real solution of the equation $\theta + \xi(\theta) = 0$. Deduce that if $X(t)$ has a compound Poisson distribution with the m.g.f.

$$\exp[-\lambda t + \lambda t(1 - \theta/\mu)^{-1}];$$

then the probability that the dam eventually dries up before it overflows is given by

$$P_u = \begin{cases} \dfrac{\lambda e^{-(\lambda-\mu)u} - \mu e^{-(\lambda-\mu)k}}{\lambda - \mu e^{-(\lambda-\mu)k}} & \text{if } \lambda \neq \mu \\ 1 - \dfrac{\mu}{k + \lambda^{-1}} & \text{if } \lambda = \mu. \end{cases} \tag{32}$$

If $X(t)$ has a gamma distribution with the m.g.f. $(1 - \rho\theta)^{-t}$, then

$$P_u = \frac{e^{u\theta_0} - e^{k\theta_0}}{1 - e^{k\theta_0}}, \tag{33}$$

where θ_0 is the nonzero real root of the equation $e^{-\theta} = 1 - \rho\theta$. If ρ is close to unity, then $\theta_0 \simeq 2(1 - \rho)$, and

$$Pu \simeq \frac{e^{2u(1-\rho)} - e^{2k(1-\rho)}}{1 - e^{2k(1-\rho)}}. \tag{34}$$

[Phatarfod (1963)].

Section 7.7

13. Beněs (1960) and Reich (1961) have obtained results similar to those presented in this section, but their approach and methods are quite different from those used here.

14. Show that under the conditions of (7.3), and for any θ, we have

$$e^{-\theta Z(t)} = e^{-\theta z_0 - \theta Y(t)} - \theta \int_0^t e^{-\theta[Y(t) - Y(\tau)]}\zeta(\tau)\, dY\_(\tau), \tag{35}$$

where $Z(0) = z_0$. If $X(t)$ increases only by jumps (35) yields (7.140) [Kingman (1963)].

Section 7.8

15. Show that $F^*(x)$, the inverse of the transform (7.162) satisfies the integral equation

$$F^*(x) = 1 - \rho + \rho \int_0^x F^*(y) g(x - y)\, dy, \tag{36}$$

where

$$g(x) = \frac{1}{\rho} \int_x^\infty \lambda(u)\, du \tag{37}$$

[Downton (1957)]. In the case where $\lambda(u) = e^{-u/\rho}/u$, $g(x)$ reduces to the function defined by (12).

16. Proceeding as in Section 2.7 obtain the result by inverting the L.S.T. (7.162). The inversion will be seen to depend on the identity (7.91) [Daniels, and also Kendall (1957)].

17. Let the input $X(t)$ be characterized by $E[e^{-\theta X(t)}] = e^{-t\xi(\theta)}$, where $\xi(\theta) = \rho\theta - \frac{1}{2}\sigma^2\theta^2 + o(\theta^3)$, and $\sigma = \sigma_1$ when $\rho = 1$. Show that the asymptotic distribution of $W = (1 - \rho)Z^*$, where Z^* is the limiting storage function, is given by

$$\lim_{\rho \to 1-0} Pr\{W > w\} = e^{-2w/\sigma_1^2} \tag{38}$$

[Downton (1957)]. A much better approximation, valid for all $\rho < 1$ and large w, is given by

$$dF(w) \sim \rho\left(\frac{1-\rho}{\rho\mu}\right) e^{-qw}\, dw \qquad (w > 0), \tag{39}$$

where $\xi(-q) = -q$, and $\mu = q^{-1}[\xi'(-q) - 1]$ [Smith; see the discussion in Kendall (1957)].

Section 7.9

18. Let $Y_0 = \tau_1$, $Y_k = \tau_{k+1} - \tau_k$ $(k = 1, 2, \ldots)$ be the successive wet periods, and $W_k = T_k - \tau_k$ $(k = 1, 2, \ldots)$ the successive dry periods in the Gani-Pyke model. Show that the random variables $W_1, W_2, \ldots$ are independent and identically distributed with the common d.f.

$$B(x) = \begin{cases} 1 - e^{-\lambda x} & \text{for } x > 0 \\ 0 & \text{for } x \leqslant 0, \end{cases} \tag{40}$$

where $\lambda = -L(0) < \infty$. Furthermore, show that $Y_1, Y_2, \ldots$ are independent and identically distributed with the L.S.T.

$$h(\theta) = E(e^{-\theta Y_k}) = 1 - \lambda^{-1}\xi[\eta(\theta)] \tag{41}$$

where $\xi(\theta)$ is defined by

$$\xi(\theta) = \int_0^\infty (1 - e^{-\theta x})\, dL(x), \tag{42}$$

and the L.S.T. of Y_0 is $E(e^{-\theta Y_0}) = e^{-z\eta(\theta)}$, $Z(0) = z$. In the case where $L(0-) = 0$, $\eta(\theta)$ satisfies Kendall's functional equation (7.80) [Gani and Pyke (1960)].

19. Let $\beta(t)$ denote the total time in $(0, t]$ during which the dam is nonempty, and $\Omega(t, x) = Pr\{\beta(t) \leqslant x\}$. Show that for fixed $a \geqslant 0$,

$$\int_0^\infty e^{-\theta x}\, d_x\Omega(a + x, x) = \exp\{-z_0\eta(\theta) - a\xi[\eta(\theta)]\}. \tag{43}$$

[Gani and Pyke (1960a)].

Section 7.10

20. Let $dB(x) = \lambda e^{-\lambda x}\, dx$, $dA(x) = a(x)\, dx$, $\psi(\theta) = \int_0^\infty e^{-\theta x}\, dA(x)$, and assume that initially $Z(t)$ is increasing. Let $Y(t)$ be the time since the epoch of the last preceding maximum of $Z(t)$, and

$$\begin{aligned} F_+(x, t) &= Pr\{Z(t) \leqslant x, Z(t) \text{ is increasing}\} \\ F_-(x, y, t)\, dy &= Pr\{Z(t) \leqslant x, y \leqslant Y(t) \leqslant y + dy, Z(t) \text{ is nonincreasing}\}. \end{aligned} \tag{44}$$

Show that

$$\text{(45)} \qquad \begin{aligned} \int_0^\infty e^{-\theta t} F_+(x, t)\, dt &= \frac{1 - e^{-x\alpha(\theta)}}{\theta + \lambda - \lambda\psi(\theta)} \\ \int_0^\infty e^{-\theta t} F_-(x, y, t)\, dt &= \lambda[1 - A(y)]e^{-\theta y} \frac{1 - e^{-(x+y)\alpha(\theta)}}{\theta + \lambda - \lambda\psi(\theta)}, \end{aligned}$$

where $\alpha \equiv \alpha(\theta)$ is the unique positive root of the equation

$$\text{(46)} \qquad \alpha = \theta + \lambda - \lambda\psi(\theta + \alpha).$$

Obtain the limiting distribution of $Z(t)$ as $t \to \infty$ [Miller (1963)].

21. Show that the L.S.T. of the nonempty period T in the model described in Complement 20 is given by

$$\text{(47)} \qquad E(e^{-\theta T}) = \frac{\lambda - \lambda\Gamma(\theta)}{2\theta + \lambda - \lambda\Gamma(\theta)},$$

where $\Gamma(\theta)$ is given by (7.210) [Miller (1963)].

22. Let $dB(x) = \lambda e^{-\lambda x}\, dx$, $dA(x) = \mu e^{-\mu x}\, dx$, and assume that initially $Z(t)$ is increasing. Show that

$$\text{(48)} \qquad F_+(x, t) = F_+(\infty, t) - e^{-\lambda x} F_+(\infty, t - x) - \int_0^{t-x} k(x, t - \tau) F_+(\infty, \tau)\, d\tau \qquad (0 \leqslant x < t),$$

where

$$\text{(49)} \qquad F_+(\infty, t) = \frac{\mu + \lambda e^{-(\lambda+\mu)t}}{\lambda + \mu},$$

and

$$\text{(50)} \qquad k(x, t) = \begin{cases} x(\lambda\mu)^{1/2} I_1[\sqrt{\lambda\mu(t^2 - x^2)}]e^{-[(\lambda-\mu)/2]x - [(\lambda+\mu)/2]t} & (t > x) \\ 0 & (t \leqslant x). \end{cases}$$

Furthermore,

$$\text{(51)} \qquad F_-(x, y, t) = \lambda e^{-\mu y} F_+(x + y, t - y).$$

Obtain the limiting distribution of $Z(t)$ as $t \to \infty$ [Miller (1963)]. For this model Miller also considers some absorption problems.

Section 7.11

23. For values of n up to 6, the probabilities $g_1(z, t)$ and $g_2(z, t)$ have been explicitly determined by Gani (1961) using (7.236). Some approximations have been derived by Gani and Pyke (1960b).

24. *Several ordered inputs.* As a generalization of the model described in this section, consider the case where the input $X(t)$ consists of nonnegative inputs $\alpha_1, \alpha_2, \ldots, \alpha_p$, not all equal, which follow one another cyclically in this order. The emptiness probabilities $g_i(z, t)$ $(i = 1, 2, \ldots, p)$ here satisfy recurrence relations of the type (5.236) [Gani and Pyke (1960b)].

25. *Dams in parallel.* Consider two dams D_1 and D_2 whose contents $Z_1(t)$, $Z_2(t)$ at times $t \geqslant 0$ are each subject to a steady release at constant unit rate until emptiness occurs, when the release ceases. Unit inputs $X(t)$ arrive one at

a time and are fed into D_1 and D_2 according to the following rule: $X(t)$ is first fed into D_1, which has the lesser initial content $Z_1(0) = z_1$, until the time t ($= t_1$ say) when $Z_1(t) \geqslant Z_2(t)$; the next input is then diverted into D_2, and thereafter unit inputs are fed alternatively into D_1 and D_2. The problem of emptiness in this model is equivalent to that in the model of a dam with two ordered inputs [Gani (1961)].

26. *Discrete dam with ordered inputs.* Yeo (1961) has considered the discrete time analogue of Gani's (1962a) model with two ordered inputs.

REFERENCES

Beněs, V. E. (1960). Theory of queues with one server. *Trans. Amer. Math. Soc.*, **94,** 282–294.

Baxter, Glen, and M. D. Donsker (1957). On the distribution of the supremum functional for processes with stationary independent increments. *Trans. Amer. Math. Soc.*, **85,** 99–124.

Downton, F. (1957). A note on Moran's theory of dams. *Quart. J. Math.* (Oxford, 2), **8,** 282–286.

Gani, J. (1955). Some problems in the theory of provisioning and dams, *Biometrika*, **42,** 179–200.

Gani, J. (1958). Elementary methods in an occupancy problem of storage. *Math. Ann.*, **136,** 454–465.

Gani, J. (1961). First emptiness of two dams in parallel. *Ann. Math. Stat.*, **32,** 219–229.

Gani, J. (1962a). *The Time-Dependent Solution for a Dam with Ordered Poisson Inputs.* Studies in Applied Probability and Management Science, Stanford University Press.

Gani, J. (1962b). A stochastic dam process with non-homogeneous Poisson inputs. *Stud. Math.*, *T.* **XXXI**, 307–315.

Gani, J., and N. U. Prabhu (1959a). Remarks on the dam with Poisson type inputs. *Aust. J. Appl. Sci.*, **10,** 113–122.

Gani, J. and N. U. Prabhu (1959b). The time-dependent solution for a storage model with Poisson input. *J. Math. and Mech.*, **8,** 653–664.

Gani, J., and N. U. Prabhu (1963). A storage model with continuous infinitely divisible inputs. *Proc. Cam. Phil. Soc.*, **59,** 417–429.

Gani, J. and R. Pyke (1960a). The content of a dam as the supremum of an infinitely divisible process. *J. Math. and Mech.*, **9,** 639–652.

Gani, J. and P. Pyke (1960b). Inequalities for first emptiness probabilities of a dam with ordered inputs. *Tech. Report No.* 1, National Science Foundation Grant G-9670, App. Math. and Stat. Lab., Stanford University.

Hasofer, A. M. (1964). A dam with inverse Gaussian input. *Proc. Camb. Phil. Soc.*, **60,** 931–933.

Kendall, D. G. (1957). Some problems in the theory of dams. *J. Roy. Stat. Soc.*, **B19,** 207–212. For M. S. Bartlett (1957), H. E. Daniels (1957), D. V. Lindley (1957), and W. L. Smith (1957), see the discussion in this reference.

Kingman, J. F. C. (1963). On continuous time models in the theory of dams. *J. Aust. Math. Soc.*, **3,** 480–487.

Miller, R. G., Jr. (1963). Continuous time stochastic storage processes with random linear inputs and outputs. *J. Math. and Mech.*, **12,** 275–291.

Moran, P. A. P. (1955). A probability theory of dams and storage systems: modification of the release rules. *Aust. J. Appl. Sci.*, **6**, 117–130.

Moran, P. A. P. (1956). A probability theory of a dam with a continuous release. *Quart. J. Math.* (Oxford, 2), **7**, 130–137.

Phatarfod, R. M. (1963). Application of methods of sequential analysis to dam theory. *Ann. Math. Statist.*, **34**, 1588–1592.

Reich, E. (1961). Some combinatorial theorems for continuous time parameter processes. *Math. Scand.*, **9**, 243–257.

Yeo, G. F. (1961). A discrete dam with ordered inputs. *Aust. Math. Soc.*, Summer Res. Inst., Research Reports (1961).

Index